Another Country

Another Country
Encounters with the Red Rock Desert

John A. Murray

Johnson Books
BOULDER

For my Father

Published by Johnson Books, a division of Johnson Publishing Company, 1880 South 57th Court, Boulder, Colorado 80301.
E-mail: books@jpcolorado.com.

9 8 7 6 5 4 3 2 1

Cover design by Debra B. Topping
Cover and interior photographs by John A. Murray

Library of Congress Cataloging-in-Publication Data
Murray, John A., 1954-
    Another country : encounters with the red rock desert / John A. Murray.
        p. cm.
    ISBN 1-55566-320-6 (alk paper)
    1. Deserts—Fiction. 2. Southwestern States—Fiction. 3. Deserts—Southwestern States. 4. Southwestern States—Description and travel. I. Title.
    PS3613.U77 A84 2002
    813'.54--dc21

2002000925

Printed in the United States by
Johnson Printing
1880 South 57th Court
Boulder, Colorado 80301

 Printed on recycled paper with soy ink

Contents

Part III

There are places where the mind dies
So that a truth which is its very denial may be born.

—Albert Camus
"The Wind at Djemila" (1937)

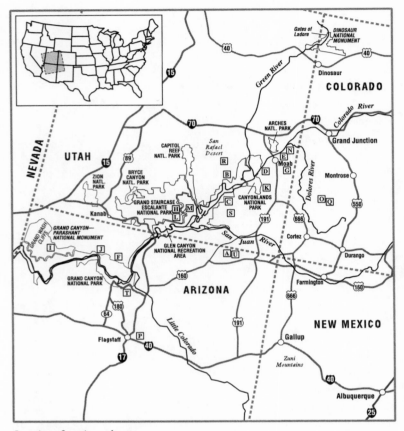

Location of stories and essays:

A. Monument Valley—"The Elder" and "Hunt's Mesa"
B. Burr Desert—"Another Country"
C. Dark Canyon—"Dark Canyon"
D. Colorado River downstream from Moab—"Bend in the River"
E. Professor Valley—"Still Life"
F. North Kaibab National Forest—"Mountain Lion"
G. Wilson Mesa—"The House at the End of the Road"
H. Coyote Gulch—"A Walk in the Desert"
I. Shivwits Plateau—"The Exact Location of Paradise"
J. Grand Canyon National Park (North Rim)—"The Heart of the Matter"
K. Needles Overlook—"Land's End"
L. Lake Powell—"The World Behind the Sun"
M. Navajo Mountain—"Navajo Mountain"
N. Professor Valley—"The Dead"
O. Dry Creek Basin—"A Very Long Time Ago"
P. Flagstaff—"The Woman Who Came with the Spring"
Q. Dry Creek Basin—"Sandpainting"
R. San Rafael Desert—"Points and Lines"
S. Grand Gulch Primitive Area—"Grand Gulch"
T. Lipan Point, Grand Canyon National Park (South Rim)—"Here Today"
U. El Capitan—"The Diamond"

Preface

DESERTS. There are deserts in the middle of crowded cities. You see them in the vacant eyes of people living without love, without faith, without opportunity, estranged from nature and themselves. There are deserts on Mars, I am told, that are older than any on Earth. There are deserts in the future where there are forests today. There are forests today where there were once deserts. There are deserts with no heat, as on Antarctica, and deserts with no air, as on the moon. Some historians refer to the European Middle Ages as a desert. To a carpenter ant, the rooftop of your home is a desert. When I think of my life, I think of times that have been deserts.

This is not a book about those kinds of deserts, although interesting books could be written about each. This is a book about the Red Rock Desert, which is a southern province of the Great Basin Desert. If the Great Basin Desert is known for its sagebrush and the Mojave Desert is known for its Joshua Trees, then the Red Rock Desert, that other northern desert, is best known for its smoothly eroded formations of red sandstone. This book will take you deeply into this wonderland, through a series of stories and essays. The Red Rock Desert is a place unlike any other, and what follows is a correspondingly unique song of praise, incorporating both fiction and nonfiction.

Another Country: Encounters with the Red Rock Desert is the first in a trilogy on the American West. I recently completed work on *Becoming the Mountains: Journeys in the Yellowstone Country*, and am currently writing the final volume in the series, *All the Rivers Run Into the Sea: Conversations with the Big Sur Coast*. The purpose of the trilogy is to explore three representative regions—desert, mountains, and sea—and thus provide readers with a unique view of the Western people and landscape.

I would like to express my gratitude to the editors who have kindly supported my other desert books: Barb Harold (*Desert Awakenings*),

Amy Sorrels (*Cactus Country*), Erin Murphy and Stephanie Buccholz (*The Colorado Plateau*), and Brad Melton (*Cinema Southwest* and *Myth-makers of the West*). Thanks as well to the dear friends who have accompanied me on my excursions in the desert, especially those of the last seven years: Katy Bosch, Fen Ying Hao, Aliette Frank, Christine June, Natalya Ryabova, and Jill Hindle. Finally, a word of special appreciation to my father, who first showed me the desert, and my son Steven, whose presence in my life is like sunshine. To all of you, my deep and humble gratitude.

As always, I welcome correspondence from readers at P.O. 102345, Denver, Colorado 80250.

Introduction: Legends and Journeys

*Reaching the extreme verge the packs are cast off, and
sitting upon the edge we contemplate the most sublime
and awe-inspiring spectacle in the world.*
—Clarence Dutton, 1882

i.

THE PARTICULAR DESERT of which I write is most distinguished by
what it is not. No large cities rise in the place. Railroads do not cross it.
The interstate highway system avoids it. Travelers peer into the canyons
and flee. Miners and prospectors toil for years until they, too, finally
leave. Cattle disappear. Sometimes whole herds of them. Sheep fatten
the local coyotes and mountain lions. Kayakers go under and occasionally never resurface, at least in this world. The same is true of rafters.
Hikers become lost and perish on the rocks, watched patiently by vul-
tures and ravens. March snowstorms blow through and for a week the
back roads become impassable. Flash floods clean out the slot canyons
once or twice a season. Sometimes they take a few trekkers with them.
The last named mountain range in the continental United States is there.
So is the deepest canyon. So are the most extensive prehistoric ruins, and
the greatest concentration of parks and monuments in the world.

So are the pollen-filled blossoms of the prickly pear cactus.

There are six deserts in the American Southwest, and the one you are
about to read about is the most beautiful. Her sisters are all lovely, to be
sure—the hot Sonoran, the cool Great Basin, the mysterious Chi-
huahuan, the delicate Colorado, the bright Mojave—but only in the
Red Rock Desert will you find such a marvelous fusion of form and
color. Slickrock canyons, blue mesas, snow-capped peaks—they are all
there, and in the most unique desert on earth. Think of the region as

an enormous equilateral triangle bounded by the Gates of Ladore on the north, the Grand Wash Cliffs on the southwest, and the Zuni Mountains on the southeast. Inside that imaginary province is an imaginary wilderness of rocks, a vast undeveloped country in which even the faintest summer stars hang like lanterns and a person can still stand on a cliff and survey a thousand square miles of uncorrupted rock.

Call this a brief history of time. The Red Rock Desert was first seen by a European, a man named Garcia Lopez de Cardenas, in 1540. In that year there were no European settlements—none at all—on either coast of North America. As is customary in human affairs, many years— forty to be exact—passed before another of his country and language visited the region. The place, after all, had not much to recommend it. Certainly there was not the wealth of the Aztecs or Incas in the province, nor was there a prosperous human population to enslave or convert. There was just the empty desert. With Arcadies like California and the Rio Grande Valley to excite the accountants, the high windy plateau was soon forgotten. Wave after wave of immigrants bypassed the desert for other regions. And so the original inhabitants of the place persisted for a few more centuries in quiet obscurity. The Hopi and Navajo lived on the ancient dry homeland of the Anasazi. The Ute and the Jicarilla Apache preferred the aspen and spruce-covered mountains. The Kaibab and Paiute roamed across the ponderosa groves of the Kaibab Plateau, and the Havasupai and Hualapai enjoyed the labyrinthine shelter of the Grand Canyon.

Fathers Dominguez and Escalante explored the region in 1776. They found no gold, no walled cities, no thronging souls to convert, and returned with the disappointing news. For half a century, nothing happened. The rivers continued to flow, of course, and the creeping vines to leaf out every spring and the acorns to harden every fall, but no one from Western Civilization (excepting a brief walkabout by Jedediah Smith) ventured inside the gates of Eden. A little while later the Mormons arrived, established a few towns, and then there was the Civil War. Following that, one expedition after another tried to gain a sense of the place—Ives, Macomb, Simpson, Hamblin, Powell, Hayden, King, Wheeler, and others. The U.S. government printing office shortly thereafter began to publish detailed maps. Modern history starts with those first maps—townships and surveyor's transits, forests and parks, paved roads, monumental dams, the uranium boom, dirt airstrips, the traveling circuses of Hollywood, the arrival of various artists and photographers, and, eventually, the modern tourist industry.

So far as geology is concerned, the landscape is an open book— eroded sedimentary beds, faulted mountain ranges, monocline folds, exfoliated pinnacles, meteor-impact craters, extinct volcanoes. During the 1960s, searching for a place to train lunar astronauts, the government chose the Red Rock Desert. Here the great-grandsons of Major Powell (who did his exploring in a wooden boat) learned about landform recognition and rock identification. They flew around in helicopters, acquiring experience for that other desert approach, and they broke apart pyroclastic rocks with steel hammers, again gaining practice for their fieldwork in outer space.

Four major rivers—the Colorado, San Juan, Green, and Dolores— carve the plateau in their wide meanderings, exposing layers that range from the Cretaceous (most recent) to the Jurassic (the age of dinosaurs) to the Cambrian (earliest). Think of the stairs from your living room to your basement. In the great canyons we have the same thing: a series of benches, each representing an accumulated segment of history, all dropping progressively toward the river. At the bottom are ancient rocks—pink granite and Vishnu schist—that range in age to 1.7 billion years. Touch the canyon walls down there and you are touching time itself, a stone that is one-third the age of the solar system. A force that is both powerful and humbling flows into you when you touch one of those rocks.

ii.

ANOTHER COUNTRY is a collection of fifteen essays and fifteen stories that have been inspired by the Red Rock Desert. It is a landscape that has been for me a continual place of happy returning, a vibrant landscape of welcome solace, a pure realm of inspiration for the restless spirit. This book is a sharing of those experiences. I have no desire to visit the deserts of Namibia, Australia, the Near East, Bolivia, or Central Asia. To see places like the Skeleton Coast, Ayers Rock, the Dead Sea, the Andean altiplano, or the dune fields of Uzbekistan. To puzzle over the lifestyle of the great gray kangaroo, or retrace from oasis to oasis the meanderings of Colonel T. E. Lawrence. These are all excellent places, I'm sure, but the Red Rock Desert is more than enough for this one lifetime, both as a landscape and a metaphor.

Dear readers, camp all you wish, hike from dawn to dusk, dance with the winds under Delicate Arch, but please do not add to the land development out there. Leave thoughts of ownership and control of the landscape at home. Help the Nature Conservancy and other worthy organizations save the Earth. Fight growth. Support your local rangers. Vote prudently. Make love on a mesa at sunset. Watch sunrises. Draw in your sketch book. Roam for hours on the slickrock. But afterwards go, leave, knowing that you will return, and that it will still be there because you chose to leave.

Part I

The Elder

THE STORY IS TOLD that in the 1930s a group of anthropologists came out to Monument Valley to interview a Navajo Elder. These were all distinguished professors who lived and worked at places such as the University of California, Berkeley, and the University of Chicago and the University of Pennsylvania. Like the venerable Johann Faustus of Wittenberg, they each held a terminal degree in their respective subject, and wore black flowing gowns and square flat-topped black hats with colored tassels at university ceremonies. They lectured in quiet halls where it was not polite to question the received wisdom and when they roamed the corridors everyone was deferential to them, especially untenured faculty who lived in mortal fear of them. Anyone who tried to be innovative or different, such as Margaret Mead, was banished to a faraway island. It was a perfect utopia, their world, and very much in keeping with Plato's vision, right down to the corner offices. For several days they visited with this Elder and interrogated him with respect to Navajo legends, myths, and cosmology. They were particularly interested in the pantheon of Navajo deities, knowing of the relationship between religion and culture, and carefully recorded the names of each deity, and the stories about them.

"But what," they inquired repeatedly, "is the name of your primary god, the one deity who is in charge of all the others?" The Elder furrowed his brow. He had no answer for them. A whole series of biases had been raised by their general line of questioning, and each had been duly noted by him. Stepping away, the professors began talking among themselves. Thinking the Elder was partially deaf and could not hear, they speculated aloud that perhaps a local superstition prevented him from speaking the word. Or perhaps he was withholding the information for some other purpose. Finally, pressed without relent, the Elder decided to give them what they wanted. He spoke a phrase and they excitedly wrote it down in their notebooks, spelling it out phonetically. Everyone was relieved. Possession of the word would elevate the stature of the new owners in their world. "That is it?" they solemnly asked. "Yes," he nodded with equal gravity. Other Navajo elders were subsequently questioned, and, after a moment of hesitation, they nodded in reluctant affirmation. "Yes, that is right."

For years this word appeared in their articles and books and in the master's theses and doctoral dissertations of their graduate students. All across Europe and America the members of the guild were reassured to know there was one all-powerful entity among the Navajo, as in their own civilization. A dispute eventually arose as to who should take credit for establishing this essential fact. One thought it should be the senior academician present. Another claimed it should be the scholar who asked the question first. Another argued that it should be, regardless of rank, the professor who was the last to pose the question. Each debated from a position of self-interest. As sometimes occurs in such matters, the territorial dispute soon evolved into a feud. Journal articles recording the battles, ambushes, and retaliatory raids can still be found on dusty library shelves. The pages will remain there forever, preserved like leaves caught in amber. The great debate went on for years, until they all died—a golf course bee attack, a falling can of house paint, an ill-advised foreign trip, the usual fare. Finally, a young woman new to the discipline went out to the reservation to check. She asked another young woman working in the gift shop at Goulding's Trading Post about the famous story of the three professors. Her peer laughed and told her the truth. The tale was long familiar to the Navajo, and its narration had enlivened many an evening around the campfire. Translated, the sacred phrase the tribal Elder had gravely dictated to his esteemed guests means "Hell if I know."

Another Country

WEST OF THE DIRTY DEVIL RIVER, south of Hanksville, and east of the Henry Mountains is a rolling expanse of salt brush and greasewood known as the Burr Desert. To the south are the deep cobalt waters of Lake Powell. The placenames of the Burr Desert—Last Chance Wash, No Man's Canyon, Poison Spring Canyon, Tarantula Mesa— suggest something of the landscape. No one lives there. Nor does anyone linger. It is the kind of place that people cross in a hurry, en route to the marina at Hite, or returning back north to the Interstate. There is a rumor, popular in the RV camps, that an outlaw, a survivalist who killed a police officer near Cortez, secretly lives there in a cliff dwelling, but all of that was some years ago. Late at night, playing pinochle on a card table beside a white gas lantern, the retirees will often devise idle plans for capturing the fugitive. The plans usually involve some manner of bait—food, liquor, guns—and an improvised device resembling a harpoon net. Most of the conversation is concerned with how to dispose of the reward money, with the men favoring Las Vegas, and the women more inclined to Paris. Others will assure you with equal certainty that the renegade is living deep in Mexico, supported by one of those separatist groups in northern Idaho, or that he has assumed a new identity and has disappeared among the twenty million souls living in the greater Los Angeles area. The government believes that, like the two other suspects whose naturally mummified bodies were found in the desert, he is dead.

The Burr Desert is that sort of country, a banished forlorn outlaw country that is forever spawning myths and legends, flat tires and torn serpentine belts, tales of death and stories of survival. The blue sky emptiness and the scorched red earth, the toxic pepperweed and thorny shadscale, the lost wandering canyons and unnamed dry washes seem to collectively say to the morbidly curious, there is no god here, there are no laws, go elsewhere if you wish to live and prosper.

Her Utah driver's license said that her name was Joy Marie Prather. She had been born on May 3rd of such and such a year, making her twenty years old. She stood five foot seven and weighed one hundred and thirty pounds. She lived at 3745 West Cedar Avenue in Salt Lake City. She had blond hair and brown eyes and was not required to wear glasses. She was not an organ donor and she was not registered to vote.

That is what her license said.

She was driving north on State Route 95 in southern Utah. The gas station map from the boat marina at Hite was unfolded on the seat next to her and sleeping on the back seat was her black terrier Casey. A young man whom she had met water-skiing the day before had told her about a shortcut across Badwater Basin in the Burr Desert. He took it all the time. It would shorten her trip by forty-one miles, nearly an hour, and she really needed to get home early so that she could finish writing a marketing term paper.

She felt relieved when she found the spot Drake the tall red-haired chemistry major from Provo had marked on the map. He had circled it and drawn an arrow indicating the correct direction. His phone number was also on the map. That was circled as well.

Just as he had promised, there was a weathered four-inch by four-inch wooden post driven into the ground one hundred yards north of the thirty mile-marker, and beside it was the sun-bleached skull of a cow, or at least a significant portion of what had once been a skull.

She turned there, leaving the asphalt highway behind and heading west into the desert.

For the first few miles the gravel road was straight as a ruler and she drove steadily at thirty-five miles an hour. At this rate she would be across the basin in around sixty minutes. The windows were up and the air conditioner was on because it was the middle of August. It was seven-thirty-four in the morning and the air temperature had just reached ninety degrees. The temperature would rise another fourteen degrees that day. It was much hotter on the Burr Desert than it was in Salt Lake City, or, for that matter, on the shores of Lake Powell.

After the fifth mile the graded embankments closed in, so that the road was reduced to one narrow lane. Shortly after that something banged up against the bottom of the car and she reduced her speed by one-half. Gradually the road became rougher and the rocks became more numerous and larger. There were hundreds of them. Most were the size of a can of soda. Every so often there was a rock the size of a car battery. By driving slowly, it was possible to avoid most of them. Five miles later there was a fork in the road and she puzzled for a moment. One fork appeared to lead toward the distant western mountains, blue and violet on the horizon. The other headed farther into the desert in a northerly direction. Drake had mentioned nothing about the fork. Perhaps he had forgotten. Perhaps he assumed the decision was self-evident and she would know what to do. But she did not. Both seemed equally traveled.

She wondered if she should turn back and take the highway, but she had come this far and besides there was no place to turn around. So she took the right fork. At least it seemed to lead in the right direction. She had no way of knowing it was a four-wheel-drive track that once, in the early 1950s, led to a uranium mine perched on the edge of a side canyon, a minor claim that had consisted of a single vertical shaft blasted into a shallow vein of green cake. No one had been on the road, not even the local dirt-bikers, in eleven months. All she knew was that it seemed to be heading north. The road, such as it was, went on for another two or three miles and she slowly picked her way along, spinning to a near-stop now and then in the sandy spots. She turned on the radio, but there were no stations either on AM or on FM, only far-away static and white noise. She turned the radio off and continued to drive. Through it all the dog remained sleeping in the backseat upon her beach towel that smelled of coconut oil.

Finally she came upon a rock so large it had to be moved. When she opened the car door the heat almost knocked her over, literally, and she remembered how it was when her mother cracked the oven to look inside while baking holiday cookies. It was like that, a shock. The body physically recoiled, reflexively turned away, as from the presence of death itself. It suddenly occurred to her, as a fact not to be ignored, that she had no water with her. No water at all anywhere in the car. In fact, she had nothing to drink. All she had in her jeans pockets were some matches from building the beach fire the night before. The only thing she had in her father's old Marine Corps sea bag was her bathing suit and spare clothes. She recalled with a stab of adrenaline that over the previous three days she had consumed no water—not one drop—only cola, wine, and beer.

When Joy tried to lift the fossil-encrusted piece of sandstone, which weighed nineteen pounds more than she did, a desert scorpion crawled out onto her shoe and she shook it off with a scream and then almost stepped on it. It was pale yellow with a black stinger and brownish-black pincers. It was the length of her ring finger and as she stooped to look at it the insect assumed a defensive posture, its fore-claws waving. On its back was a perpetually moving swarm of baby scorpions, each a tiny replica of the adult. When she saw the scorpion was a mother she could not kill it, and after awhile it scurried backward toward the shelter of some dead alkaligrass.

Inch by inch, foot by foot, the young woman pushed and shoved and pulled the giant chunk of ancient sea bottom far enough out of the way so that her car could pass by, barely. The exertion required for this was considerable. The sweat from her forehead burned her eyes and on her tongue was the persistent taste of salt.

There is a point at which a situation mutates from being mildly unpleasant to being genuinely bad and that point was reached when she turned to open the car door and saw that her vehicle had been leaking black liquid down the middle of the road. It resembled a blood trail—a few drops here, a larger spot there—and it formed a line that pointed to the bottom of the car beneath the engine where the oil pan had once been firmly bolted.

Back in the car, the amber check engine light was now on but the red oil warning light had yet to flicker to life.

She considered the latter an encouraging sign.

There was only one thing to do now, and that was to turn around at the first opportunity and head back to the paved highway, which was only a few miles away, she thought. Half an hour farther there was a dry wash. A year before there had been a heavy rainstorm in the Henry Mountains and a flash flood had torn through the drainage at the speed of an untethered horse startled by a gunshot. The wash was littered with debris from that violent event—flat rocks, angular boulders, whole shrubs, tree branches, an entire embankment of blackbrush, a dead Hereford cow, a rusted half-collapsed oil drum, a shattered four by eight sheet of plywood from a mining shack. On the other side of the wash, though, there was a sort of pad, a small flat place where a car could turn around. For an hour the young woman cleared a path through that wash, all the while remaining alert for scorpions and snakes, all the while becoming drier and drier. She worked with a skill and energy she normally did not possess and in the end the car traversed the wash without much difficulty. When she reached the other side, she got out and studied the situation from several positions, calculating exactly how best to conduct the maneuver.

As a living thing she was mostly made of water and at this point, after three days without replenishment, most of the water she needed to live was gone. Her cheeks were strangely flushed when she checked in the car mirror, and she realized that, however it was done, it had to be done quickly and right.

With consummate precision she carefully maneuvered the car on the roadway, inching this way and that way, and the wheeled machine was almost free—literally inches away from the final angled turn—when the back tires hung up in the sagebrush and the front tires began to spin down into the sand. Within seconds the sand had reached the axle, and the smell of burning rubber filled the air. The oil warning light came on then, as well, and the noises from under the hood were like the sounds of a creature dying—a death rattle that comes up from the lungs and causes all to take a step back, even physicians, as they realize what will occur next.

It was at that moment that she was overwhelmed by a wave of frustration and panic and, hitting the steering wheel with both of her clenched fists, screamed out loud. It was not a desperate scream for help but, rather, an honest expression of pure terror. The sound of her voice was so strange, so alien and detached, in that vast uncaring place that it alarmed her, and she resolved not to cry out again. This was not, she could see, a place for screams or for tears. The desert did not care either way. What would happen next, life or death, would depend entirely on her.

The dog was frightened and badly in need of water but still regarded his owner with loyalty and trust, and she spoke gently to him. He, too, had not had water in a very long while.

She considered what to do. There were two alternatives. She could remain with the car, and hope someone came along. The problem was that the road was in the middle of nowhere and no one knew where she was, other than Drake, who said he might call in a week or so. That would be at least six days too late. She could build a signal fire, but if she did and waited a day and no one saw it she would then be too weak to walk out. That meant she had to walk out immediately. The choice was to walk out during the day, or walk out during the night. The problem with walking out at night was that it was the dark phase of the moon. She knew that from the previous night when they had built the fire on the beach and watched the Perseids meteor shower. With no moon, she might wander away from the jeep road out into the desert. All bearings would then be lost. Therefore she had to leave right then, while she still had energy, and not waste a moment longer.

She was thinking very clearly now, or at least she thought she was.

And so with that she stepped from the car and started back down the sun-baked track, holding her ten pound dog in her arms because it refused to walk on the scalding hot ground. Every so often she would feel light-headed and want to faint, but she kept going. The first three miles took about two hours, and then the weight of the late summer heat came fully down upon her and she had to sit and rest. She had no choice. It was either stop or fall over. The sun at that point was near the middle of the sky, with the hottest hours still ahead. Her tongue was swollen and dry and stuck to the top of her mouth and if she moved her head suddenly to one side or the other side she became dizzy and the far horizons tilted this way and that. Her skin was tingling and prickly—pins and needles—in the extremities. Her fingertips and toes were numb. She had no hat but she had tied a red bandana around her head and at least she was still sweating. What had once been a dark summer tan had now become a blistered sun-burn, the clear bubbles covering her cheeks and shoulders and arms and legs. She was dressed in a halter-top and cutoff jeans. She hadn't thought to bring a light-colored shirt to protect her shoulders and arms.

After another two miles, only three or four more to go she thought, she came to a rocky gulch and thought she heard water but when she walked up the drainage she found only the world's smallest fully grown cottonwood tree, its green heart-shaped leaves rustling in the breeze. Long ago a migrating thrush had deposited a cotton-feathered seed in the midst of the dry watercourse. After a monsoon the tiny black seed had dutifully sprouted and found water a few feet down. It wasn't much of a tree, about twice as tall as her, but it kindly offered a patch of luminous blue shade and so she sat there.

She vaguely remembered that drinking water could be found in cactus—she had seen it in a Roadrunner cartoon or a Western movie once—but there were no cactus anywhere in sight. She had no way of knowing that the soil in the basin was too salty for cactus. Her heart was racing now—*thump thump thump*, pounding like a framing hammer on a sixteen penny nail, almost loud enough to hear—and her head felt slightly detached from the rest of her body. The dog, having absorbed the desert sun with its black fur for quite a while, had closed its eyes and was panting furiously. There was a white crusted saliva around its mouth and its eyes were dry and closed and as she lay there sleeping it stopped breathing with a series of spasms that shook its entire body.

When the young woman awoke the sun had gone down and the desert was filled with the last purple light of day. There was a single star, actually a planet, in the eastern sky. There was not a sound, nothing, over the entire desert. All was still, as it had been since the beginning of time and would be forever more. It was a supernatural quiet, like the silence that accompanies a single cloud that hovers motionless in the sky, or a beam of light that cuts across the desert from a break in the mountains, or a perfectly balanced pair of scales in a place where people do not exist. For a moment she did not know who she was or where she was or whether this was a bad dream or something real and then she remembered most of it.

For a full minute she could not recall whether she should start down or up the ravine, and then remembered she had to head down the ravine. Twice she became thoroughly confused and headed the wrong way. When she finally returned to the road she decided it was safest to sleep there for the night. She laid the dead dog nearby. As she slept in the road that night, her head on a rock that was somewhat shaped like a pillow, a desert fox, smelling the dog, came near, but seeing that she was still breathing, continued on the same route he took every night. It was a young fox, born that May, and he had never smelled a human before. The scent of a human was not as musky as a ground squirrel, but not as faint as a mouse. It was not the smell of death, not yet, but there was some promise in it still.

At first light she awoke, sat up and in a loose shaky hand wrote a brief note on the back of a five dollar bill with the face of Abraham Lincoln on it identifying who she was and she also wrote something for her parents. She thought of them sitting at the butcher block table in the kitchen back home, worried about her being late and wondering who to call, and she wanted to cry. They had no idea where she was and they would be fearing the worst. She thought of some more things to say and then she added them to the note. They were simple words shaped in the form of an apology. She then put her hands together and prayed that her life be spared. She wanted to live, she wanted to have a baby one day, she wanted to see her home again.

Before standing up she looked around at the desert and saw for the first time how beautiful it was in the early morning light. There were flowers scattered widely over the landscape in all directions. She did not know their names—rabbitbrush, groundsel, aster, verbena, thistle—and so she identified them by their colors—yellows and blues and pinks and occasionally a red. And it was all so very still, so quiet. She saw that there was really not that much to fear in the desert. It was a living thing, just like she was. It was doing the best it could and, really, it was full of wonders. She was not angry anymore, or frightened. Her only sadness was that she would not be able to share her discovery with the world.

One step after another, more a shuffle than a walk, she started down the road. After a mile, which took one hour and ten minutes, she stopped to rest. Her skin was badly scorched and her lips were cracked open and her mouth was as dry as the dust on a rock and her whole body had begun to gently tremble. Every so often it would shudder, but mostly it was a steady trembling. If someone would have seen her at a distance they would have thought she was a very old woman. She was hunched over and moved in slow motion, stopping often, and seemed disordered, gazing at fixed points that were far away, or at objects nearby that did not merit close attention. Sometimes she was on her hands and knees, whispering to the earth, which was as heavy and still as she was.

It was while she was resting there at the bend in the road that she thought she heard a distinct repetitive sound coming from the south, from the direction of Lake Powell, and by degrees a memory came back to her. She had overheard a conversation at the hot dog counter in the gas station the night before she left Hite Marina. Two rangers were discussing the need to check on a smoke plume from a lightning strike in the Henry Mountains near eleven thousand six hundred foot Mount Ellen. They decided they would run the flight early the next morning before it became hot and the air molecules expanded and the fully-loaded helicopter didn't have sufficient lift on its rotors to safely reach higher altitudes. She remembered almost every major word of it now with something approaching clarity and she recalled the matches in her jeans pocket and pulled them out. There was a dry greasewood bush beside her and, with one match, she set the tangled mass of branches, twigs, and dried leaves ablaze. She ran from bush to bush, setting each on fire, and within seconds a quarter of an acre of the parched desert was burning. One by one the desiccated oily plants burst into flame and, in the windless air of morning, the gray-white smoke rose in a ragged column straight up toward the center of the blue heavens. The helicopter spotted the smoke in due course and was almost overhead now, and she ran into the middle of the road, screaming and jumping up and down and waving her red bandana. She could see the pilot looking down and he waved back and she knew then that she would be saved.

When the red helicopter landed in the middle of the road she stood just outside its airwash, still waving, and one of the two men, dressed in an orange fire-resistant flight suit, came running over. He lifted the darkly shaded visor on his white helmet and handed her a clear plastic bottle of water and she began to drink.

"Not too much at first, now," he cautioned, his voice a shout over the roar of the twin turbines, "too much water can kill you just as much as too little."

It was at that moment that the first light of day struck her face and she opened her eyes and, rising on an elbow, realized that it had all been a dream. Nothing had happened and nothing had changed.

She was still in the great quiet desert and everything was the same.

She heard something nearby, a rustling, and turned to see a raven in the middle of the road, feeding upon Casey. Its feathers had a blue-black sheen to them and they were glistening in the sun. The raven paid no attention to her. The abandoned mining spur was outside its customary feeding area along the main highway, but today, not finding any fresh roadkill, it had flown west over the desert. The reconnaissance didn't require much energy—just a flap of the wings now and then—and sometimes there would be a dead ground squirrel the desert foxes hadn't found yet, or a jackrabbit that was too large for the horned rattlesnake to swallow or an injured mule deer that had wandered off and died in the brush.

Yes, she was still in this desert place. She knew with certainty that she must begin walking, but she also understood that she did not quite have the strength to rise from the ground and begin walking. She felt like a discarded husk, a shadow of something that passes in the imagination, a wilted shell waiting to be blown away back into a dream.

She lay there for some minutes, not so much contemplating her situation as floating outside her body in an exhausted daze, drifting between this world and the next. She understood now how close the two worlds were, side by side actually, and how easy it was to cross over from one to the other, and back again. There, she had done it. Now she would do it again. It was so simple. Back and forth. Like a dance that stepped now on the ground and now in the stream. There was nothing difficult about it. She could go back, a year in the past, or forward, a year in the future. Everything was fluid. All time was present in every moment and all things were filled with the same light. She saw that now. The world was spinning, spinning and she was dancing and in a moment or two she would dance one way, in one direction, and would not come back to the other side. There would be no reason to. She understood that now, and that it would all happen on the beautiful sandy desert where things were being born and dying every moment, and that it was all the same, really, because even when things were dead they were still alive, only in another way. Even the warm rocks on which she stood. If only people knew, she thought, how differently they would live.

It was then that she heard something.

She stood up stiffly and put both hands to both ears and listened. It was a rhythmic metallic sound, distant and nearly inaudible but still definitely there, a persistent signal barely registering on the furthest edge of the senses. She turned methodically in a circle, listening in every direction with every fiber of her being, and three-quarters of the way through the second rotation she spotted a red Forest Service helicopter on the southern horizon coming directly toward her. It was as tiny as a mosquito, but it was definitely there. It was real. This was not a dream anymore. She had awakened from all that. She reached into her pocket and found the matches and knew then exactly what she had to do.

Becoming the Desert

You have much to do.

The first task is to find a solid rock with a fine prospect. There is a good place high on the south canyon wall of the Colorado River near Spanish Bottom. There is another spot about forty miles down the Pariah River from Bryce Canyon, a purple clay hill above an arroyo, but you will naturally find your own. Sit on the rock for an hour before sunrise. It is important to be there for the full hour. Eventually the sun will strike your face. Close your eyes and feel the rays in your bones. Let them fill your form with warmth and light. Do not think of any dark thoughts. Forget about your past. Do not consider the future. Empty yourself of anything that is not filled with warmth and light and happiness. Relax. Breathe in rhythm with the sky, which breathes as we do.

Eventually you will be at peace and you will be relieved of a burden you did not realize could be so easily lifted.

Do not be reluctant to feel joy, but avoid euphoria, for it is made of the same sand as the heat mirage on the desert.

Listen then to the canyon wrens among the green cottonwoods in a dry wash. They have much to teach you. Do not bother taking notes. They will be there again tomorrow morning delivering the same lecture. If you attend every day, you will learn much from them.

There is a collared lizard in a crevice above a rock with a hole in it that is as tall as a quaking aspen tree. If you sit there for awhile he will come out to visit. Study his eyes. They will tell you what to do next.

Now you've found it. The ruins, I mean. The Anasazi cliff dwelling in the canyon near where the collared lizard lives. Do not go inside. That would be disrespectful. Picture a family there, a mother, a father, a child. Remember that they lived here in the rocks every time you think that your life is hard.

You are back in the city now. Go to the downtown library and study the books of John Wesley Powell and Clarence Dutton. Read Van Dyke and Stegner, Abbey and Fletcher. Read Thomas Merton's essay on the early Christian fathers and the deserts. Avoid all writing that is not filled with the light of the desert. After that proceed to the museum across the street and study the work of Thomas Moran and William R. Leigh. Seek out the photographs of William Henry Jackson. Compare Timothy O'Sullivan's image of the White House ruins at Canyon de Chelly with your memory of the place. Edgar Payne, Maynard Dixon, Everett Ruess—they will soon be familiar to you. Find the images of Laura Gilpin and Joseph Muench, Ansel Adams and Eliot Porter. Notice how Georgia O'Keeffe painted not landscapes but single rocks.

Watch a silent film from 1925 entitled *The Vanishing American* and all of John Ford, especially *The Searchers*. Visit a place called The Hole in the Wall where the rocks still remember the shadows of Butch Cassidy and the Sundance Kid.

Listen to the music of the Navajo as they chant to a deer-skin drum in a hogan along the San Juan River. Listen to the young wrangler as he whistles the song of a hermit thrush that he just heard along the trail. Listen to the young mother in a cabin at the end of the road, as she whispers a lullaby to her restless baby, a melody that just came to her in the night. And listen to the elk that bugle every September in the ponderosa groves along the South Rim, and to the white-throated swifts that fill the Escalante Canyon each spring, and to the autumn wind in the cattails along the Green River north of the confluence with the Colorado.

After you have experienced all of these things, discard them. Forget this whole part of your experience, but remember that it will always be there like the earth, part of the landscape on which you walk and which you need in order to walk.

You are back in the desert now. After much practice you have learned to use the pelvic bone of a deer, held above your head like a lens, to focus the light. And you have also discovered that your heart can be made into a nest of mud and twigs, attracting the darting arrow-shaped birds of love.

Coming out of the deep shadows of a narrow slot canyon near Page, Arizona, in early July, the noonday sun will strike you and almost knock you down. Remember the power of that light, and how something that came to you across space once made you stumble for a moment. And that it occurred in the desert. And remember that the light of the sun is not on you, but in you, and that your substance was once part of its fire, and will be again. And know, too, that your spirit is part of something larger and older than the sun.

Join the coyotes as they sing the stars up and then run with them through the night, learning all of the secrets of the dark world. They will show you places that you did not know existed, however familiar you are with the landscape. A cave where a man hid the body of his business partner a century ago. The dry wash frequented by desert bighorn sheep where the dinosaur tracks have not yet been found. A sparkling black meteorite the size of a pinyon pinecone that fell burning to earth three nights ago and still smells of sulphur. A rock shelf where the musky rattlesnakes gather when it is cold. When morning comes you may wash in the river. There will be blood on your muzzle that is not your own blood. Take particular note of the prints you now leave on the sand and of the juniper berries in your hair.

Walk, too, a night or two with the lion as she drifts among the pot-holes at the base of Navajo Mountain. She will take you to a starlit oak tree beneath which the rabbits pass on their way to water. You will see that an hour before dawn she always crosses the canyon at a place where a wandering ghost sometimes appears, the figure bent over the water as if in search, a sight which can easily be seen by the green luminous eyes of the lion. You will notice that even the lion is disturbed by the sight, and hurries off into the cedars, her pregnant belly swinging.

Study the four and five-sided maps that form on dry river beds after the rainy season. They will lead you to other universes, parallel to our own. In them you may meet people identical to yourself, but who have made other choices. The stories they tell you will help you in your journey. You may wish to keep these maps but if you try to take them home they will crumble in your hands.

If you are hiking along the Virgin River one day when the alders are turning and come upon a white-haired man who observes that seeing such a fine place he feels as though his life in a faraway city was wasted, give him a handful of acorns and tell him to walk up farther into the canyon and plant each in a good place.

Draw a line anywhere on the sand in the desert and realize that any line drawn anywhere on this or any world is part of a much larger circle.

Any of the major rapids in the central canyon will do—Grapevine or Serpentine or Kanab. Position yourself on top of a dislodged chunk of Vishnu schist. You will know it by the smooth glassy touch and the gray-blue density. Be well above the water line but not completely out of danger. Let the water soak you. The roar of the river will be louder than the sound of one hundred waterfalls. Hurl your questions in its general direction and you will immediately receive a reply. Hear the big bass drum, *boom, boom, boom,* calling out over the waves. At first it will puzzle you, but then you will understand. Every few minutes a large curious wave will come up out of nowhere and embrace you. Once you are completely soaked by them you will have been accepted by the river. You will hear tales of drowned kayakers and spring floods and floating logs that came down the side canyons like arks with baby owls and corn snakes and squirrels. The river will tell you of the quiet place where it was born, at the bottom of a glacier near a valley called Kawuneechee, and of the place where it dies in the palmetto marshes of the Gulf of California. And it will tell you that it is continually dying and being reborn, and that this is the same for everything in the universe.

After you are done, you will notice that the red silt of the river clings to your body, and that your clothes are now forever stained red. Consider this a gift from the river, a garment finer than any made of silk or any other cloth.

Watching an approaching storm from your campsite at Point Sublime on the North Rim, you will note the lightning on the South Rim and then count the seconds before you hear the thunder. Remember that your life is as brief.

In Grand Gulch when the snows on Cedar Mesa are melting and the thrushes have returned and the pasqueflowers are blossoming there is a waterfall that drops off a shelf of sandstone like the long blond hair of a young woman. If you go there she will sing to you. These are songs that are too beautiful to be sung by anything other than the water of early spring.

There is a natural arch in Monument Valley that is the color of a mariposa lily in the shade. Touching the smooth stone, elders have been known to become children again, and children, walking through the aperture, have been known to speak with the wisdom of the ages. Mourning

doves, flying through the portals, have turned into hawks—I have this
on reliable authority—and rain whistling through the portals often becomes snowflakes—this I have seen. Be careful where you step near such
places in the desert, for they are openings not only in the rock but also
in the spirit.

If you are an artist and wish to paint the last light of the sun as it
touches a high cliff on Capitol Reef, dip your brush not onto your
palette but into the nearby blossom of an orange globemallow. You
will notice that the honey bees are covered with a similar orange, and
that they return to the same flowers often to restore the purity of their
own color.

Gather the fallen blue petals of the lupine and the flax, the larkspur
and the harebell. Save them in a turtle shell—preferably the shell of a
western box turtle. On an overcast day you may then scatter them across
the sky and everyone will be grateful. With a single sunflower tossed into
the air the picture will be complete.

If you see a young man and woman quarreling at the trailhead to the
Bright Angel Trail over who left the camera at the Denny's Restaurant in
Page, Arizona, let them use one of your cameras for the day and you will
be amazed at their amazement.

A skull in the desert is a fine thing. But always return it to the place
where you found it.

Here is an exercise that may seem easy. The month is now January.
The holidays are past and you drive out to the desert for some star-
gazing. Pick a clear night with a full moon and wear warm clothes. Hike
up a drainage that has some water in it. Any of those streams draining
west from the La Sal Mountains behind Moab will do. They will be half-
frozen, of course, and that is why you want to be near them. Kneel beside the stream in a place where the banks are thick with snow and the
water is covered with ice. There will be yellow aspen leaves caught in the
ice, and heart-shaped cottonwood leaves, and the long slender leaves of
willow. Some will still be green. Here and there a bit of sand may be
caught in the ice, sparkling where it fell. Elsewhere there will be twigs
the squirrels dropped and branches half submerged and half exposed to
the air. You will see another world, a frozen cosmos with nebulae and
galaxies and black holes and pulsing neutron stars. Note how time and

space warp around an empty place, an air bubble with sides as smooth as your eye, or how miniature tunnels form from one realm to the other. There is no need to set up a telescope to look for the edge of the universe. It is much closer than that. The edges are everywhere. They are even inside us. As is the center.

Before you leave drop a heavy angular rock the size of your hand into the open current just below the ice. You will observe that the water splashes in all directions, upstream and downstream. Remember that the next time you sense what is going to happen, or when you are suddenly splashed by something that occurred long ago. Time has many metaphors, but the stream has only one.

Try this—imagine that there is a worse predicament in the desert than to be buried beneath it.

If you are talking to someone who has died in a deep canyon where no one else can hear, telling them how much you love them and how much you miss them, know that they are listening. Know that when you touch the canyon wall, and the canyon wall feels warm, they are touching you back. Know that their silence is not reticence but the highest form of speech.

In after years, caught in rush hour traffic somewhere, you will recall— the smell of the sage in the desert that afternoon when it rained and the car got stuck in Bullfrog Creek; the scent of aspen leaves underfoot on Wilson Mesa that morning you found the clay pot that you never told anyone about, leaving it there for the mouse to live in; the fragrance of the blossoming cliffrose the day you walked the trail to Bridger's Knoll for the first time; the cedar campfire that night on the cliff above the Needles when you stayed up and watched shooting stars; the musk of the elk in the ponderosas near Zuni Point, and the lingering smell of the sap on your fingers.

Try this—imagine something more tragic than the inability to love.

If you should ever find anything of value in the desert—a piece of sky-blue turquoise the size of a Fremont Canyon apple, or a freshly broken rock that appears to be sprinkled inside with golden dust—discard it immediately, for these things will lead you into a canyon where many people have been buried before they died.

One last thing.

The next time you are in the desert you should go looking for a stone. This could be a moon-colored geode from the oak canyons near Monticello, where the rock hunting is always good. Or it could be a smooth riverstone from the banks of the San Juan River—a black volcanic egg with a cream-colored band, perhaps, or a red sphere with a polished surface. Or it could be a milky agate from an aspen-covered mountain that rises high above the low desert near Tarantula Mesa. Whatever the case, this will be your dreamstone. It will find a place beside your bed, and, in your hand, transport you far away whenever you need to be taken far away, and provide you a sleep as restful as any that you had in the desert.

Dark Canyon

THE SPRING WAS LOCATED at the head of a side canyon eleven miles south of the Colorado River. The side canyon had no formal name, nor did the spring. Neither was drawn on any map, nor were they represented on the quadrangle sheets stored in the wooden chart drawers of the government offices in Monticello. Both had somehow been missed by every ground tracking party ever sent into the wilderness. The general region was as rugged as it was remote, and was rarely visited. People flocked to Monument Valley, or to Natural Bridges National Monument, but not to this place. It was far from the river, quite a distance from the backcountry roads and deeply buried in a sprawling desert closed for half a century to anything other than foot travel. And so it remained unchanged, year after year. It was a place well known by the birds, especially in the hot days of the summer, when the doves and wrens and swifts came each morning to drink. They trusted the spring as a place of constant water, even during droughts. They would rest in the branches of the single cottonwood tree that rose, massive and gray-trunked, above the spring, or in the nearby ponderosas, their shaggy bark the color of wild turkeys. Below the spring there was not much of a stream. The water ran for fifty yards over the dusty red shale and then disappeared underground. It would not resurface until just above the Colorado River, a clear waterfall that dropped over a sandstone ledge before running across some rocks into the muddy current.

The desert bighorn sheep came to the spring every third or fourth day. There were two groups of them. The first was a mixed band of ewes, spring lambs, and young rams whose horns had yet to inscribe a half circle. The second group were the resident bachelors, five in all. Their horns were massive and full-curled, and appeared more like chiseled stone than living matter. One ram in particular carried horns that were heavier than the rest, and flared widely at the tips. The sheep lived together in two separate bands until December, when they all assembled in a grassy pasture high above the spring for about a week. The rest of the year they lived apart in different regions of the canyon. The only time they went near the Colorado River, where they could possibly be seen, was late in the winter. But no one floated the river late in the winter.

When the sheep came to drink at the spring, they would make their way down the rocks very slowly, constantly testing the air with their black noses and listening carefully with their oval ears. Their eyes, however, were their best defense. They could see the collared lizard sunning itself on a rock near the water long before it was aware of their presence, and they could watch the squirrel that had just dropped a pinyon pinecone from a branch in a tree a mile away. Most of the mountain lions lived over the ridge in the Blue Mountains, where the hunting was good for mule deer. Every once in a while, though, a mountain lion would tire of venison and come hunting for mutton. The older sheep knew about these lions, and remembered with fine detail how the big tawny cats suddenly leapt for the neck from behind, and how every line was a bold controlled curve. Most distinctly, they recalled the peculiar scent of the lions on the wind.

The bighorn sheep lived peacefully in this canyon for many decades, alone and largely undisturbed. Elsewhere, the world went through its usual mutations. Presidents good and bad came and went. New wars were fought in old places. A steady stream of inventions were unveiled to the public. Saints and sinners were paraded on alternate weeks in the press. But nothing in this place was altered. It remained an obscure corner of the earth, lost and forgotten. All things must pass, the eastern philosophers observe, and so the anonymity of this place, too, would ultimately change. The transformation would begin with a whitewater kayaker from Flagstaff. This young man, whose name was Grisham Bell, was different from most river-travelers. When he glimpsed a waterfall on the tangled south bank of the river he was impelled to come ashore and investigate. He carried his kayak up into the brush and, curiously casting about, soon found a vertebrae. Grisham was a graduate biology student. He knew from the robust flanges that flared like wings from the central ring that this was the lumbar vertebra of a desert bighorn sheep, a species thought to have been killed off locally by the uranium prospectors who scoured the country in the 1950s. This particular bone was not an ancient relict, he observed, but was, rather, a fresh specimen, with strands of brown-red fiber still attached to the core.

Intrigued, he filled his pack and hiked up into the canyon. Half a day and eleven miles later, he found the side canyon and the spring and spotted the bachelor band, which bolted stiff-legged for the cliffs as soon as they saw him. Grisham had a camera in his pack, however, and photographed the giant ram just as he turned his head to look back. A copy of the image soon found its way to the state wildlife headquarters, and the senior managers there duly made inquiry of the local game warden. Bob Franklin of the Colorado River district had known about the isolated herd for over a decade, but had told no one, other than his wife, so as to protect the rams from poachers. The next week he was called to the regional office for a meeting with the sort of people who rarely leave offices, and a letter of reprimand was inserted in his permanent file.

The photograph of the ram shortly appeared in newspapers across the West. It was not long before the chief executive of Safari Club International in Las Vegas called his annual one-shot antelope hunting partner, the governor of Utah. His plan was straightforward and appeared to have its virtues, even if it employed a bit of negative logic. It went something like this: "We all know this magnificent animal will be illegally taken if someone does not legally harvest it, so let us agree to hold an auction for a single license and then all the money will go to desert sheep management. That way everyone wins, even the endangered sheep." One month later, an auction was conducted on the Internet, and continued for one weekend. Bids came in from wealthy sheep hunters around the world—Argentina, Russia, Germany, Brunei, and Saudi Arabia. Everyone was certain this would be a new world record.

The winning bid was two hundred and seventy-three thousand dollars.

ii.

THERE IS A PICTURE OF Leonard Cross that shows him with his friend Donald "Cisco" Doogan, both of them in Marine uniform in Honolulu. Cross wears the rank insignia of lance corporal. Cisco was a private first class. This was during the Second World War. Whenever someone comes into his office and asks about the picture, Cross tells the story of how he and his best buddy Cisco once asked two hula girls out for dinner. After the young women ordered, he and Cisco realized they did not have enough money to pay for the meal. They then politely excused themselves to the restroom, and proceeded to crawl out the back window into the alley. Cross always laughs good-naturedly at this point, and the visitor laughs, too. The point of the story is to emphasize to everyone in the room that even the renowned Leonard Cross was once just another poor guy who could not afford a proper date.

Cross's personal fortune has been variously reported at various times in various amounts. The consensus seems to be that he is among the twenty or thirty wealthiest people in the country. After the war, he and Cisco returned to San Diego and began to salvage junk metal from decommissioned naval vessels. At first they only had a surplus two and a half ton diesel truck. Later they had a fleet of flatbed trailers and eventually they became part-owners of a rail line. In 1950 Cisco died in a commercial plane crash over the Grand Canyon. After that Cross ran the company. The profitable salvage operation soon turned into another business, which led to another, and so on, until, forty years later, even he was not certain what the nature of all his activities were. It was an empire that spread around the globe and included everything from hotel chains to television stations to a professional football team. He even owned an art museum in Phoenix, which featured the traditional Western paintings collected by his second wife Phyllis, who had drowned while they were boating on Lake Powell. Cross was currently in the fifth year of his fourth marriage, his wife a thirty-one-year-old former beauty queen from Terrebonne, Louisiana, who had also enjoyed a brief modeling career in Manhattan.

It was late October now and Cross and his wife Peyton Lacombe were getting off a raft just below the waterfall on the Colorado River. The biology graduate student Grisham Bell was with them, serving as the hired guide at Cross's request. It took about an hour for the gear to be carried to the bench above the river. After organizing the supplies, they then deflated the raft, concealed it and some wooden boxes in the brush, and packed into the canyon. Cross was in good spirits, for the ram would complete his "grand slam" of record North American sheep. The summer heat had gone off the desert and the days were getting shorter now. The rams would be spending more time with the ewes, as they prepared for early December. They would be less wary, even when coming to water. The hunt had every prospect for success. At sixty-four, Cross was still in reasonable shape. His wife was also in good condition. She often accompanied him on his hunts, and was herself an accomplished shot. They both carried full packs, and both carried loaded rifles as they followed Grisham up the canyon.

The hike in took the better part of one day. There was no trail, other than the game paths scattered here and there among the rocks. It was a hard climb in places, but it was not a particularly difficult climb for people accustomed to walking under a pack in the outdoors. The three of them established a base camp in an adjoining side canyon several miles below the spring. It was a protected spot where they could live in relative comfort and not disturb the sheep. There was a constant spring nearby, and all around was a vast supply of deadfall that had blown off the cliffs in windstorms. There was even a natural bridge a quarter-mile up the side canyon that no one had ever seen before. It had no name and was not recorded on any map and its presence reminded them that they were, indeed, in the back of the beyond.

After dinner the first night they sat around the cedar fire and Cross told stories about his sheep hunts around the world. He had hunted the argali in the snow mountains of Iran with the Shah before he was deposed and he had pursued the mouflon in Cyprus and the audad in France and the bharal or "blue sheep" of the Himalayas. He had managed to bag an *Ovis poli* in Marco Polo's China, the first western hunter allowed in the wilderness province since Theodore Roosevelt. Up north he had hunted Dall sheep with Lynn Castle on the Wood River in the Alaska Range and stone sheep with Ned Frost in the Cassiars of British Columbia. All of the ranges of Alberta and Montana were familiar to him. He had stories of a plane crash in Wyoming and frostbite in the Yukon and dysentery in Baja and armed bandits in Mongolia and runaway horses in Yugoslavia and broken ribs in the Atlas Mountains and this went on until after midnight at which point he and his yawning wife retired to their backpacking tent. Grisham slept on his foam pad beside the fire beneath Orion and a nearly full moon that kept him awake.

The next morning the three of them rose before dawn and hiked up to the spring and conducted a general survey of the area. Cross decided they should build a blind. A place was selected about one hundred and fifty yards downstream, and they worked on the blind until noon. As Grisham gathered wood for the blind Peyton often stared at him. She liked his beard the color of red sandstone and the blue bandana he wore around his neck that was the same faded blue as his eyes and the way his chest swelled beneath the Poison Spider Mountain Bike Shop t-shirt. At one point Grisham called her over to look at the petroglyph of a ram that had been scratched on the desert varnish by an earlier hunter, some ten or twelve centuries earlier. As Grisham pointed at the petroglyph, she reached out to touch the rock and instead touched his finger. She then pretended to lose her balance, and grasped his hand for support. Cross saw none of this because he was busy with the blind.

For the next two days they waited in the blind from dawn to dusk, speaking only in the lowest tones, and through all those many hours of sitting together watching the spring not one sheep came.

At dinner on the third night Cross declared that they must now climb into the cliffs and take the hunt to the sheep because, with the full moon, the herds were obviously drinking at night. Grisham remembered a trail that could lead them into the heights and the next day they hunted the cliffs. They hunted there all day, looking for sheep. They found plenty of fresh tracks, but no sheep. On the way down Cross slipped on a ledge while looking to see where his wife was and fell about four feet, smashing his knee against a sharp rock and damaging his rifle scope. His face went white with pain and he only returned to camp with some difficulty.

That evening a new plan was formulated. Cross would rest in camp with a wet bloody towel wrapped around his badly swollen knee. Grisham and Peyton would hunt the ram. When Peyton killed it with the backup rifle, she would give credit to him. Cross said he had done this once before in the Mackenzie Mountains of the Northwest Territories, had sustained an injury and then paid a native guide to shoot a Dall ram for him and then lie about it. Such practices were common among trophy hunters, he explained. The main thing was to get the animal, no matter what. That was their code. Grisham's face remained expressionless through this. Peyton was accustomed to such pronouncements.

Two hours after sunrise the next day Grisham and Peyton finally reached the rim of the canyon. They used their binoculars all morning, glassing the terrain below, but saw only one ewe and one lamb, which had apparently been left behind when the herd left the area. They could see the smoke plume from the campfire, rising narrow and pale, from the terrain far below. It was a fine day and they admired the panorama and pointed at distant landmarks. The Henry Mountains were visible to the far west, colored light purple. Island in the Sky rose to the north. One tiny part of the river was visible. High above, a golden eagle was circling in the cloudless sky. They were sitting very close against a rock, as they had in the blind, with their shoulders touching and they remained this close as they ate their lunch. An hour or so later they hiked over the ridge-top to the head of another canyon. Here there were tall ponderosas and deep blue shade and Peyton suggested they lay down on the bed of fallen pine needles and take a nap. Several minutes later she mentioned that she had a chronically sore neck from a gymnastics accident when she was fourteen and asked Grisham for a back rub.

The next day they returned to the same place and made love again. It was after this that Peyton began to tell Grisham what her life with Cross was really like. Grisham, being a scientist, was not accustomed to facts being casually mixed with fiction, and so he believed it all, every word of it. Peyton told him that Cross had made her sleep with business partners to consummate deals, which was only partially true—she had slept with business partners. She told him that Cross had murdered his second wife Phyllis when she asked for a divorce, which was not remotely true—he had dived in and tried to save her when she fell into the lake. She told him that she had fallen in love with him, Grisham, and that she wanted to live with him for the rest of her life and bear his children. She told him that Cross would have them both killed and that the only way for their love to survive and for their children to be born was for Cross to have an unfortunate mishap. She suggested to Grisham how this event might occur. He, Grisham, would be unloading the rifle across the campfire and it would go off in his hands. She would be the only witness and she would swear that it was an accident.

After that they could be together, forever.

Grisham said he needed more time to think about it, even when she cried and begged him to do this for her, for them, for their future together.

For the next two days they kept returning to the trees, Peyton memorizing every pinecone above.

On the third day they returned early to camp with wonderful news. The ram had at last been spotted. They knew just where he was. Tomorrow he would be theirs. It was time to celebrate. Cross opened a flask he was saving for just this occasion. He proceeded to drink the entire thing, and to fall asleep against the deadfall he had somehow dragged into the clearing. Peyton said she had to go up the canyon and whispered in Grisham's ear before she left. While she was waiting in the shade under the natural bridge, she heard a shot go off. Just one. It echoed through the canyon for a long time. A raven called out once. A small rock tumbled from the cliffs above. Nothing more. And then there was the silence of the desert.

She returned along a sage-covered ridge. Beside a broken ledge of sandstone near the bottom of the ridge she found the place where she had earlier put Cross's rifle. She picked the gun up in her gloved hands and confirmed a round was chambered and then made her way slowly toward the campsite, following the tang of woodsmoke. Soon she was very near. From behind a cedar she saw Grisham sitting across the fire from Cross. Grisham's head was in his hands. It appeared as though he was crying. The rifle was in his lap. She walked on the sides of her feet in the sand, not making a sound. All that could be heard was the crackling of the fire. She stopped when she was standing directly behind her dead husband. Peyton then called out Grisham's name. When he looked up she shot him in the chest. He slumped over and it was quiet again, except for the crackling of the fire. She then placed the rifle in the hands of her dead husband. That way it would appear the two men had killed each other in an argument over her, which would be her story.

iii.

THE NEXT MORNING Bob Franklin hiked in from the river on schedule to check on the progress of the hunt and found the hysterical wife and the two fly-covered bodies. He listened sympathetically to her account, and let her sob for a time against his shoulder, but he also stared off thoughtfully into the trees. He had been in law enforcement all of his adult life. He had learned to be skeptical, to trust no one but himself in the pursuit of the truth, and to carefully assemble the facts and see what they told him. After awhile, Peyton was sufficiently composed for the hike out. On a steep embankment just above the river a leather-covered notebook fell from her backpack and Bob Franklin picked it up and quietly put it into his own.

The notebook turned out to be her daily journal.

At the trial, held in the county seat of Monticello, a jury of nine local people was duly seated. It consisted of a Navajo sheepherder, a working single parent, a coal miner, a convenience store clerk, a disabled veteran, a retired elementary schoolteacher, an out-of-work realtor, a secretary at the BLM, and an elderly housewife. There were five women and four men, and seven had resided in San Juan County for their entire lives. Peyton's lawyers, and there were three, tried to convince the jury that the journal was a fabrication. That was after her lead attorney had tried to have it ruled as inadmissible because it was obtained in a manner that compromised her right to privacy and appeared to violate certain Supreme Court guidelines in such matters. The jury did not believe her, deliberating only forty-five minutes, nor did the appellate judge, nor did the State Supreme Court. In the end, the sentence of life in prison without the possibility of parole was sustained in every venue.

Bob Franklin was provided with a substantial bequest from the estate of Leonard Cross, in gratitude for his service to the family and the community. He retired from the state shortly thereafter. You see him sometimes on the road south of Monticello in his new truck and horse trailer. He still checks on the desert bighorn sheep in Dark Canyon, but he prefers to take the scenic route over the Blue Mountains. The old ram is still there, his battered corrugated horns growing larger every year. He doesn't breed anymore. He just follows the other bachelors around. Bob's intention is to see that the ram dies a natural death, even if it is the sudden blow of a mountain lion from behind.

Hunt's Mesa

THE BEST PLACE TO BEGIN with a physical description of my friend Tom is with his face. It is a broad face, with a square jawline, a prominent chin, and a strong nose. It is not the kind of face that a person originally possesses in young adulthood. It is something that life—its mysteries and paradoxes, comedies and tragedies, reversals and injustices—slowly imparts to a person. It is an earned face, the expression of decades, the quintessence of the deeply lived journey. It is, for lack of a better word, the face of a philosopher. You see it in the look of a cottonwood in a dry wash that has survived a hundred winters or a weathered sandstone butte out on the sage flats or a length of smooth sculpted driftwood beside a canyon river. It is the look of something that has been reduced to its essentials, and from which everything irrelevant has been removed, so that only the simplest of forms, the core of beauty, remains.

Tom's skin is a light terra rosa, like the standing monuments of the valley where he lives, or the fallen acorns up on the mesas in the autumn. He wears his black hair in a single braid down the middle of his back. It reaches nearly to his sacrum. Although he is past fifty, he has not a single gray hair. His eyes are dark umber, but you won't see them, for he wears sunglasses in the bright sun of Monument Valley, even when it rains. He rarely smiles because he is missing a minor tooth. His voice is low and gentle and he never raises it. Most days he wears a white cowboy hat, some sort of a t-shirt, faded blue jeans, and well-worn cowboy boots. He is solidly built, with a big frame. Although he is not tall, he has the presence of a tall man, and so he appears so. When he is hiking, which is often, he wears old tennis shoes. As with anyone who has spent any time in the desert, he always carries a gallon of water with him wherever he goes.

Tom lives in a hogan about ten miles south of Monument Valley. Like all Navajo hogans, it has eight sides, and the door faces east. He lives there with his thirty-year-old wife, who is from Austria, and their little girl, who speaks only Navajo and German. He also has a family of Blue Healers, a few Appaloosas, a herd of woolly sheep. This is his second marriage. He does not speak much about his first. In the spring, summer, and fall he operates a guiding business in Monument Valley. Long ago and far away, he worked for a well-known tour company. One year the business was purchased by some people from the east. They began their brief reign by insisting that the Navajo guides wear uniforms. Tom walked out the door and started his own outfit.

In the winter he flies to Frankfurt with his wife and child. There he goes on the lecture circuit. The Germans, he observes, are fascinated with Navajo culture and always treat him with kindness and respect. He has grown to love their delicious beer, spiced potato salad, steamed bratwursts, and hot butter rolls. This cuisine, he sadly notes, has had a notable effect on his waistline. Once he taught Navajo at the Navajo Community College in Window Rock. He also taught Navajo for awhile at Stanford University. He believes that language is culture and despairs at the loss of language among the young. He is well read, and has pored over the complete works of Edward Abbey, and other poets of the desert. He is also a student of cinema, and can tell you exactly where John Wayne or Henry Fonda, Dennis Hopper or Tom Hanks stood in a celebrated scene of a particular film that was shot in Monument Valley.

How he and I became acquainted is a complicated story that in its simplest form goes something like this. One October there was an unusually powerful hurricane in the Caribbean that sank a number of ships, among them a lovely sloop from Belize with five or six courageous young people on board. The equinoctial storm moved north over the Yucatan Peninsula, the Gulf of Mexico, and the whole of the state of Texas and then proceeded, in its wandering course, to finally stall out over the Four Corners Region. I was camped in Monument Valley at the time, waiting for the weather to clear so that I could find a cover photograph for a book on the desert I was writing. I waited there for three nights and four days in the fog and rain and finally I could not wait anymore. I had several thousand more desert miles to cover before the snows of November. So I left, vowing like the wild geese and the green grass to return in the spring.

When I did return seven months later the May skies were blue and the summer crowds had not yet descended on the valley. I was standing in the parking lot of the visitor's center at Monument Valley admiring the view, when Tom, an alert and friendly entrepreneur, walked over and introduced himself. I explained what I was doing and he told me about a secret place at the south end of the valley called Hunt's Mesa. We would hike there on the mesa all day and it would be wonderful and the only drawback was that it would cost one hundred and twenty dollars. "No problem," I said. "Let's go." And so we did, driving south by southeast over the dirt tracks in the red sand with his nephew at the wheel of a beat-up Chevrolet Suburban.

The trail to the mesa began at the farthest bend of the farthest road, the nephew departing in a dust cloud after promising he would return at three-thirty. That would give us eight hours to make our climb. We loaded up, me with a backpack of camera equipment weighing forty pounds, and Tom with his gallon jug of water, and headed up a dry streambed into the wilderness. I had been to Monument Valley for years—it is a mecca for photographers—but I had never ventured very far out into it. For one thing, you must have a Navajo guide. For another, it is the sort of sacred landscape in which a human figure seems an unwelcome intrusion. Walking away from the dirt track, the ground felt palpably different. It always does, away from roads. I was so happy to be out there that day with someone who truly knew the valley that I wanted to shout with joy or let out a rebel yell, but, out of piety, I restrained myself.

As we hiked up the drainage Tom explained the country to me—what this plant is used for, what that rock is called in his language, where various animals can be found. Much of the conversation focused upon the natural color dyes used in making Navajo rugs. All of the colors, it turns out, come from native plants on the reservation. Pale yellow ochre, for example, is produced by boiling yarn in sagebrush leaves and twigs. A much brighter cadmium yellow can be obtained from the flowers of rabbitbrush. Bright orange is created from fresh sunflower petals. Red is derived from juniper roots or sometimes wild holly berries. The fruit of the prickly pear cactus produces a really nice purple. Black walnut shells make a brown so dark it is almost black. A lighter brown comes from sumac bark. And so on.

It was a slow march over the Martian red sand on that hot morning in May and so after awhile we stopped in the checkered shade of a lone juniper to have some water. One thing led to another and we somehow discovered to our mutual amazement that we were both ex-Marines. Instantly there was that bond of brotherhood that comes from having shared a common trial of the spirit. It turned out that we had also both served in the 1970s. To further the coincidence, we had also both gone through basic training at Paris Island and so, like two friends long separated, we cheerfully exchanged stories from the past.

After an hour or so, talking and walking side by side, we reached a sheer rock wall from which a rope dangled. The frayed rope hung from a rock shelf about two or three stories above us. At the top of the cliff was a colony of swallows. The blue air was filled with the sharp-winged birds. They sang in rolling churrs and squeaks and occasional grating sounds and all the while flew with ceaseless energy among their mud and twig nests. There were literally hundreds of them. The rope was the only way up the barrier that stood between us and the rest of the mesa and so it had to be scaled. We each inched up the rope, me going first with the pack full of bricks and he with the gallon jug in one hand, and then we rested for a moment on the narrow ledge on top, catching our breaths and watching the birds before continuing along the slickrock bench. There was no trail at this point and so we simply followed the steep ridgeline higher and higher up the north face of the mesa. To a golden eagle we would have been two inconsequential specks lost among the junipers and pinyons. To a mule deer we would have been a familiar scent on the wind. To a mountain lion we would have been part of a passing dream that came and went during the morning slumbers. Over my shoulder, to the north, an incredible view began to open up. The higher we climbed the more I wanted to stop and look, but I knew it would be best at the summit. We pressed on, drawn to the heights as all dusty pilgrims are.

Finally we were there, the view from east to west unobstructed, and I had to sit down. It was a sacrilege to remain standing. The entire valley was spread before us—solitary rocks, flat-topped mesas, heroic pinnacles, cathedral-like outcrops, far-away buttes, and all set upon a flat red sea of sand. The monuments were not grouped together, but stood apart in wide spaces with hazy violet mountains in the far distance. Taken as a whole, the scene looked like the remnant of some ancient city that Sven Hedin might have discovered along the Silk Road in the 1890s, a prehistoric site in which all the wooden buildings had been blasted away by time and only the monolithic stone structures remained. I thought of Wordsworth on another subject—"The city now doth like a garment wear/the beauty of the morning." The desert valley was wearing the morning like a translucent article of clothing, and the graceful light fell uniformly over the vast desolation, saturating earth tones and shadowing far rocks. It was all too much. I opened my camera pack and Tom disappeared without saying a word, knowing that I needed time to myself.

After an hour or so he returned and we had lunch on a sun-baked rock. All around us the tough cedars twisted from the ground and their branches filled the wind-swept heights with an aromatic scent. We could have found on this planet no finer place to dine. As we ate there, as happy as hawks and sharing what we had, we watched some Maynard Dixon clouds slowly build over the valley. There would be no rain that day, but they were building anyway, as if to practice. They drifted around like football players out on a field in a lazy scrimmage, just playing, not close to doing the real thing. I was glad they were not creating weather that day—lightning, downpours, flash floods. I had seen all that on other days. As we sat there watching the clouds we idly formed a list of our favorite places in the Southwest, places most people have never heard of, such as The Maze, The Gulch, The Narrows, The Wave, and The Racetrack. I had yet to visit The Racetrack—a dry lake bed where large rocks move hundreds of yards in straight lines for reasons not fully understood—and Tom explained how he had once driven a 1978 Toyota Corolla down the twenty-five-mile road to the place by using lifters on his underframe. The fact that he had actually driven out there, quite a distance from Monument Valley, to see those rocks impressed me more than anything else he told me that day.

I asked Tom if he knew Richie Nez, my Navajo friend from college days who had gone on to be a tribal lawyer, and he said no, but that it was a common name on the reservation. There followed a story about the time twenty years before when I found a dead golden eagle on Parkview Mountain in northern Colorado and took Richie to the place, Richie harvesting the wing and tail feathers for his grandfather, a medicine man on the Rez, as he called it. I then related a few more stories about other confluent matters that can not be recorded in print, as did Tom. We were both students of human nature and were comparing field observations.

Sometime after lunch we descended from the heights and retraced our route down the rocks and through the sun-bleached sand washes to the drop-off location. We talked less now, because we were running low on the water. It had become very hot, the sun now having roasted the desert for nearly twelve hours. Once at the spot we waited patiently for about thirty minutes. It seemed safe to then assume that the nephew was not going to show up and so we decided to start walking. For one thing, all of our water was now gone. For another, Tom confided that his nephew was not always wholly reliable. Besides, he could always follow our tracks along the road. We walked at a steady pace past distinctive rock formations such as the Totem Pole and the Yeibichai, both well known to those who watch John Ford films. At the Sand Springs we decided to take a shortcut to the North Window—a picturesque gap in a rock wall—and turned off through the dune fields.

A hundred yards later it seemed a well-intentioned mistake. Our pace had dwindled to a slow-motion stumble and our thirst was growing with each step. The temperature was well into the nineties and the sand was not a coarse friendly riverbank sand but a diabolically fine beach powder sand. For the first time all day, there was a Stoic silence. But then something miraculous happened. The late afternoon sun began to create beautiful shadows among the red dunes. Wherever the wind had rippled the loose particles of sand a shadow was born, and each was in a long delicate curve, and frequently they were formed in parallel sinuous rows—dozens, hundreds, thousands of them. Once again, the tripod was planted and photography began in earnest. It was one of those rare magic moments of light and landscape. I recalled the lines of Ernest Blumenschein on first seeing the Taos valley—"I saw whole paintings right before my eyes. Everywhere I looked I saw paintings perfectly organized, ready to paint." What I was seeing were whole photographs right before my eyes, everywhere. Tom waited patiently, and the only complaints heard from his direction were in the form of jokes. Finally, the heat subdued even my creative fire.

A mile later we reached a four wheel drive track and collapsed there in the lovely relentless desert sun, waiting for a ride. Two discarded saddle blankets would have appeared to have had more life. The nephew never showed, but we finally hitched a ride with an acquaintance of Tom's who was driving his pickup truck through the desert looking for a lost herd of goats. As we rode in the back of the pickup, drinking some water the man gave us, we discussed the possibility of bringing people to the southern valley for three-day workshops in writing and photography. Tom remembered that he had a dozen backpacking tents left over from a film shoot, a gift from the producer, and I was already imagining various modules. We didn't even notice the potholes in the road that lifted us from the bed of the truck and brought us crashing down, or the fact that the metal on the bed of the truck was too hot to touch, or the coyote-like dog who didn't want us anywhere near his corner of the universe.

The day ended exactly where it began, although the sun was now on the opposite side of the sky. Much remained the same, but much had changed. It was one of those days you always remember, as when you cross a wide pass from one country to another. As we shook hands I learned my first Navajo word, *Ahe-hee'h*—which means "Thank you."

Bend in the River

THERE HAD BEEN A GROUP OF THEM, at first, five kayakers running the river west of the Highway 191 bridge. Gradually she had lingered behind, tiring of their conversation and how it distracted her from the landscape and her own thoughts. Finally she had waved them on. Now she was alone. She paddled in the middle of the river for awhile, but the trip was going a bit too fast and so she angled the kayak toward the south bank. She found a channel where the water was deep and slow, and stayed there, paddling now and then to remain with the current. The channel was like a stream in the midst of the river. The bank with its shallow water was to her left and was overgrown with willow, tamarisk, and the occasional cottonwood. All around her, north and south, rose the sheer red cliffs and standing rocks of the desert.

This was not her first time down this stretch of the Colorado, but this was her first time without companions.

Everything along the river was in shades of tropical green, for it was June, and the birds were everywhere—herons and egrets, mallards and geese, sandpipers and seagulls, mourning doves and red-winged black-birds, a kingfisher and a pair of osprey. They were all vocalizing. One bird was defending its nest in the cattails. Another was searching for a fallen hatchling. Still others were attracting mates or calling out for assistance or sounding alarms. The canyon bottom was one continual song. As she listened to their music she began to quietly sing an old folk standard. It was a melancholy tune that she liked to sing when she was alone. She looked around to see if anyone was around, and, not seeing a soul, she began to express herself with more resolve. Soon she was sustaining notes with the volume and vibrato she had once used in the college choir back in Chapel Hill. She sang the song several times and then some Broadway show tunes and then her throat was sore and she stopped.

All of that, the dream of a career in music, was a long time ago. Now she was a physician, a senior resident, and was about to begin a practice in rural Utah. It was, by any standard, a fair arrangement. For each year she worked in the small town, the government would forgive one year of her medical school debt. In four years she would be released from that burden, and then she could be a pediatrician anywhere. She was thirty years old and all of her life was ahead of her, or at least what was supposed to be the good part.

Something was moving in the water ahead. At first she thought it was a beaver, but then she saw from the length that it was an otter. She had seen otters before on other rivers, but this was her first otter in the West. It must have, she thought, come in from the Dolores. The otter had not noticed her yet and so she approached silently from behind. The animal was cruising with the current, pushing steadily with only its eyes, nose, and ears showing. All of his lines were sculpted and swept back. It was a lovely slender body with a short muzzle, a broad and flattened head, a muscular neck and trunk, and a powerful tapered tail trailing behind it to a point. Everything about the otter was made for the water, from the head curved like a river stone, to the tiny ears flattened into the dense fur, to the fur itself—a dark brown coat so fluid and fine it seemed he wore the element in which he swam. Only his stiff white whiskers protruded visibly outward.

She followed him for awhile and then he turned suddenly and swam over to the bank and got out of the water. He paused for a moment— she noticed that he was a male—and looked at her and then he disappeared up a muddy slide into the vegetation. With some effort she worked her kayak into the shaded cove, pulled herself out of the craft, and then dragged the ten-foot kayak up the twelve-foot slide and onto the clay bench. She heard some rustling in the leaves and branches not far away and followed the musky sound until she was completely lost. She then returned to the slide area—the remains of catfish and suckers everywhere—and was about to get back on the river when she noticed a deer trail off in another direction and this she followed.

It was a green, winding tunnel filled with mosquitoes and black flies and honeybees, and one hundred yards later she found herself facing a red sandstone cliff. The deer trail angled back and forth over the crumbling ledges and she scrambled upwards until she emerged on a vast expanse of slickrock. It was an enormous piece of sandstone shaped like a horseshoe and the views upriver and downriver were wonderful. There was no sign or sound of any person, nor was there a single contrail in all the chromium blue Utah sky. It could have been five hundred years ago or five thousand years from now. She could have been the first person or the last person.

On seeing this, she was glad she had decided to stop and sat down and opened her hip pack and had some water and a Jonathan apple.

A raven called as she was about to leave and she turned and looked over her shoulder at the rock wall behind her. It was a huge affair, vaguely Gothic in appearance, with dark varnish on the terra rosa ramparts and broken talus scattered at intervals along the base. Not far from the raven nest there was a prominent notch in the wall, indicating the entrance to a side canyon, and so she walked over to the narrow opening. The walls on either side of her were ten times higher than she could reach, and there was a faint cool breeze coming from the depths of the canyon. She felt very small as she walked into the place. There was a sort of permanent evening at the bottom of the canyon. It was the best of the golden twilight, suspended for hours. A contoured turn shortly put the world behind her. There were no tracks on the sand. The floor of the canyon was flat and unbroken. No deer, no coyotes, no other living thing had entered this realm. She would be alone. There were no plants, either, for there was no water. It was a smooth-sided tunnel in the extended shape of a serpent, and it was open on the top to the sky, and it was curling deeper and deeper into the earth.

A winding and dusty quarter of a mile later she discovered that it was a cul-de-sac, a box canyon. It led to nothing more, or less, than the dry remnants of a seasonal waterfall. There were no petroglyphs here, no marine fossils imbedded in the sediment, no dinosaur vertebrae protruding from the stone. There was nothing unusual or particularly interesting to recommend the place. In its own understated way, though, the nondescript dead end was quite beautiful, for it consisted of an immense grotto of sculpted stone. The chamber was filled with a pleasant mixture of direct sunlight and reflected light. It was an intimate sanctuary of soft beguiling radiance, and the acoustics were remarkable. She thought of a carpeted gallery in a museum, a small country church emptied of its parishioners, a music practice room in which the silence was complete. She imagined an empty place in the center of it all that would be as simple and pure of form.

She felt safe and comfortable in this humble dry room at the end of the nameless side canyon and so she did something she had never done before in nature. She removed her clothing and lay down on the sand. She lay in a place where the sunlight did not directly fall on her body. She was in the shade beside where the sunlight fell. If she reached over, even with her eyes closed, she could feel the warmth of the sun beside her.

She liked the feel of being separated from everything and anything that physically connected her to the life she led in the city. For this moment it would just be her and the Earth. Her weary spirit, her out-of-tune body, and the soft flesh-colored sand. The experience was liberating and it was cleansing. It transported her far from her own life. The truth was, she had needed something like this, a healing interlude of solitude, for a long time. She was exhausted—too mild a word—from the last four years at the hospital, and every third night an all night affair. She was still appalled at what she routinely had to witness. No person should see such things, she thought: a five-year-old girl impaled on the deer antlers she had pulled off the wall, a golden-haired two year old who had choked to death on a penny, a high school honor student in a coma from a pill her best friend gave her. Sometimes when it was late at night and she was passing down a corridor to visit a patient she would glimpse her reflection in a window, and the sad drawn face that stared back would startle her. The person she saw was not even a person she wished to know. But it was worse than that, for the darkness of what she experienced at the hospital had permeated her life away from work, as well—her home was filled with somber tonal paintings, her musical tastes had shifted to the minor keys, and her coffee table was littered with the adumbrated novels of nineteenth-century Europe.

Her fantasy went something like this. It would be a Friday evening, or perhaps a Saturday morning. She would return home from the hospital and she would load up her truck with her Dalmation Molly and her alley cat Max and a few personal things and drive far out into the desert—to a nowhere place like Bluff, Utah or Fredonia, Arizona. She would find a local lawyer who had not been disbarred yet and declare bankruptcy and move into a little house and become a river guide. It would not be much, that life, but at least she would never again have to tell two parents that their nine-year-old child with Down's Syndrome now had incurable leukemia. At least she would never have to do that again.

She pictured the home in which she would live. It would have white-washed adobe walls as thick as a bale of hay and it would have the permanent temperature of a cave. There would be a grand piano in the corner of the living room, and there would be framed black and white photographs of the rivers that she knew and loved on the walls. The windows would be small, with antique glass and wrought iron frames and there would be fragrant cedar wood stacked by the fire. Bookcases filled with novels and histories and works of philosophy would line the walls. There would be rugs in the warm colors of the desert on the hardwood floors. Her four-posted bed would be the sole piece of furniture in one room. The kitchen would be immaculate, and there would be a shelf of cactus in the south-facing window. The bathroom would have an over-sized tub, and there would be scented candles scattered all around. Out back there would be a vegetable garden with everything in it but lima beans, and beside the greenhouse there would be some fruit trees—peach and apple and pear. Further back, in a fenced pasture of sage and grass, there would be a beautiful quarterhorse mare with a little Arabian in her.

That is how it would be.

Even as she imagined it, though, she understood that it would never be.

She lay there for a long time in the sand with her hands outstretched behind her head and her legs crossed at the ankles, staring up at the sky between the walls of the canyon as if it was a movie screen in a darkened theater. Every so often a slow cloud would drift by. After awhile she closed her eyes and fell asleep.

An hour later she awakened toward the end of a dream. It was a powerful dream that had swept her far away. She had visited a strange place—a windless beach beside an enameled blue sea—and many things had been revealed to her but now she could remember nothing of it. Even as she pursued the outlines of the dream it was disappearing into the air of the canyon. Daytime dreams were like that, she knew. They were here and then they were gone.

She thought about herself for a long time in a detached and clinical way, as a physician considers a patient under an examining room light.

She looked at herself in every way possible, taking careful inventory, and the sum of it was that she still had no idea why she had only loved one man in her life, or why she had remained a virgin until the age of twenty-five, or why she was the way she was. She knew that she could blame her parents, whose issues had become her own, or she could blame medicine, which had hurt her in the way that a husband sometimes does a wife. She was honest enough, though, to know that it was deeper than that. This was the way she was put together. She was all alone with herself now at the bottom of that canyon and for an instant she saw some bones and strands of fiber and a handful of teeth and little more.

The truth was she had no one to love her in the world, and if matters proceeded unchanged probably never would.

When she came out of the canyon the heat and sunlight were almost overwhelming. She stepped back for a moment, not sure if she wished to continue. But it was late, the sun was sinking toward the west and blue shadows were forming on the cliffs across the river. She had to move on. Reluctantly, feeling the pull of duty and promise, she continued along the slickrock toward the place where the deer trail emerged from the forest. Midway across the great round of curved stone, though, she stopped. There was a claret-cup cactus growing from a fissure in the rock. Something about the plant caught her eye and drew her near. On impulse—it was a day for such things—she lay down and curled her body around the cactus. She nestled as close as she could to the plant without touching the spines. Being a scientist, she instinctively began to count. There were twenty-three individual stems. Some were short and others were long. Some were young and vibrant and others were older and beginning to brown in places. Together they formed a tight mass that was formed roughly like a hemisphere—individual cactuses radiating literally in every direction.

Here they had grown over the years, like the closely knit family they were, and all from one seed. This year they were particularly full with stored water. It had been a bountiful winter, and the snowmelt had saturated the soil in the fissure. At the top of nearly every stem was a bright red flower. In the center of each flower was an erect golden stamen, covered with pollen. The scent was faintly sweet, more a suggestion or a rumor than a statement or a declaration, but it was still definitely there.

Occasionally a butterfly—a yellow sulphur or a blue harebell—would approach, but then would flutter away, uncomfortable with her presence. Once she thought she heard a hummingbird buzzing in the neighborhood, perhaps attracted by the red color.

She touched a single blossom with her finger as gently as she would touch the purple-pink hand of a newborn baby. The petals were as soft as an infant's skin and left a fine dust on her fingertips. Touching the flower was different than touching a rock. It was living, this thing, in the same way that she or any person was.

As she lay there with the cactus in the late afternoon sun she pondered the harmonies between herself and this living thing. She, too, lived in an arid harsh place, where resources, such as love and freedom, were scarce. She had found a sheltered place and anchored herself there with strong roots and was trying to survive. She had covered herself with the human version of spines so that no one could get close. If a man tried to get too close, he would soon be repelled by her defensive array—a broken promise, a sharp response to an innocent remark, a natural opportunity foregone. She could exist in this way for a long time—self-sufficient, alone, and protected from compromise or risk. She could even go proudly to her grave in this way, as many had before.

She wondered, though, for it was a day to wonder, whether this is the way she really wanted to live. Was it a noble thing she was doing—sacrificing her best years to heal the sick? Or was it folly? Had she been bold and decisive in her choice, or had she taken the most obvious path? Was she courageous, or was she the opposite of that? Could both be true? Was she deceiving herself about everything? Was medicine her true calling? Could she do what others had done, such as Anton Chekhov or Eliot Porter, and turn her back on it? Was it too late for change? What, in the end, was the truth?

But she was not strong enough for the truth, not yet anyway and perhaps never, and so she eventually retreated into the comfort of familiar modes of thinking about herself and her past and her future. She stood up and gathered her things and left the rock and the cactus and the sun as a student might leave the office of a professor who had posed a difficult question, without looking back, deep in thought, secretly doubting if she was up to the task. It was an afternoon for partial revelations, but not for wholesale change. She would, instead, go back to the kayak and continue down the river to the take-out point where the others were waiting.

MANY YEARS LATER, dying alone in a hospital emergency room following an automobile accident, surrounded by nurses and doctors but detached from them as the dying always are, she would recall that moment when she was still young and the sun was in the middle of the sky and the future was yet to be lived, and realize what she should have done that day. It had been, she would understand then, her only life.

What We Found

MANY YEARS AGO my parents lived at 2146 Eighteenth Avenue in San Francisco. The house is still there. You can see it. Like most homes in that residential area, it is what would be called a townhouse elsewhere: a street-level garage over which the carpenters of a century past raised a single long floor. In back of the house there was a walled garden. Even in late December, when I would come to visit, the pale red roses would be blossoming. Everything in the garden—trellis, leaves, thorns, flowers, seashells, rocks, ferns—was perpetually wet from the fog. This was a good time in their life. During the week my father worked downtown at a job he loved, and my mother, who was an artist, painted regularly at the conservancy. The weekends were reserved for expeditions to places around San Francisco: the Marin Headlands, Point Reyes, Napa Valley.

In April of 1986 the Friends of Photography organized a one hundredth birthday celebration for Edward Weston (born March 24, 1886). At that point Weston had been dead for twenty-eight years. Like all great artists, he was, notwithstanding the minor inconvenience of cremation, still very much alive. The event, sponsored by family and followers, was held in Carmel, where Weston had spent most of his career. My parents were admirers of Edward Weston, Ansel Adams, Imogen Cunningham, and the other members of Group f.64. Naturally they had to drive down the coast to attend. The event would also afford them the chance to finally meet Charis Wilson. It was in Carmel that Weston had spent fourteen years with Charis, who was his model and wife during his most productive period. Oftentimes the two had worked together in the California desert, trying to uncover the resonances between the landscape and the human form. At times they achieved images of tremendous power and virtuosity. In her 1998 memoir *Through Another Lens, My Years with Edward Weston*, Charis wrote that,

Edward was ... a robust lover of life ... a man who found the world
endlessly fascinating. With his camera he pored over it, probed it, and
sought to comprehend it, and to render for others its beauty, complexity,
and inexhaustible mystery.

Toward the end of the first day, a few of the guests—Charis Wilson,
Virginia Adams (Ansel's widow), the three Weston sons (Brett, Cole,
Neal), my parents—moved from the gallery to the old wood-framed
house on Wildcat Hill. This was the home in which Weston had lived
with his wife and many cats. A tour of the grounds followed, and my
father tells the story of the unusual darkroom in which Weston
worked. At one point during the visit he asked Charis Wilson if it
would be possible to see the room where Edward Weston died. Weston
had suffered from Parkinson's disease during his final decade. On the
last morning of his life—January 1, 1958—he had somehow raised
himself up into a chair and turned the chair to face east, toward the
rising sun. That is how the seventy-two-year-old artist passed away, facing the dawn. Although Weston's body had been destroyed, his spirit
was still drawn to the light of the sun that had created him. After
Charis led my father to the room, he asked if he could photograph the
chair, which still faces east. Charis graciously gave her consent. That
photograph is among his treasures.

Over the years, growing up in such a household, I often studied the
day books of Weston and the nude figure studies that he and Charis
made as they explored the sand dunes around Stovepipe Wells in Death
Valley and the Oceano sand fields near San Luis Obispo. All of these
were eight-inch by ten-inch black-and-white contact prints that Weston,
always a purist, refused to enlarge or alter in any way. At such times I
would find myself wondering if I could ever find someone, as Weston
did, with whom to collaborate on such a project. It seemed to me the
Red Rock Desert was better suited as a landscape than the Mojave
Desert. For one thing, the slickrock provided a closer analogue to the
human form. The flesh-hues of the sandstone similarly offered a useful
metaphor. Color film could also be used to advantage. Most importantly,
no serious work of this nature had ever been done before in that part of
the Southwest. The possibilities for original work were unlimited.

ii.

ONE SPRING SEVERAL YEARS AGO I was out in the Red Rock Desert in an area that is now known as the Grand Staircase–Escalante Canyons National Monument. At that time it was BLM grazing land—unfenced cattle allotments, seasonal line camps, wood corrals, and empty cactus desert. I had parked my vehicle and raised my tent among the junipers near a place called Twenty-Five Mile Wash. From there I was well situated to explore a vast country that extended from Davis Gulch on the south to the Kaiparowits Plateau to the west. Every day was different. Some days I hiked from dawn to dusk, exploring the beautiful canyons. Other days I remained in camp, watching the clouds, napping, cleaning my cameras, and writing. I was happy to be far from civilization and its discontents, and I felt fortunate when I recalled other times in my life when I hadn't enjoyed such freedom. I was alone and happy and I would sit there and think that no one, at least no adult, had the right to be that content. In retrospect, I see now that it was also a healing time—not long before I had stood in a hospital room and watched as the doctors had tried in vain to save my mother's life.

Every three or four days I would drive the thirty miles back to Escalante—sun-darkened, smelling of sage, a bit of the deer in my eyes—to buy fresh provisions at the grocery store on Main Street. While in town I would call my nine-year-old son in Atlanta and my father in Denver. Whenever I am away on a trip my father picks my mail up at the post office, and then opens and reads the letters to me over the phone. One night he read a letter from a woman in Albuquerque who was writing on behalf of her daughter. Apparently the mother had read one of my books and had concluded that the two of us—a forty-three-year-old writer and a twenty-year-old Bennington student—should become acquainted. I found the whole concept somewhat difficult to believe. The letter was the sort of unexpected plot development one might find in a nineteenth-century novel of manners. When I returned to Denver two weeks later, though, there it was. One afternoon I called the number. The father answered and observed that my timing was perfect. His daughter Anna had just returned that morning from New Zealand, where she had been climbing Mount Cook.

One thing led to another, as they sometimes do, and I found myself one week later picking up Anna at the Denver International Airport. She saw me first and walked over with bright blue eyes and a broad smile. She had the muscular, lean body of an athlete and moved with the confidence and vigor of someone who has just ascended a snow-covered mountain in the southern hemisphere. Her hands were the strong weathered hands of a technical climber and her hair was sandy-colored, with blond highlights from the alpine sun. Her nose and cheeks and the bottoms of her ears were still peeling. She spoke in rapid spurts and her voice was high and sharp. There was no subject about which she was not curious.

The next day we drove back out to the desert, she to join me in doing whatever it is I do out there in the desert. Not far from Arches National Park, there is a lovely road that leads from Seven-Mile Canyon to Grandview Overlook. The asphalt road passes through a narrow box canyon where the rocks are scattered and broken, climbs a series of steep switchbacks, and then flattens out on a high plain where the grasses are thick. The wild pasture there—acres and acres, a windy bay extending in every direction—seems not part of the Red Rock Desert but a landscape imported from elsewhere, the plains of Mongolia or the savannas of East Africa. It is a place where one half-expects to see a herd of Przewalski steppe horses or a reticulated giraffe. It was on that road, somewhere in the vicinity of Mesa Arch, that I expressed, as I sometimes do with travelling companions, my admiration for Weston's pioneering work in the California desert, and my intent to one day pursue my own vision along these lines. Anna, an avid photographer, was familiar with Weston and his milieu. To my surprise, for it certainly was not my intent, she declared that we should begin work on the project immediately.

The following day, in the Needles District of Canyonlands National Park, we did just that, and at a special place. Twenty years earlier I had gone out for a walk one morning and, over the course of several hours, wandered a considerable distance off the trail. I had then gradually found myself inside a labyrinth of rocks that brought to mind the Greek parable of Theseus and Ariadne. It was an enclosed maze of passageways that simultaneously seemed to lead everywhere and nowhere. I eventually followed a deer path that led to a human trail that led to a four-wheel-drive track that led to a road that led me back to the world. Along the way, I discovered several things, not the least of which was a remarkable amphitheater I called "Point Solitude." The route to this sanctuary is about six miles in length, and winds through a network of red sandstone canyons. For the last two miles there is no trail, only a line of sight navigation over a series of slickrock ridges. Only a person who has been far off the traveled path in that part of the desert would ever find such a feature. Over the years I had often returned to the place, which had proven itself to be an ideal location for solitary camping and meditation.

When we reached Point Solitude our work began. To this day, some of those first photographs, taken with little regard for convention or concern for anything other than improvisation, are among my best. I will always be grateful to Anna for her courage, trust, and faith, as well as for her insight and imagination. In this process we were very much creative partners. Although I had by that time illustrated over a dozen books, photographing at locations ranging from the northern foothills of the Brooks Range to the depths of the Okefenokee Swamp, nothing in my experience had approached the challenge of fusing the human form to the desert landscape. It is one thing, in such a situation, to take a picture. It is quite another to create a work of art.

Over the next two weeks we sought to do just that. We found, among other things, that the time of day was even more important than is normally the case. Midday sun on desert rock is a harsh visual environment for the human form. The situation poses a number of challenges in terms of integrating the foreground with the landscape, as well as in striking a balance with the tonal scale. Although interesting effects can be achieved, as Weston and Charis often demonstrated in their collaborations, early morning and late afternoon offer a more forgiving light. We agreed that natural light was essential. We used no reflectors or flashes or shields. My subject was washed in whatever fell from the desert sky—unobstructed sunshine, diffuse cloudlight, the luminous glow that accompanies rain, the rich reflected light at the bottom of a sandstone canyon, the noonday shadow beneath a cottonwood tree, the brief fires of sunrise and sunset, the cold rays of a full moon setting on the Grand Canyon—and for this illumination we depended solely on god and the weather.

Our favorite place among these natural galleries, as we called them, was not a panoramic overlook, a picturesque ghost town, or a painted hoodoo garden. It was a nameless slot canyon in northern Arizona. These gulches are among the most unusual features in the Southwest—deep, narrow trenches in the desert floor formed by flash floods in the summer thunderstorm season. You pass through a portal, a gateway in the rock, and enter another world, a silent realm washed in warm red and orange light. In places the slot canyons are as narrow as your shoulders. Elsewhere they widen to accommodate your outstretched arms. Throughout, they are filled with soft reflected light, as the sun beams are bounced off the smooth tapestried walls of golden sandstone. In the depths of these canyons there are otherworldly patterns of light and shade, hanging gardens on the walls, standing pools, desert owl nests, womb-like silences, and striking petroglyphs scattered here and there. These places are magical, and I have often wondered what Weston and Charis could have done in such locations—in fact, I have often asked myself exactly what they would have done, because they had such fine artistic instincts.

When we returned from the desert Anna decided to stay for the summer. We often hiked in the mountains with my son, who comes out during the warm months, and in August I introduced them both to one of my oldest friends, the Canadian Rockies. Along the way I taught her how to play the guitar and how to oil paint, and she soon exhibited her first works in a juried show. In the fall, though, she had to return to college and her promising future in the east. We had remained close friends throughout, but would now, because of the natural course of her life, see each other only rarely. I realized at that point that my work had only begun, and that the most essential part—the learning phase—was now complete. Her visit had been a blessing, one of those rare moments that life gives you, but the rest would now be up to me. In order to find a collaborator, I placed an advertisement in the local arts paper, explaining who I was and the nature of what was now a named book project (*One Hundred Photographs: The Female Form and the Desert Southwest*). Over the course of the next week I received eighteen inquiries. Most were not suited for the project, a fact that became apparent as I explained that the task involved rising before dawn, hiking across endless dune fields, wading up seasonal rivers, following game trails when conventional paths gave way, trekking through slot canyons, climbing eroded rock pinnacles, and trying not to pass out while standing on the edge of a 900-foot cliff.

Six I agreed to meet with. All were in their early twenties. Their backgrounds could not have been more diverse—an artist, a photographer, a personal trainer, a physical therapist, a dancer, and a waitress. Ultimately I chose to work with a young woman named Charlotte. She had grown up in Muninsing, Michigan, the daughter of a ranger in the Hiawatha National Forest, and had spent whole weeks of her early life camping in the north woods with her father, mother, and sister. She would be comfortable in the desert. She bore a strong resemblance to Charis Wilson, and I could see the red hair would be beneficial, given the terra rosa hue of the prevalent Navajo sandstone. There was also a distinct echo, in her face and form, of Helga Testorf, the model with whom the watercolor and tempera painter Andrew Wyeth had worked so effectively in the 1970s.

There was finally this—Charlotte had experienced an unusually difficult life journey, and I believed the desert might be a healing landscape for her, as it had been so often for me. In the end she and I spent most of October in the desert, working clockwise from Arches National Park to Monument Valley to the north rim of the Grand Canyon, and then back north through Zion National Park, Bryce Canyon National Park, and Capitol Reef National Park. This was the same approximate route that Anna and I had taken in the spring. The advantage on the fall trip was that, in each location, I knew exactly where to go and, just as important, when to go during the day.

A year and a half passed. The project, which occupied an entire table in my office, was passed over as other pressing literary or photographic tasks came and went. The opportunity to work on the book arose again when my former New York editor, Laurel, traveled west for a spring visit. She was twenty-six and a graduate of Middlebury College. She worked as an English teacher at a private secondary school in Vermont and also served as the cross-country skiing coach. Both of her brothers were artists, and she had a broad knowledge of painting and photography. We had first met over the phone when she worked for one of my publishers in New York, and had developed a friendship, as people often do, through phone conversations and correspondence. During the course of our travels through the Red Rock Desert, Laurel expressed interest in the project and so we worked at several locations, including Natural Bridges National Monument and Canyonlands National Park. I had begun to realize at this point that every human form presents its own unique land-scape, and poses interesting challenges in terms of the basic objective of unifying foreground and background. Like Anna and Charlotte, Laurel was very much an equal partner in the task of composing images, and offered many compelling ideas in different situations.

What I learned over the course of these efforts was that, for all my years of exploring the desert, I knew little of it. I knew less of the human form and still less of the many obvious and subtle ways in which the two are bound together in a single harmony. Each time I anchored the tripod and held up the light meter, I was aware of my challenges and my responsibilities. I learned, too, that as the form is unclothed, so is the spirit, and that a muse may then share thoughts and memories which are normally withheld. Such epiphanies of pain or loss or hope are often ab-sorbed into the compositional process, and are silently reflected in the image that will endure when those who made it have been returned to the earth. Throughout these trips, I made every effort to create images unlike any that have been seen before. I had no desire to imitate the past, or to record the visual moment as anything less than a revelation. Each image was a focused meditation, a celebration of the eternal present, and an attempt to honor all that is evoked by the word life.

iii.

TWENTY-TWO YEARS AGO, on a gray December day, I walked into a light-filled gallery of the Museum of Fine Arts in Boston and viewed the painting by Paul Gauguin (1848–1903) entitled *"D'Ou Venons Nous? Que Sommes Nous? Ou Allons Nous?"* Translated, these questions are "Where do we come from? What are we? Where are we going?" The over-sized painting stretches out to roughly five feet by twelve feet (54 inches by 147 inches). Gauguin worked on his masterpiece for a solid month in what he later described as an "unbelievably feverish state." There were no preparatory studies. He painted the scene wholly from his imagination. His canvas was a wrinkled piece of sac cloth. His brushes were whatever he could find in that remote place (the South Pacific). His paints were similarly improvised. Gauguin saw this complex image as his *ultimate verba*, his final statement to the world, a summary of all that he knew and wished he could know. Even then, in December 1897, he understood that his time among the living was limited.

The painting depicts a clearing in a forest. In the opening are twelve people—the old and young, sick and healthy, happy and sad. Some are clothed, others are unclothed. To the right of center a figure reaches for a ripe red fruit that carries with it all the symbolism of the Old Testament. Not far away, two young women sit pensively near a baby, its head turned in sleep. Elsewhere an elderly woman sits mournfully with her head in her hands. Nearby is a young woman, her eyes turned from the old woman. Behind them is a blue-green statue of a deity, the expression inscrutable. To the side a woman stands in profile, her eyes stealing a glance of the viewer. And there are others—a child eating a piece of fruit, two figures in night clothes wandering down a path. In the far background one can see an ocean, a distant mountain, and drifting clouds. The color blue pervades the painting. Mixed into almost every other pigment, the dull ultramarine conveys an impression of melancholy. The painting can variously be looked at as an hallucination, a vision, or a penetrating examination. Perhaps even its creator did not know which.

In the upper left corner, against a golden background that is also the brightest region of the canvas, Gauguin boldly painted his three questions. I say "boldly" because at that time, before the more experimental era of Picasso and Braque, artists did not place philosophical questions on their paintings. It has often occurred to me, in this regard, that my desert figure studies are an attempt to visually respond to Gauguin's three questions—"Where do we come from? What are we? Where are we going?" Each person I photograph is a microcosm of the human race. Each scene I preserve is a concentrated fragment of the universe at large. Implicit in all of these images is, if not a series of answers, then an alternative framing of the questions. Taken as a whole, the suite is meant to remind us that we all come from nature and that we will all ultimately return to that realm, no matter where or how we live. The images are designed, in that sense, to be both uplifting and cautionary. Because of their setting, they also remind us of the oldest myth—that we, as a race, have wandered from the garden, but that, through the purity of art, which eschews all that is worldly, we can re-enter paradise, and be at one with it, again.

Still Life

THE BABY SAT IN ITS CAR SEAT, dressed in a t-shirt and a diaper. The mother sat beside the baby and they were both under a cottonwood tree. The mother had been reading aloud from a book of stories the baby liked. The village of the Tropuloids had invaded the village of the Mutanians, searching for the golden lollipop tree, and Grandfather Turtle had risen from his slumbers to bring peace to the world. And now the restless child had finally fallen asleep. After awhile the young woman went to the car and pulled a gallon water jug from the cooler and returned to the blanket under the tree. It was August and it was hot at the bottom of the canyon and she and the baby were drinking alot of water. A month before she had stopped nursing the baby. After a brief period of turmoil, the child had settled into its new world of formula and solid foods.

Every few minutes a car went by on the road and she looked up hopefully.

Three hours earlier her husband and three people—a young man from Italy, his wife, and her sister—had put their mountain bikes into the back of a pickup truck. There was an automobile commercial being shot in a redrock canyon south of Moab, and the four of them were going to observe the filming. Julie could not go because of the baby and the heat on the desert during the middle of the day.

She looked over at the baby, sleeping angelically in the soft blue shade that fell from the cottonwood tree. She saw her husband in his features, but little of her own. She had come to realize that what she had given the baby was more inside. The baby had her mellow personality, and none of his father's tension. But he did have his father's face. There was no doubt about that. He would one day be as handsome as his father.

In her hand was a piece of paper that she unfolded now and then and read. Each time she read it she would purse her lips, or shake her head back and forth, or rub her forehead with her fingertips. A day earlier she

had found the note in the pocket of her husband's fleece jacket when she
went into town to do the laundry. It was not in one of the side pockets
where he would have left it. It was in the breast pocket where he would
never look, but where she, the wife, would be certain to find it. It had
been placed there by someone so that she would read it. It was a love
note, expressing gratitude for this and for that and there was a kiss on it.
It was about as incriminating a piece of paper as has ever been placed in
the pocket of a husband.

She sat there for a long time reading the note and thinking, and looking up expectantly each time a car came by on the road.

After awhile the campground host, a woman of around fifty, came
over and asked if they were going to spend another night.

"I'm not sure."

"Are you all right?" the older woman asked.

The young woman hesitated for a moment, and then shook her head
slightly back and forth.

"Is it your little boy?"

She shook her head again. She was afraid that if she tried to speak she
would begin to cry.

The older woman sat down on the other side of the baby and smoked
a cigarette and said nothing for a long time. Her skin was tanned the
same color as the sandstone of the cliffs that rose all around the river.
Her hair had once been brown. She had the physical presence of a
woman half her age—alert, mobile, animated.

"You know there are some ravens up there."

"What?"

"Across the river. Up there in those rocks. You see?"

She was pointing to a ledge on a sandstone cliff.

"They raise a new family up there ever year. It's a good place for them.
Lots of roadkill. And of course there's always the campgrounds."

"What kind of fish were those guys catching earlier?"

"Catfish mostly."

"Where do you go in the winter?"

"I stay here."

"You mean ... *here?*"

"Uh-huh."

"Doesn't it get cold?"

"Well there is such a thing as propane, you know."

After awhile they got up and walked over to the older woman's trailer. Her name was Ginny and she lived in the farthest campsite. On one side it was all woods and on the other side there was the Colorado River. Because she had lived there for a long time, she had made some improvements. There were homemade wind chimes hanging from the lower branches of the cottonwoods, and among the trees she had placed unusual sculptures built with things she had found along the road. Someone had once given her half a truckload of redwood beams and she had used them to make an outdoor patio, over which she had hung a canvas tarp attached to four wooden poles. On a flat place just above the river she had built a redwood hot tub. She filled the tub with river water heated in an oil drum beside her barbecue pit. There was even a drainage system. Nearby was an outdoor shower.

Inside the trailer everything was a mildly cluttered mess. Her flute was in its case on the kitchen table, and there were photographs of her various husbands and children and grandchildren and favorite pets on the refrigerator. Above the sink was a framed certificate commemorating her retirement after twenty years as a fire manager in the Deschutes National Forest. Scattered over the kitchen table were a few library books, works of philosophy mainly, and some polaroid pictures of her recently belly-dancing at the only bar in Moab. There were also some watercolor paintings of the desert she had done for the open competition at the new art gallery on Main Street.

She apologized for the cluttered condition of the trailer and Julie paid her a compliment on the comfortable way she lived. The baby was asleep in its car seat on the floor beside Julie. As he slept his eyelids fluttered and his fingers moved gently.

They were drinking coffee now, and the conversation had turned to the note. The two analyzed the note from every possible angle and as they talked many of the truths about the marriage emerged. Rick was not a lawyer as he had told everyone at the campground. He had once been in law school in Kansas City, but had flunked out in the second semester. Now he worked as an independent ticket scalper in Denver. He would buy up large blocks of tickets for sports events or music concerts on the Internet using a special system he had devised. He would then sell these tickets for whatever price the marketplace allowed, and this price would naturally increase as the day of the event neared. The beauty of it was that he paid no taxes, or at least he saw that as the beauty of it.

The worst part of the situation was not all this but, rather, the fact that he was not faithful.

"I had a husband like that once," Ginny observed.

"What did you do?"

"I stayed with him. Just like you are. But then finally one day after about ten years he got some young woman pregnant and left me. Left me with two kids and a Thanksgiving turkey in the oven. Sounds like a country-western song, doesn't it?"

"I don't want to wind up like that."

She had spoken reflexively. She was deep in her own thoughts. She was debating about whether to tell Ginny about her own mother, or her older sisters, and how the women in her family always seemed to marry men like Rick, and then suffer quietly for the rest of their lives.

"Then leave him before he leaves you."

"But the baby."

"You know, there's an old country saying that a man needs a woman but a woman with a child will do very well."

"But a son needs a father."

"You are a free woman in a free country. You—"

A car drove from the road into the campground and Julie looked nervously out the window.

It was not Rick and she sat back down.

Ginny had met women like Julie before at the campground. She understood what was going to happen. Sometimes they would return year after year, and she would follow their stories. The installments were like serial novels from the Victorian age. Every summer there was a new development, but always there were the same central characters and the same core problems. Julie was talking in circles now, repeating herself as she tried to rationalize her choices. Ginny looked at her watch and told Julie that she needed to go into town to pick up the mail.

A few minutes later Ginny's two dogs, Skipper and Shorty, returned from their morning reconnaissance in the woods. Skipper had something in his mouth and Ginny took it away and threw it in the river. Not long after that they all left together in her vintage microbus, which appeared to have once served as someone's home.

She waved out the window as she drove through the campground in a cloud of dust.

Julie was back at the cottonwood tree now and it was later in the day. The baby was awake and drinking a bottle of water. She was holding the baby's hand as the baby drank the water and the baby was looking steadily into her eyes with his father's blue eyes. Every time she smiled, the baby smiled too. It was a game they were playing. The baby's name was Rick, too.

After awhile the baby was finished with the bottle and she changed his diaper and took him for a walk down by the river. She carried him most of the way because some boys in the next campsite had killed a rattlesnake in the grass the day before. She watched the river flow for a long time. Occasionally something would float by, the branch of a tree, a fallen leaf, a cup that had dropped from a boat.

The baby was becoming restless now. It was almost time for his lunch.

Before she left she took the note from her pocket and stared at it for a moment and then threw it into the river.

She watched until it was gone.

Mountain Lion

COMING BACK TO THE NORTH RIM is like returning to the sea when you have been absent from it for a long time, or the embrace of a lover. The old logging roads wind through dark woods and open clearings, and always there is the expectancy of the view at the end of the road. At night, the thunderstorms awaken you from sleep, and you listen to the thunder, and to the rain falling on the tent. In the morning the clouds dissipate rapidly in the dry air and by nine or ten it is clear and you gaze out at the great canyon as at some Shangri-la. Birds sing throughout the day in the ponderosa groves. These are tall, heavy trees with smooth cinnamon bark. Some of the forest birds make a song like a mandolin being tuned, and others produce a melody like wind chimes tinkling in the breeze. Downy woodpeckers can sometimes be heard thumping in the trees, and the Kaibab squirrels with tufted ears are always alert sentries for their neighborhoods. The North Rim is best visited in the summer, when the sun burns and scorches the low desert, for that sort of heat never reaches the place. The magic of the high plateau settles like a fine yellow pollen on all who visit, and few depart—Thomas Moran, Theodore Roosevelt, Zane Grey, Ansel Adams, Edward Abbey—who do not eventually return.

On the day I am thinking of it was early August. The fireweed was mostly past its prime, although a few of the lilac-purple racemes still waved in the breeze. The sunflowers were coming into their own, and every morning there were more of them along the roads and trails. In the clearings there were brilliant gardens of violet-blue iris and red paintbrush, each with the purest of colors. Here and there the prickly pear cactus held up scarlet knobs of ripening fruit, and the cliffrose were hung with sunny blossoms. In the shade there were yellow columbine, easily lost among the heart-shaped leaves, and soft living mats of pretty pink fleabane. The warm air was thick with the scent of fallen ponderosa pine needles and sagebrush and native flowers and everywhere there was the gentle soothing whisper and murmur of insects. In the aspen groves the eyes on the white-barked trees stared from the gloom made by their own green shadows. Out in the grass meadows each individual ponderosa had a circular pool of blue coolness underneath it. Sometimes there would be a maroon and cream colored Hereford beneath a tree, and nearby would be her spring calf, a miniature replica of the ponderous mother.

I drove without a map down gravel roads through the forests and meadows that I knew from previous trips. I remembered each road as I came upon it as I do the features of a friend. I turned left here, took a right fork there and proceeded steadily through the labyrinth to a place I knew well, a rocky point where I could camp near the rim and be alone with the gulf for awhile. The North Rim is a big country, and I drove for many miles without seeing any other drivers. At one point a small herd of elk crossed the road, and I stopped the car and turned off the engine to let them pass undisturbed by my presence. They were all bulls, a bachelor band of seven animals, and they walked slowly on their split hooves over the roadbed, their antlers arched back over their raised shaggy necks. The antlers were still in velvet and would not be hard and sharp for many weeks. The elk were like the shadows and the sunshine of the forest given life, and legs. They were free-ranging creatures of the high meadows and they belonged to the wilderness that was their home.

Several miles farther I took an obscure fork to a less-traveled road, and then there was one last fork, and soon I was entering the outer edges of the most remote corner of the forest.

At a blind turn in the road I suddenly came upon a couple of green government trucks and a private truck with wooden dog boxes. As I passed I noticed a culvert pipe on a wheeled trailer off in the trees. A tarp had been thrown over the culvert pipe. A hundred yards later I turned around, thinking that perhaps they had captured a black bear.

There were four men, three in uniform. I stepped from my car and introduced myself. The bald man with glasses was a biologist from the state of Arizona. The other two with baseball hats were rangers from the Kaibab National Forest. The civilian with the cowboy hat and boots was the owner of the five Plott hounds that had recently treed the animal. He was about to leave for the veterinary clinic in Kanab, as one of his hounds was bleeding from the shoulder and the muzzle. He was also putting a check into his shirt pocket. They were all burly men and deeply tanned. They made their living in the out-of-doors. These forested highlands were their office. They had the presence of men who were proud of the fact that they had gotten the job done.

The biologist invited me to look at the animal in the culvert trap. It was, he said, a mountain lion that had killed a spring calf and a pony on a grazing allotment in the past two weeks. The men then returned to their paperwork, which appeared considerable, and continued to converse by radio with the bureaucrats back at their base.

The lion was half-asleep, and still drugged, for they had darted the animal in a tree. It was a female and she was lactating—six of her eight mammaries were swollen with milk. She was on her side, panting, her eyes fixed at some vague point on the edge of consciousness. They had put some fluid in her eyes so they didn't dry, and I could see the effects of the anesthetic were beginning to wear off. The lion regarded me as from the depths of a dream, or a nightmare. It was a fairly muted look, but there was annoyance in it, and the first stirrings of a fury. Her eyes were flickering to life. They had a radiant darkness about them and the lines of Blake came to mind: "What immortal hand or eye, could frame thy fearful symmetry?"

I had never seen a lion up close. Who has? My sole sighting, in thirty years on the desert, had been a year earlier on State Route 64 just south of the Desert View entrance to the park. But that was a brief sighting, my friend Natalya Ryabova pointing out two lions on the road as we approached by car around seven-thirty in the morning. We saw the two lions for all of five seconds, only long enough to positively identify what was likely a mated pair. My chief memory is that the head was quite small relative to the rest of the body, and that the tail was tubular (unlike that of the coyote or the wolf). The tawny color was also different from that of any other animal I'd ever seen.

Other than that there had been exactly one verified track in the snow at a place called Bull Canyon back in the 1970s. I remember this much about the track—it was about the size of the palm of my hand. And, too, there was an episode down on the Gila River in the mid-1980s, when my father and I heard a lion crying out in the night above our camp. It was an eerie sound, like a woman screaming.

Of course, I'm sure lions have watched me many times.

So I was immensely curious to be so near a legend rarely seen, and to observe this famous recluse so often discussed around campfires from Alberta to the Andes.

My chief impression was of the size of the animal. I would later learn that she weighed one hundred and thirty-two pounds and measured just over six feet from pink nose to dusky tail tip. Her fur color was a reddish sandstone on the top and sides. A shade of white limestone ran underneath from the chin to the base of the tail. There were light charcoal markings around her eyes, nose, and mouth. Her eyes were green—the color of pale jade—with tiny black pupils like black suns. White and black whiskers protruded like stiff radio antennae from her nose and from the region above her eyes. There were traces of blood around her mouth. Her nose was the same color as a wild rose blossom. Her smell was the same as that of any cat.

She was gradually becoming alert, and shaking the dizziness and confusion from her head. When she realized the nature of her predicament she gave me a terrible look, erupted in a hiss and struck at the wire door, catching her claws in it. I backed away to give her a modicum of privacy.

After awhile the biologist came over and said that the cat was being sent to a zoo in Ohio. I asked about the fate of her kittens—would it be possible to radio-collar the lion and then backtrack to the den site? Unfortunately not, he said, there was not the manpower or the financial resources for such an operation, and of course the existence of the live kittens was speculative. If they still existed, the kittens would have to fend for themselves.

Becoming an easy meal for a coyote, I silently thought.

He walked back to talk with the others about something and I was left alone with the mountain lion. To be honest, I was tempted to open the door and let her run off. I understood, though, that she would only be tracked and caught again.

The lion could not conceive of the degradation to which she was going. Once she had been a proud and self-sufficient animal, an independent spirit that knew these forests and meadows and rock outcrops as no man or woman ever would. She had been as much a part of the North Rim as the ponderosas or the pinyon jays or the passing storms.

Now she would only know captivity—the damp steel and concrete cage, the urban noise, the dreary boredom of a place in which every day is exactly the same as the day before.

Crowds would file by and look at her. They would stare and laugh and mock her. Children would throw hot dogs and peanuts. At night she would pace back and forth until she was so tired she would collapse in fatigue.

I wondered what she would dream of there. Would she remember the high sweet air, and the smoldering blue of the high sky, and the smell of the woods in October? When the full moon rose over that gray town would she remember what it was like to hunt along the canyon rim beneath the full moon? When the thunderstorms came would she remember the scent of the sage on the breeze and how the sound of the rain made for good stalking? When a wind passed through the zoo, bringing with it the scents of the deer and the elk, would she recall the animals she had known on the high plateau? When the snow fell, would she remember how she followed the great herds off the plateau to the desert canyons where they wintered?

She stirred then, in a cage that smelled already of imprisonment. I have known the same. You have known the same. Jobs and marriages and all those responsibilities that fetter our natural freedom, but nothing that we will ever know can compare with what a wild animal goes through.

Good-bye, I said to her. Good-bye, old friend. I salute you as a hunter with the heart of Diana and the spirit of Artemis. Your kind has seen me often, over the years, in this desert and elsewhere, and though they could have killed me many times they have always spared my life. I thank you as a representative of your kind for that. I hope that you die on the journey before you reach that city in the Midwest, where there is nothing like the Grand Canyon. I know that world. I grew up there. I spent seventeen years there, and it is nothing like this place where you are now.

The House at the End of the Road

HE LIKED THE WAY HIS LIFE WAS NOW, living in the mountains above the valley and the paved roads, with the national forest at his back and the desert below. Whole weeks, whole months would go by and he would not be disturbed, especially in November after the snows began to fall and the main road over the mesa was often closed. At such times the only sound would be the quiet music of the stream in its narrow rocky course below his cabin, and the waxwings and sparrows that over-wintered in the junipers. He liked mornings best, when the amber light hit the Henry Mountains sixty miles to the southwest, and then slowly came up on Island in the Sky directly to the west. Finally the sun would climb above Mount Peale and find his cabin set among the pinyon pines on Wilson Mesa in what used to be a half section of irrigated hay fields. Over the last eleven years the fields had largely returned to sage and na-tive grass, and the deer had gradually come back. Summers he would often sit on the front porch in the late afternoon and watch the thunderstorms build over the desert to the west, towering cumulus clouds that grew even as he watched, forming hard-edged and white against the radiant blue sky. At night the lightning would illuminate amphitheaters and antechambers of darkness and after many seconds the muffled thunder would reach him. In the fall the elk hunters would come to the door now and then, asking for directions to the Owl Creek trailhead, but generally no one climbed over the locked gate and walked up the winding gravel road to his home.

He had known the other way of life, the busy crowded days of serv-ice and career, during the six years he had worked as an art professor at a state university in the upper Midwest. Sometimes he would see some-thing—a report in the paper, an article in a magazine—that would re-mind him of that time. It was all in the past now, and had receded from the present as a mountain range does that you climbed in once, but which is now just a distant violet rise on the horizon. But sometimes he would see something and it would all come back—how the older faculty, unsettled by the angle of his ascent, had leveraged his departure in an intrigue worthy of an Elizabethan play. He remembered it all and for a moment he would be poised on the edge of regret, but then he would remind himself that they had done him a favor.

His life after that had entered a new period. At first it had seemed a bit unnatural, not having to go to work in an office every morning, as his father had and his father before him, but now it seemed the only way to live. He had built a studio in the field beside his home, with floor to ceiling windows facing north, and skylights on the roof to bring in more light. Most days he began painting after the sun rose, and continued off and on until late afternoon. Four times a year he traveled to meet with the dealers who represented his work in Carmel, Santa Fe, New York, and Frankfurt. He always sent his paintings ahead and he would help the gallery staff with the unpacking and with the hanging for the show. He would then stay for the opening and visit friends in the city for a few days. The truth was, he had become wealthy as a result of his work, but only his accountant in Salt Lake City and his attorney in Phoenix knew about that. His paintings, which came out of the Maynard Dixon line, were most concerned with the landscapes of the Southwest, particularly the desert. He realized that the desert was both a place and a metaphor, and that all of his paintings were in a sense self-portraits, even those, especially those, that consisted of nothing more than a dry wash.

In his seventh spring on Wilson Mesa his mother in Denver had died of ovarian cancer and shortly after that his father's spirit and health had begun to fail, and so he had invited his father to come and live with him. He had built a second cabin in the woods near the stream and his father lived there among the cottonwood trees. Most of the time his father read books or corresponded with friends on his computer, but he also enjoyed sports and that is why there was a satellite dish on top of his cabin. During the summer months he tended to his garden and in the winter he worked in his greenhouse. Over the years a change had slowly come over the relationship, so that they were now not so much parent and child as they were two bachelors who had known each other for so long they could each read the other's mind. He had an older and a younger brother but they lived far away and were pursuing professional careers in the city. They had wives and children and every few years would come out to visit. The three sons had grown apart over time, as siblings often do, and he felt as though he did not have much in common with his brothers anymore, even if he loved them as one always loves family. He knew that they were busy being husbands and fathers and quite often they were in silent despair and that they would rather be doing what he was doing. He also knew that either brother could have done what he was doing, but that they had made other choices. In this way he felt a responsibility not only to work for himself, but also to work for them, for what they might have done.

It was a sunny frosty morning a week before the spring equinox and he was cutting wood at the woodpile. The wood came from high up on the mountain where a lightning strike had caused a small ragged burn the summer before, during the drought. The forest service had opened the burn to the local people and let them cut down whatever they wished. There was a lot of good wood up there, because the fire had burned through fast, scorching the needles and the bark, but leaving the trees intact. He kept the wood—raw chunks of spruce and fir and aspen—piled up against the shed where he kept his tools.

He had been splitting wood for about a quarter of an hour when he heard a voice and turned around.

There was a young woman standing there in a lilac-colored fleece jacket, a white reindeer sweater, and faded blue jeans. She had on a gray wool beanie and her blond hair was in two braids to her shoulders. Her cheeks were flushed red and her eyes were the lightest blue. She had the broad shoulders of a swimmer. Her posture was immaculate. She was wearing the orange liners to a pair of ski gloves.

She smiled at him and spoke again.

"Well are you?"

"Am I what?"

"Are you the artist James Clark?"

He paused as was his habit with strangers. He surveyed the clearing to see if she was alone, and stared for a moment at his twelve-year-old golden retriever Sally, who was sound asleep on the back porch. He was standing there in a t-shirt stained with oil paint and blue jeans that he had worn for the past three days and well-worn basketball shoes. The t-shirt clung to the middle of his chest because of the sweat. He was forty-four years old and of average height and build. His beard and hair were the russet color of the scrub oak in the fall and his eyes were pale green and his face showed that he had avoided all those things, from idleness to envy to anger, that destroy people over time.

He gave his standard answer.

"I'm his younger brother."

"Well do you know when he might be back?"

"He's out of town for a few days."

"Ok. Thanks anyway."

She turned and walked away.

"Who should I tell him stopped by?"

"That's between me and him."

She continued to walk back down the road. She was walking with a quick step and she had very long legs. When she was about fifty yards away he asked her to come back.

She returned, walking briskly, out of breath now and apparently upset about something.

"Alright, I'm Jim Clark. What is it?"

She took out some tissue and blew her nose. He saw that she was ill and that her hands were trembling.

"Could we go inside? The other day I caught a cold from my little girl."

"Alright."

He put the axe down on the woodpile and grabbed an armful of kindling and whistled to Sally, who awoke with a start and came over and smelled the woman from ankle to waist.

"Ouch. What is she doing?"

"Don't worry, she always does that."

They walked in through the front door and he went over to the stone fireplace and added a few chunks to the fire. He asked her if she wanted something to drink and she answered and he came out of the kitchen with two ceramic cups of orange juice.

"What's your name anyway?"

"I'm Danielle."

They shook hands and sat down in different chairs on either side of a wooden table. She drank the orange juice and scratched the head of the dog that had taken up residence at her feet.

There was a silence, with only the fire crackling.

"Do you mind if I look around a little?"

He shrugged his shoulders as he opened a bag of mail that had sat there for a week.

She stood up with her hands in her pockets and began to explore the contents of the living room.

"You sure do have a lot of books."

He said nothing.

The books were organized by subject. She went from one bookcase to another, inspecting each shelf carefully, taking out books and looking at them. There was one entire case of art books, and then another of history. Nature and science books were in the same bookcase as philosophy. The same with poetry and fiction. Scattered on the walls were some of his favorite paintings, the ones that he would never sell and that the world would not see until he was gone, and she looked at these as well.

"I didn't know that you painted in Canada."

"We go up there every fall."

"We?"

"My father and I."

"Where is he?"

"He has a cabin down by the stream."

"You mean he lives here with you?"

"Uh-huh."

"Do you play the piano?"

"A little."

"Yeah, right. A little. That's Rachmaninoff."

She bent over the piano and played a few bars of the concerto.

The dog looked at her with a puzzled expression.

One wall was covered with photographs of family and friends. She walked over and pointed to one of the pictures.

"Isn't that Alice Weurthner?"

Weurthner was an obscure Australian painter whose work blended the dreamtime sandpaintings of the Aborigines with the colors and rhythms of Kandinsky and Klee. He had met her several years earlier at an opening in San Francisco.

"I'm surprised you're familiar with her," he said.

"I'm full of surprises."

Nearby was a matted photograph of a dozen men at the edge of a tropical forest. They wore helmets and packs and carried rifles. They were young and tanned and appeared happy. They were all smiling. She put her finger on what appeared to be his image and turned to him and he nodded.

"I didn't know you were in the service. Where was this picture taken?"

"I forget."

"What did you do?"

"I was a diesel mechanic."

"Who are the other guys?"

"To be honest, I can't even remember their names."

"Yes you can. You just don't want to tell me."

She moved to another part of the wall.

"Were you ever married?"

"Once."

"Which one is she?"

"The ballerina."

"What happened?"

"Long story."

"Is there a short version?"

"She ran off with her dance teacher."

He would have to be more restrained. She might be from a magazine, or worse, another lunatic fan.

She wandered into the dining room and began studying the paintings there and he was left alone with the memory of that name, and others.

The truth was that he had been successful in every way but one. He had loved many women and many were still his friends, but he had never found permanence in the heart. Anymore the women were younger because those further along in the journey had turned from the light. The same could be said of his older male friends, as well. They expected the world to disappoint them and it had, for the world will fulfill any prophecy made of it. In either case, he avoided people who dwelled in the shadows, for given time they would adumbrate the lives of those around them. When women came they would stay awhile, weeks or months or even occasionally the better part of the year, but they would

always leave. At some point, even with the regular trips, they would want
to move to a more exciting place. In the end they could not see that he
needed solitude to do what he did. If he moved somewhere with inter-
ruptions and distractions his work would fail and then his life would fall
apart. He had let that happen once when he was younger, but he would
never let that happen again.

She walked back into the living room.

"Where did you park anyway?" he asked.

"My car got stuck in a snowbank about three miles back. It took me
an hour to walk up."

"By the South Mesa turnoff?"

"I'm not sure. I only had this map they drew for me in town."

"They?"

"The man at the post office."

He made a face and glanced at his watch.

"Look Danielle, I've got a commission on deadline waiting for me
over in the studio. What is it that brought you here?"

He had already calculated another lost hour driving her down to the
road and pulling her car out of the drift. That would leave only six
hours of passable light to lay in the sky on the large canvas for the col-
lector in Los Angeles, a retired businessman who wanted to present the
landscape to his wife on their fiftieth anniversary. The colors for the sky
had to be painted all at once, mixing the blues down from the ultramarine through the cerulean to the azure, and it had to be done in one
sustained and continuous physical effort, adding zinc white and a bit of
Mars orange at each stage, or it wouldn't work. He had developed a
complicated system for his Southwestern skies. If he waited even a day,
the oils on the canvas would be at different stages of drying and would
not mix properly.

She sat back down and finished the juice. She looked at him nervously. Then she tried a smile.

"Mr. Clark—"

"—Please don't call me that."

"I have something I need to show you."

She reached into the pocket of her jacket and pulled out a picture and
handed it to him.

"Do you know the woman in this photograph?"

He took the photograph in his hands and his face immediately changed. It was a color picture from long ago. A young blond-haired woman in sunglasses was sitting against her backpack at the top of a mountain pass, surrounded by midsummer snowbanks and smiling into the camera. She was wearing a halter-top and cutoff jeans and heavy socks and waffle-soled hiking boots. It was a sunny day and the view was to the horizons. The mountains to the west went on forever, blue and blue-gray and grayish-purple in the extreme distance. Far below the glacial turquoise of an alpine lake was visible. He remembered that day on the tundra with the pikas chirping on the chilled wind and his back to the warm sun and being careful that his shadow did not show in the picture.

When he looked more closely at the image

it all came back to him in a rush from the past and the sense of how it was then, even the sweet pollen scent of late July in the high country, returned with a vividness that pulled him far away. They had met in a course on the art of the renaissance. They had been friends for a long time, taking bicycle trips east of town and talking for hours in the field behind Old Main, before anything had happened. She had thick luminous hair that fell to her shoulders like the spring light in an aspen grove and eyes the color of the sky when the sun has gone behind a cloud and her form was like something the river has sculpted in the pink granite at the bottom of the Grand Canyon. On the night of his eighteenth birthday in January she had come to his room with her sister Rose and asked if he wanted to have some three-two beer now that he was of legal age. He said no at first because he had to finish reading a biography of Juan Gris for a class but then eventually he was persuaded and they went to Giuseppe's on the Hill and drank watered-down Coors from a pitcher and watched a local bar band named "The Regulators" attempt to cover British Invasion tunes. They danced twice, first to a loose rendition of Ray Davies' "Victoria" and the second time to a rocked up version of Mick Jagger's acoustic "Dead Flowers." On the last song all three of them danced together on the packed dance floor.

Around eleven her sister Rose began to yawn and said that she had to make it back to Golden before the snowstorm and then Katrina pretended to accidentally spill beer on her jeans. This was all part of a plan of which

he had no knowledge. He and Katrina went back to her room—more a glori-
fied storage closet—in the basement of a university cottage on Thirteenth
Street, so that she could change and they could then go to Tulagi's and see
the last set of the Linda Ronstadt concert, but they did not leave the room
until the next afternoon, instead lying in bed and listening to Bob Dylan's
"Blonde on Blonde" on her cassette player over and over again. She told him
everything that first night, but most of the stories were about her older
brother Eric, who had been killed a year before on his first solo flight at the
Jefferson County airstrip.

Two days later she had moved all of her things into his dorm room.

That summer they backpacked over a high pass in the mountains west of
town. She had been there before with her other sister, Teresa, and knew the
way. The trail was endless switchbacks up boulder-strewn slopes and on top
at twelve thousand five hundred and forty one feet they turned and saw the
prairies spread flat and blue-gray like a morning sea against the eastern horizon. The first night they camped at an alpine lake among the wind-flagged
spruce on the far side of the pass and after they made love in the tent she remembered she had forgotten to bring her birth control pills, but they agreed
it would not be a problem because she could resume taking them when they
returned to Boulder. Two weeks later her body didn't seem quite right and
they went to the student health clinic, where the doctor was of no help. Then
one day she told him that everything was fine and not to worry. A month
later she moved out, leaving a note that said she had decided to quit college
and go back home and work for awhile and not to call.

He flunked his courses that semester and shortly lost his student deferment
and soon after that was drafted. Two years later, in May of 1975, he was a
twenty-one-year-old corporal stationed on an amphibious assault ship in the
Gulf of Siam when the word came down that the Khmer Rouge had seized
a U.S. merchant vessel and taken hostages. He remembered lifting off in the
heavy transport helicopter and flying over the blurred tropical water and
looking out at the rosy fingers of dawn which are equally lovely everywhere
in the world and then above the reef seeing red tracers just before the lead
helicopter exploded in a fireball. After that they too were hit by ground fire
and there was a long spiraling sickening drop with the pilot who was about
to die struggling to regain control all the way down and the sudden flare-up
and the hard nose-in sideways impact on the coralline beach, and the one

person who survived with only bruises and broken ribs climbing through a hole in the wreckage before it burst into flames to join up with the men in the third helicopter that had miraculously not a single hole in it.

They were moving inland then without words using only hand signals in echelon formation through the former French coconut plantation toward the assembly area near the Buddhist temple. He remembered the first shots going off ahead like tree branches cracking in a windstorm and the two squads dropping all around him, wounded young men calling out in pain and confusion but never in panic, and he remembered shouldering a coconut palm and firing single shots to conserve ammunition at the moving helmets and shoulders and stomachs and legs he found in his rifle sights at the edge of the jungle fifty yards away. And then they poured out of the trees in a frontal assault and the grenadiers were all down and not answering and the rifles were jamming in the automatic mode and Lieutenant Ray Archer of Beaumont, Texas spoke the last words he ever spoke which were to fix bayonets.

And he remembered then how long it was before the second wave arrived even if it was according to the official reports only fourteen minutes.

"Yes," he said. "I remember this woman."

"Well, she was my mother."

Some birds came to the feeder outside of the window. He saw his first thrush of the spring.

"Was?"

"She died six weeks ago from breast cancer."

There was a silence.

"I'm sorry. She was—"

"I know what she was."

He began to feel a little dizzy. There was a ringing in his ears. He had the sense that he had been present in this conversation before, sitting with this person in this room, and he wondered if such fluid intersections could occur, in a passing dream or in a period of reflection. The moment had the familiarity of a previously lived event, and yet it was all new and unfolding in ways that he could not anticipate.

"And your father?" he asked.

"My mother married a very good-looking, very worthless piece of garbage the fall after I was born named Dino Sereni. He worked, when he *was* working, as a salesman. Every couple of months it was something different he was selling. They divorced when I was four. He was always jealous. One night he threw her down a flight of stairs and broke her back."

His face was expressionless.

"So," she paused. "She raised me by herself."

He took a full breath and looked outside. A pine squirrel had come down the branch to the feeder and chased the songbirds away.

"What did she ever wind up doing, anyway?"

He was trying to appear calm, but she could see through it.

"She was a landscape architect. She won a lot of awards. I was proud of her. Business was good with the new subdivisions going in north of Denver."

He nodded, remembering how she had known the names, even the Latin binomials, of the wildflowers in the mountains. There were the yellow avalanche lily and pink bistort she found in the talus near the top of the pass, and the alpine forget-me-not and white columbine on the shores of the lake, and the bluebell and monkshood growing shoulder-high on the lower trail in the canyon, and the marsh marigold and globe-flowers around all the springs.

"Was she sick very long?"

"About two years. It wasn't bad until the end."

"Right."

There was a pause.

"Last week I drove up to Fort Collins and was cleaning out her house and I found her journals in a sealed box underneath her bed. There was one for every year since she was fifteen. I think she wanted me to read them after she was gone. That's when I learned the truth."

"The truth?"

She paused again, staring at the diamond in her wedding ring.

"I think you know."

He studied her appraisingly, searching for echoes of himself in her eyes, her nose, her chin, her ears, the shape of her head, her hands, her fingers, her shoulders, her body frame. He searched for harmonies and, one by one, he found them. It was all coming together now, the multiple loose ends of an unfinished story now twenty-five years old. It all

made sense and it all made no sense and in the end it was as he had suspected from the beginning.

"I guess I do."

A piece of kindling broke in the fireplace, the sparks flying upward.

"You have to understand. She was young and scared. She was afraid
your family would take the baby. Your parents were well off and hers
were poor. Her mother controlled all of her decisions. You remember
what she was like."

He recalled a religious woman in a modest wood-frame house on the
north side of Golden who had worked hard to raise her three daughters
and one son pretty much by herself, her husband having been disabled
in the war. For some reason the mother had never thought that he was
good enough for her daughter.

"After many years my mother really wanted to tell you, especially after
her own parents died. But she was always ashamed of what she had
done, separating us, and never could bring herself to do it. It was easier
to live with the lie that Dino was my father."

He glanced out the window and lifted his eyes to a place high on the
mountain where the snow was still deep and the wind was pulling the
fresh powder out in banners.

"You don't have to worry," she said.

"Worry about what?"

"I don't want money or anything."

"I hadn't thought of that."

"Yes you did. I just saw it in your eyes."

He looked at her.

"There's one more thing."

"What?"

"For the past three and a half years you have been—" She reached into
the breast pocket of her jacket and took out a small gold-framed photograph and handed it to him "—a grandfather. Her name is Alexandra and
she's in town at the Best Western motel with my husband Cameron."

It was a studio picture. The little girl with the two blond braids in the
pink flowered dress was smiling toward the waving mother behind the
photographer's camera and the innocence and joy in her bright blue eyes
filled the picture. No one could view her angelic face and not share in

her smile. He saw, too, that the little girl resembled the baby pictures of his own mother. The resonance was there and it was haunting. He stared at the picture for a long time. A mystery he had often pondered was now gradually becoming clear, and like this, on an ordinary morning in March when he had almost forgotten about it, and had finally surrendered to the absurdity of what had occurred and had let time bury the memory the way a new forest grows up around an old burn. If only she and her mother had trusted him, what a different life they could have had, the three of them. Of course, he would not be what he now was, but he would likely be something similar, and yet something perhaps fuller and happier in other ways. He was filled with thoughts that made him feel happy and sad at the same time.

She said nothing. Her hands were folded in her lap as if in prayer and her feet were crossed at the ankles. She was waiting for him to speak, to accept her as his daughter, because she had always known something like this was true, and that somewhere there was another man who was her real father. She had waited all of her life for this and now the moment had arrived. Her heart was racing in her chest. She wanted to put her arms around him and finally hug him and call him Daddy and tell him how much she wanted to love him but she restrained herself, waiting for him.

An ancient country of his spirit, a realm that he had never entered before, was slowly filling with light. Peaks and valleys and distant vistas were coming into view. It was a strange new landscape and he had much to learn beyond what instinct and experience would provide. In his mind, a dozen equally urgent thoughts were simultaneously arising and competing for attention. Questions were spawning questions. Being a practical person, he would begin with the essentials.

"What does your husband do for a living?"

The back door opened just then and they heard labored steps across the wooden floor of the kitchen. A much older version of James Clark appeared at the doorway, supported by two steel canes and wearing trifocal glasses. An expression of pleasant surprise registered on the elderly man's face.

"Well, I thought I heard some voices over here in the main house. My goodness, son, we've got a visitor! And what a beautiful young visitor she is!"

Part II

A Walk in the Desert

BY THE TIME I ARRIVE at the trailhead, after driving all day, it is
evening. The sun is down and the desert is filled with a soft and beguiling radiance. A light peach color weights the air. The dust stirred by my
passage over the road drifts slowly, a beige mist, over miles and miles of
lavender-green sagebrush. To the west are the eastern cliffs fronting the
high plateau known as the Kaiparowits. To the east is a deceptively open
country. Beyond the near hills are dark canyons, a vast number of them,
and through the center of the plateau runs a lovely passage known as the
Escalante. Night comes quickly, the first stars gather. A hush falls over
the land. Somewhere Keats' solitary cricket chirps, but that is the only
sound. I crawl into my ancient sleeping bag, so tired and so glad to be
back home that I swear to myself that I could sleep for a hundred years.

But I do not, and I am up an hour before the sun, waiting impatiently
for first light. The trail down Hurricane Wash, it turns out, is easy to follow. The trail is the dry wash. And there are tracks on the sand, dozens
of them. I am not the first, nor the last. Hundreds, thousands have trod
this trail, all on a pilgrimage to see the natural arch that is to this desert
what an inner altar is to a temple, an essential valve is to the heart, a resonant metaphor is to a poem.

For years I have wanted to see Stevens Arch. Today I will.

What can I say of the first few miles? The open sage desert in early
spring has all the excitement of central Wyoming. But gradually, something wonderful begins to occur. The wash begins to sink into the earth.
The canyon walls steadily rise on either side of it. At first these walls are
insignificant—the height of a hound, the height of a horse, the height
of a house—but with each step they acquire more stature. By the third
or fourth mile they give promise of what is to come. They are heavy,
looming walls, unclimbable in places and streaked with desert varnish.
Soon, too, the first water appears and along with it the first willows. It
being spring, the cliffrose are blossoming and they fill the canyon with a

sweet fragrance. The scent is to the desert what wisteria is to Savanna or orange blossoms are to San Diego. Deer tracks abound, too, as well as the miniature human footprints of *procyon lotor*, the common raccoon. Here and there are the familiar tracks of my old friend, coyote.

The wash cuts ever-deeper and deeper into the rock—cool shaded undercurves and sturdy cliffs and contoured alcoves—and the walls become three to four times higher than the canyon is wide. Cottonwoods appear, tall and slender, reaching for the sky with their spring leaves. Waterfalls tumble freely over the rock. With so much water, and the trail basically in the stream bed, I soon switch to tennis shoes and slosh up the middle of the stream. The cool water feels good, but slows the travel. I keep an eye out for poison ivy.

Eventually the trail reaches Coyote Gulch and a mile later I come upon Jacob Hamblin Arch, named for an early Mormon explorer. A mile farther is Coyote Natural Bridge. Both are nice, and would form the centerpiece of a national park in Delaware, but serve on this trail as something of an opening act for what is to follow. The experience of viewing them is similar to that of patiently listening to a warm-up set by an unknown local band before B. B. King comes out, or politely enduring a reading by a college professor before the Nobel Laureate who spent ten years in a Siberian concentration camp takes the podium. They are functional, they work well in their setting, they are in many ways accomplished, but I understand they will pale beside Stevens Arch.

I press on.

A mile beyond Coyote Natural Bridge I take my pack off and place it in the branches of a cottonwood, far from the rodents that live here in abundance. With only my canteen, camera, and tripod I resume the march. I am now only a few miles from Stevens Arch. The canyon walls are prodigious at this point—the height of a seventy story building—and the canyon is filled with a strange golden light, reflected and refracted from the polished stone. It is an intimate subterranean place and the mind becomes absorbed in details—a leopard frog swimming across a pool, the sound of the water, the wind in the wild plum leaves. Everywhere there are hanging gardens and springs gushing from the walls and little waterfalls supporting maidenhair fern and red monkey flower and yellow columbine. Sunlight slants in at straight angles from above, and wherever it strikes the scene is transformed. The canyon is full of charm and grace. I imagine Eden to have been such a place, or the land of the lotus eaters that Odysseus visited, where the men and women rested in idle contemplation forever, having forgotten, and been forgotten by, that other world.

At one juncture an entire wall of the canyon has fallen away. The freshly cut rocks are each the size of a city bus. I am dwarfed by them and move with caution, as one might among the feet of titans.

After awhile I reach the confluence with the Escalante. The mother stream is about fifty feet wide and running deep. I wade upstream toward the arch, the sand giving way beneath my feet, and I am reminded of my days of river-walking on the sandy Pariah River to the south.

Half a mile farther, at the first major turn, I glimpse Stevens Arch. It is set high in the weathered rocks above the river. I can only partially see the arch, and so I climb the canyon wall. After some scrambling, the entire formation becomes visible. I plant the tripod and begin to compose an image. The arch is both a larger and more impressive feature than I thought it would be. Blue sky completely fills the opening, which rests beneath an immense arm of orange-red sandstone. The opening is a mutation between a triangle and a square—a little of both, with gently rounded edges. The rough dimensions appear to be about one hundred and fifty by two hundred feet. It is a structure of extraordinary beauty. It looms like a portal, a gateway, an entrance to some other realm. The light pours through it as from another universe. The ranger in Escalante mentioned that some years ago a man illegally flew his single-engine plane through Stevens Arch, but it is difficult to see how that could be done, except perhaps in a suicide mission. The arch was, she said, named for Al Stevens, a local rancher. As one who lives among words, I can't help but think that the arch should be provided with a more lyrical name—something multisyllabic and rich in vowels from the Navajo lexicon, or a more fitting English noun such as Imperial or Panoramic.

The contemplation and photo-taking finished, I stop for one last look. This may be the only time in my life that I stand in this faraway place. The arch is so beautiful that I blow it a kiss. A sentimental gesture, perhaps, but I love such places with all my heart.

I return to camp. So far as I know there is not another soul in this canyon. One of the virtues of visiting this place early in the year and in the middle of the work week is that you are often alone. Solitude is fine, I learned long ago, except for the end of the day.

Evening comes early to the bottom of the canyon and I lie on my back and look up at the sky, watching it change color and wondering about matters large and small. Finally I settle down beside my fire of twigs and fallen branches. Before going to sleep I say my prayers as I say them every night. Who knows if they do any good, but I say them every night in case Bertrand Russell was wrong. I pray first for my son, and then my father, and then my brothers. I pray that my mother is resting in a place of love. I pray for various friends who might benefit from divine intervention. I pray for good people that they may continue to be good and I pray for bad people that they might see the light. Sometimes I pray for someone I do not know. Once I read in the paper of a person in a terrible situation and I said an extra prayer that night asking for a special favor, and the next day I read in the paper that this individual had been miraculously saved. Just a coincidence no doubt, but still I pray. Who knows how the universe works?

The next morning I am up before the sun, which is an easy feat to accomplish at the bottom of a one thousand foot deep canyon. It is a long hot walk out and almost to the trailhead I finally meet some other hikers. Their names are Ted and Karen Knight and they are from Evansville, Indiana. They are high school science teachers on spring break.

"Where have you been?" they ask, "Do you know where we are on the map? Where are you headed?"

Good questions, I think. Very good questions, indeed. I provide them with the answers they want and we part on the trail. I understand that these are not the real answers to the questions. Perhaps there are no real answers, only questions that we continually rephrase and refocus with ever-greater clarity. And perhaps the desert is in its own way a question, as well, a question that we must each answer in our own way.

The Exact Location of Paradise

IT WAS DECEMBER and the fog was flowing from the ocean into the bay. In the time it takes to remove a book from a shelf and open it to page one the bridge supports of the Golden Gate were gone. Only the steel towers and support cables stood above the fog. Everything below was as gray and insubstantial as the passing cloud into which it had disappeared. Next was Fort Point. Its reinforced brick walls that could withstand a sustained barrage from a ship of war and its heavy cannons that once could fire a one hundred pound projectile across the bay to the Marin headlands and its rusted machine gun turrets were lost just as quickly. They were taken without a single shot being fired or a flag of surrender being raised. The capitulation was as thorough as it was swift. Down below the sea lions barked and indignantly grunted, feeling the winter chill through their thick skins, but that did not slow the fog. They, too, were absorbed into its depths, vanishing one by one into an opaque mist that dissolved their forms and muffled their cries. Then came the gray humped mass of Alcatraz, the warden's house and concrete cell blocks fading like an elusive memory into the void.

From here the fog poured into the central bay and steadily claimed every battleship and sailboat, skyscraper and side street, intersection and alleyway of the city. Nothing escaped its touch. The rich and the poor, the good and the evil, the young and the old. All were influenced by its presence. Curtains were closed. Sweaters were put on. Umbrellas were found to be useless. Thoughts began to turn inward and moods to shift downward, even though it was the week before Christmas. After filling the bay and obliterating the lower city the fog began to climb the surrounding hills. At the Presidio the fog crept up the grassy embankments, drifting past the eucalyptus trees and the drab barracks of the enlisted men and the fine old Victorian houses of the officers. Everyone was asleep. No one noticed. There was no wind that night. Not even a slight breeze. No dogs barked because they were all asleep at the foot of their masters' beds. The wandering cats felt the chill as they explored the obscure places of the night and so they came in through the pet-doors and tiptoed across the kitchen floors, leaving wet tracks on the polished wood. They would find an easy chair in the shadowy corner of a silent room in which to spend the rest of the night.

Eventually the fog reached the military cemetery and floated specter-like around the graves. The headstones were as varied as the people buried beneath them—plain crosses and granite monuments, marble tombs with tiled roofs and sturdy tapering obelisks. Common or elaborate, large or small, each stone and marker disappeared with the same weightless effort into the fog. It was a cold night in December and no one was around. Even the army private in the guard house on Lombard Street was asleep at his post, still badly hung over from the night before. He did not notice the man who walked briskly by at eleven, his collar turned up, and who made his way up to the graveyard. Nor did he notice the second man who followed an hour later.

Far up the farthest hill in the Presidio there is a special area reserved for those who have received the nation's highest award for military valor. This is known as "The Hill of Honor." There are officers from the Civil War and cavalrymen from the Indian Wars, marines from Belleau Wood and paratroopers from Normandy, sailors from Pearl Harbor and riflemen from Vietnam. At the center of the burial ground is the tomb of a young marine pilot named William Upshur. The lieutenant died in a suicide attack on an aircraft carrier in the early days of the Second World War. The impact of the plane caused a fuel explosion that destroyed the carrier deck and helped determine the outcome of a desperately fought battle. Lieutenant Upshur's father was a United States senator representing the state of Ohio. He wanted a permanent place on the western coast where the grieving family could come and pray in solitude and dignity. Because the body was never recovered the memorial structure is empty. There is no coffin, no ceramic urn. There is nothing inside but wind-blown spice-scented eucalyptus leaves. The gated door to the tomb appears to be padlocked, but the lock arm was long ago filed away. Only a careful inspection would reveal the tampering, but no one ever makes such an examination. Here the dispossessed sometimes come to sleep when the nights are long and cold and wet in December.

That night a young veteran of the last war came to the wrought iron door and quietly opened and closed it. Once inside he spread his bedroll neatly on the floor and curled up on his side. He had just begun to fall asleep when he heard the door creak open. The man could tell from the bulky outline of the dark figure that the stranger was not a cemetery guard and so he told him to go away, that this was his place for the night.

"But I don't have any other place and it's raining."

"Why should I let you stay?"

"Because I have food. Warm food from that Chinese restaurant over on Filbert Street. I started a fire in the trash cans and grabbed these take-out bags when they went to put it out."

The two lit a candle and ate in silence. The food was good and warm and it improved their perspective. The world was not as forlorn as it had been an hour earlier, because their stomachs were now full and they were dry, at least until morning. It is also always better to have a companion when alone in the night. Gradually they began to converse and it turned out they both had served in the same branch of the service and after their recent discharge had both suffered similar injustices and misfortunes. Everything that could go wrong had, and nothing right had occurred. So here they were, trapped in an unlikely predicament in which they did not belong. The first man was named Carl Husk. The other said his name was Howard Guffy. Howard asked why the tomb was empty and Carl related what he knew of William Upshur. It was a sort of a bedtime story. After that they fell asleep on opposite sides of the tomb, each slipping into a deep dreamless sleep in which they could forget for awhile that they were homeless and sleeping in a cemetery.

In the morning they parted. It was a damp dreary day and the sun would not shine for a minute that day but at least the fog was gone. One man went one way and the other went another way.

Three days later on a bright sunny morning the young man named Howard Guffy was down on the docks. He went there often, looking for day jobs. The shipping companies would hire vagrants like himself for unpleasant or dangerous jobs that no one else wanted—cleaning the bilges, caulking the decks, painting the forecastles, lifting heavy objects, handling dangerous or illegal cargo. Howard wanted to save enough money so that he could go to Orange County where he had a sister and could perhaps start a new life. Had he been attired differently, he would have appeared as a young man with a bright future. He had straw-colored hair and broad shoulders and an honest intelligent-looking face. His eyes were the color of the blue sky in southern California and when he smiled people wondered how such a person could wind up on the streets. His presence made them uncomfortable, for they saw how similar he was to them and how little, really, separated their lives from his. The loss of a job, an accidental injury, a devastating fire and they, too, would be eating at the soup kitchen of the Little Sisters of the Poor.

As he walked behind a warehouse below the Oakland Bridge he heard a loud commotion and, peering through a broken window, saw two men fighting in the back of a storage area. Fights were common in this area, where the only law was often a closed fist. There were cards scattered on the top of a shipping crate and it was evident the men had been playing cards and that one had caught the other cheating. Howard recognized one of the two men as Carl Husk. He remembered that Carl had done him a favor several nights earlier and so he found a length of pipe and walked in and struck the stranger with the knife over the head. It was easy. He just swung the thing as if it was a baseball bat.

Carl thanked Howard with a handshake and a slap on the shoulder and bent down to examine the man. Carl noted that from the condition of the man's head and the fixed quality of his eyes that he appeared dead, although he was still breathing a little. Howard agreed. Carl unbuttoned the man's shirt sleeve and found the cards he used to fix games. When he found the cards he stood up and kicked the man in the side and exclaimed "Serves you right you ugly son of a bitch. Stealing from a man down to his last five dollars. You ought to be ashamed of yourself." Howard cautioned Carl to keep his voice down and suggested they dispose of the body. Before doing so they removed everything from the man's pockets and put these items into their own. There were coins, a wallet, a gold watch, and some papers they could examine later. They then stuffed the man into a canvas sack. He was not a large man and so he fit into the overseas shipping bag easily. They put the bag on a dolly and wheeled it a few blocks to the dog food factory. The worker on the receiving platform spoke perhaps one hundred words of English and so Carl indicated mostly with sign language that the bag was full of meat scraps collected from the local restaurants. The functionary, who was relieved to learn they were not field agents from the federal immigration service, weighed the bag on an oversized scale and paid them one dollar and fifty-two cents—a penny for each pound—from a cigar box on the floor. Carl personally lifted the bag onto the greased steel conduit and watched as it disappeared with a series of crunching sounds into the depths of the machine. He then observed that the only justice in this world is that which a man makes himself.

Their victim had over a thousand dollars at various places on his person, and so Howard and Carl hailed a cab uptown to The Flying Dutchman where they rented a corner room overlooking Golden Gate Park and cleaned up. Later they bought some fashionable clothes at a nearby store. Carl looked completely different in his new suit, and was transformed as if by Pallas Athena into a genuinely impressive man, standing just over six feet with thick blue-black hair and a chin of the sort Hollywood loved in the Thirties and green eyes that sparkled merrily in the sun. With their deep outdoor tans, they both looked as if they had just returned from a month in Hawaii.

After several hours of feasting at various fine restaurants the two wound up at the Blue Note night club on Russian Hill. While drinking at the bar they met a pair of young women who went by the names of Maya and Cheyenne. Maya had the lines of a ballerina, which she had been in high school, and stood with her back straight and her shoulders back. She had curly black hair and a sharply featured face and thin lips that disappeared when she smiled. Her eyes were the flat predatory eyes of a hawk. The other girls in the neighborhood had nicknamed her "hatchet-face." Maya did most of the talking. Cheyenne was the prettier of the two and also the more voluptuous, with dark blond hair and a freckled nose. She had lovely fine hands with long slender fingers. Her eyes were as blue as cornflowers. Cheyenne was blessed with an easy grace and it was not necessary for her to do much talking. They both smelled of tropical flowers and wore brightly colored sundresses and platform heels. After an hour of pleasant conversation the girls walked Carl and Howard across the street to the establishment at which they were employed, The

Green Garden. The men were asked to take showers. Afterwards they were led into separate curtained rooms. There was slow music playing through speakers set at intervals in the hallway and each girl danced awhile in the soft purple light, removing articles of clothing along the way. Eventually they had everything off.

At a certain point nature took over.

Later the four sat on the roof in lawn chairs and drank cold German beer from bottles and looked at the silver pepper of the stars and the lights of the city and talked. The girls were wearing thongs and the men had on their boxer shorts. Howard and Carl had discovered the girls' real names were Mariah Sweeney and Amanda Samples and that they were both twenty years old. They had come from Kansas City where they had grown up together in the same boring neighborhood and they had only been in San Francisco for one month. They were living in Amanda's car over on Kearney Street. They had no plans other than to save money and try to get an apartment. This was the only work they could find that paid decently in such an expensive city and after awhile they had become somewhat accustomed to the bizarre way of life. It was all only temporary, though. Both dreamed of going into the theater, or so they joked.

For the next three days the quartet lived in the rented corner room with double beds at The Flying Dutchman. The girls enjoyed the chance to sleep in real beds for a change with clean private showers and the guys relished the opportunity to call room service and watch the holiday football games and generally feel as though they were members of the human race again. At first Amanda slept with Carl and Howard slept with Mariah, but then Mariah only wanted to be with Carl, and that left Amanda and Howard together in the same bed. It was the sort of arrangement that couples quietly sort out among themselves in such situations, gradually reaching an accommodation with circumstance.

On Christmas Eve they slept in late and then opened their presents, such as they were. After that they ordered brunch, watched part of a football game and went back to sleep. It was raining steadily and it was a good day to be inside. While the others were asleep Mariah started cleaning. The place was a mess, and she organized clothing on different chairs by owner. Everyone was still asleep and so she began to examine what few things the two men had. In a pocket of Carl's sports jacket was a brown legal envelope, which she opened. Her eyebrows lifted as she read the contents, and the more she read the more the expression of astonishment grew on her face. The document was a deed to a gold mine in northern Arizona. It provided the exact location of the mine by latitude and longitude, as well as by township and local survey markers. There was also a complete history of the prior ownership, as in the official provenance for a work of art. The property had once belonged to a man named Dr. Clarence Farney from Muscatine, Iowa, who had signed it over to Gideon Nettles from Wolf Hole, Arizona, who had signed it over to Pinkerton Vaughn of Carson City, Nevada, who had then signed it over to Carl Husk of San Francisco, with Howard Guffy as the witness.

So that was it, she thought, Carl had somehow come into ownership of a gold mine.

Mariah woke Carl up by shoving him repeatedly on the shoulder and he finally turned over and rubbed his eyes, not sure of where or even who he was.

"You never told me you owned a gold mine, you idiot!" she exclaimed, waving the deed playfully at him and giggling in that somewhat unnerving giggle of hers.

Carl stared at Mariah incredulously and thought for a moment and then explained that he had recently won the gold mine in a card game, and that he had never been to the site. She then proposed that the four of them go out to the desert and visit the place. Carl sighed and admitted that he was nearly broke and that out of state travel would sadly have to wait for better times. He fully expected her to leave—he was actually hoping for her imminent departure—but instead she laughed and said she had known all along that the two were not what they seemed. She now had a brilliant plan to obtain the seed money for their venture.

Everyone got up and listened to the scheme.

The next morning was Christmas. The Green Garden was closed because there was no business that day. This fortuitous coincidence would present them with the ideal opportunity to liberate the office safe. They could break in through a rear window—they had to make it appear an outside job so as not to implicate innocent employees, protested Amanda—and then rip the safe from the wall. Carl could use a sledgehammer to break apart the drywall and then knock the safe free of the two by fours. It would not take long, for Carl was strong and certainly would have the motivation. No one would hear because everyone was gone for the day, from that building as well as from the surrounding businesses. The owner would never call the police, because everything that happened on the premise was illegal and the money technically did not exist.

Three hours later, shortly after dark, they found a locksmith who worked from a van with expired plates and charged them one hundred dollars in cash up front to open the safe, no questions asked.

What they discovered inside startled even Mariah.

After each appointment the girls put one-half of the money they had earned into a small hole on the door of the safe. It was not merely an honor system—there was an older woman, Mrs. Kincade, who closely monitored the internal operation and also made sure the police received their ten percent in a glass pickle jar set aside for that purpose. Every week the owner drove down from Napa Valley and personally emptied the safe. His name was Mr. Young and he had a number of legitimate enterprises through which he laundered the profits. There were always at least five girls employed at The Green Garden and they worked in twelve hour shifts for three days every week, and sometimes more during busy periods. They each had between four and six appointments per shift, and they each charged a large fee and usually more, depending on the customer. In an average week there would be around five or six thousand dollars in the safe. On this week, because Mr. Young's mother had died and he had missed a week, there was eleven thousand dollars.

Mariah immediately put herself in charge of the treasury. She allotted everyone a modest allowance and began making detailed plans in a spiral-bound notebook. They shortly moved to a less expensive hotel near the university that had rooms with kitchenettes and began cooking their own meals. After all, they would need mining equipment, explosives, and any number of horses or mules to reach the site, given its remote location. Mariah even went to the downtown library and undertook a day of research, obtaining topographic maps and learning precisely what materials were required. To save money they would rent, not buy, a car and drive to a place called Bowie Pass, where they could then obtain whatever provisions and livestock they needed to reach the canyon.

On the day of departure, Amanda did not show up at the appointed rendezvous site. Mariah explained that Amanda had decided to return to Kansas City. Howard was sad to see her go. He had grown fond of her. They had even invented affectionate pet names for each other—Blondie and Pierre. Mariah assured him that girls like Amanda were easy to find. There were at least ten thousand in every American city, and more were graduating from high school every year. Girls like her were as easy to find as the next city bus.

Later she bought him some chocolate cake from a convenience store to cheer him up.

In reality, Mariah had sent Amanda on a last-minute errand and then given her elaborate misdirections. Amanda had waited at the wrong place in the rain for three hours before returning to her car and the solitary drive back to Kansas City.

ii.

SAGE AND CACTUS SPREAD from horizon to horizon. There was no sign of the human race anywhere. The country was a desert—a deserted place—and therefore unpeopled. It was located somewhere in that arid, empty, bleak quarter north of the Grand Canyon and south of the Utah border where the largest living thing is a deer and whole weeks go by without a single cloud. Because it was the hour before dawn, the land was still in shadow and was filled with silence. It was so quiet that the sound of a coyote digging its day bed carried one hundred yards, and attracted the attention of a burrowing owl sitting on a rock. It was so quiet that the last star winking out in the western sky seemed to make an audible sound, a kind of wuuush like a candle being blown out. It was so quiet that the sea that once covered the place could sometimes be heard, a gentle breaking surf that resonated from the grains of sand held in the buttes.

As the light came up on the earth, the country began to reveal its secrets. It was a desert land, spare and disciplined, and there was no fat on it. The colors were dry and sun-washed, like the colors of dusty pottery sherds. The floor of the desert was covered with coarse beige sand, dotted here and there with sage and cactus and yucca. Along the winding stream courses, junipers and pinyon grew, branched in delicate ways and colored olive-green, like bonsai. Otherwise there were no trees, only shifting sand dunes and fossil-encrusted rocks and hardy plants with waxy leaves and clustered thorns. The early-morning air was cool, and scented with the smell of sage. Sometimes there was a breeze as frigid as ice water, for it was January. Other times, there were milder currents, as the air of earth and heaven began to mix.

First light across the desert came with a force unknown to dwellers of the city. The amber rays and beams moved and shifted powerfully across the land, striking first the distant mountains and mesas then moving downward. The fractured walls of the nearby cliffs displayed stronger hues than the rest of the landscape, as if they had, over the ages, absorbed the fire of more than one Arizona sunrise. They seem to glow with an inner light. Their weathered rock was faded bronze and bright copper and the burned red of kiln-forged bricks. Here and there the rocks were colored weird shades of green and purple and gray. In the first warm shadowy light of dawn every fine detail—the folded stratifications and immense pediments and individual fallen rocks and majestic projections and hidden alcoves—were for a few moments visible. The tall stony masses were constructed in a mixture of the Byzantine and the Gothic, the Egyptian and the Greek, the plutonic and the antediluvian. It was an architecture of a scale and beauty against which any structure ever raised by the human race however monumental would seem insignificant.

And then suddenly the sun broke free and the entire landscape from horizon to horizon was flattened by a blinding radiance.

One of the scenes the sun illuminated that morning was the campsite of three people who had stopped the previous evening at the mouth of a canyon. The trail they had taken to reach this place was not evident, although anyone following their tracks would have found they began at the end of a dirt road some twenty-five miles to the north. The three were camped in a flat place among the rocks. There they had stopped, too exhausted to raise a tent, and there they had slept on the frozen ground. With the three people were three riding horses and two pack mules. The stock was hobbled in the canyon and wore their saddle blankets against the cold. Rising behind the gorge was a large forested mountain that was three times longer than it was high. The mountain sat by

Sell your books at sellbackyourBook.com!

Go to sellbackyourBook.com and get an instant price quote. We even pay the shipping - see what your old books are worth today!

Inspected By: soledad_hernandez

00059991557

itself on the edge of a plain, and there were other mountains like it scattered around the landscape, each positioned as if dropped randomly from the skies. This particular mountain had been christened "Black Mountain" by a government survey that had wandered through the area after the Civil War.

A little after ten that day the outfit got under way and shortly before noon they reached the mine, which was five miles up the narrow rocky canyon. The mine was set on a shelf of rock about fifty yards above the canyon floor. One hundred years earlier a midwestern college professor named Clarence Farney had worked the claim for several months after he retired. He had found some gold particles in the outwash sand on the canyon floor and had then located a small exposed vein in the quartz monzonite above. A bit of dynamite had been used to blast an exploratory tunnel in the formation. The tunnel went back around seventy-five feet. Here Dr. Farney had encountered a common form of nonmineral bearing rock, and had abandoned the site. All totaled, he had just about broken even on the project.

Carl emerged from Dr. Farney's tunnel and said he had not seen anything resembling gold in the rock but admitted that he didn't know exactly what he was looking for.

"All this way for nothing!" exclaimed Howard, who was developing a bad cough from the exertion and the dust and the cold.

Mariah wanted to see for herself and so she took the kerosene lantern and came out half an hour later with a fragment of gold no larger than the tooth of a mouse. They all agreed it was probably worth at least enough to buy a loaf of bread. Carl and Howard dejectedly went down the slope to establish camp for the night. This time they were going to raise the tent and this time they were going to gather enough wood to build a good fire. Carl had noticed that scrub oak was abundant in the canyon and he knew that oak burned well. He had decided to leave the next day because the radio had warned that a major Pacific storm would cover the area in snow the day after tomorrow. They had to get down to lower ground by then.

Mariah wanted to explore the countryside. She would be down later. She followed a deer trail for awhile as it ambled among the rocks and bushes and when it ended she climbed a line of rocks and walked along the edge for some distance. At the end of the line of rocks there was an obvious route that rose toward a ridgeline that would offer a commanding view for further reconnaissance, but Mariah did not take that route. It was her nature to always defy convention and reasonable expectation, and so she followed a lower contour along the canyonside. Half a mile later she came to a rock overhang and there she sat to rest her blistered feet for awhile before turning back. A stiff wind had come up and the rock offered some protection. She lay back and put her hands on her sunburned face and wondered how she had ever gotten to such a godforsaken place.

When she opened her eyes she noticed that there was a curious pale yellow streak in the grayish rock above her head. It was as wide as her leg and it ran through the rock for ten or twelve feet. On the floor of the cavern were pieces of the rock that had fallen over the ages and she picked one of these up and studied it closely. The rock was raw quartz and it appeared to contain granular crystals of gold.

Mariah had a wooden-handled geologist's hammer with her and she struck the rock several times. The surrounding quartz crumbled and fell away, but the hard bright mineral did not fracture or turn to powder when it was hit.

She knew then what she had found.

iii.

IT WAS A GRAND MANSION, one of the most distinguished on the Kona Coast, and it was surrounded by extensive lawns and coconut palms and stately banyan trees. In the sixteenth century, the great King Umi had moved his royal court to the same rocky point, and there built a royal estate. He liked the dry sunny weather of the western coast, and the fine views out across the calm blue sea, and the gentle trade winds that kept the annoying insects and court intrigue away. When he died he had his bones buried under a pile of lava stones in the place, believing his spirit would always occupy the point. He had been a good monarch, generous and caring of his people, and he wanted to continue to be a benevolent presence on the big island in the afterlife.

The rocky point was the same now as then, except that it was occupied by another sort of sovereign in a different sort of home. The cultivated lawn began at the road a quarter of a mile away, and ran over red brick walls and brilliant tropical gardens and Roman statues and stone-lined pools with swimming goldfish and when it reached the house it became a green wall of red flowers as big as plates and spreading tree ferns and banana trees heavy with ripening fruit. The house was a huge rambling three story affair with floor to ceiling French windows of the style favored near the equator. It was painted titanium white to reflect the sun and there were open porches on all four sides, and from the roof there was a flagpole with the American flag, for one of the former owners was an admiral who had married a plantation heiress. Behind the house was a sloping hill and beyond it a cultivated forest of Ohia trees and gray-barked koas and bamboo groves. The forest was rich in shades of green and the sky was not always visible through the foliage. In places the moss grew like beards on the trees and the creepers and the orchids hung as if there was no gravity, and everywhere the luminous shadows imparted an atmosphere of intimacy and secrecy. Birds of every color sang from the branches each morning and each evening and many would call out at various times during the day. The air was always cool like spring water and filled even in January with the sweet scent of citrus blossoms and exotic imported flowers from places like Nepal and Burma that even a trained botanist would be hard-pressed to identify.

Carl Husk and Mariah Sweeney had lived as husband and wife in the house now for two and a half years, ever since filing a formal claim on the deposit and discovering that, formidable as it seemed, it was nothing compared to the major body sleeping quietly below the surface of the canyon. They were as wealthy as medieval lords now, and led a perpetually busy life at their palatial residence on the Kona coast. They traveled frequently in their own yacht, or in their own airplane, and they were known from Carmel to Cannes as being among the nouveau riche. Everyone in that crowd liked them, even if no one knew much about them. Their house was filled with objects of art, for they loved to collect things of value, however unfamiliar they might be with what they were. In the main living room there was Renoir's "Luncheon of the Boating Party" and Picasso's "Seated Woman." Elsewhere hung crayon portraits by Seurat and a representative canvas by Gauguin from his Tahitian period and a rare early watercolor of the Dutch countryside by Van Gogh.

There was one entire room filled with antique furniture from the English Renaissance, and there was a music gallery with a grand piano, and there was a library filled with books that neither of them had ever had the time or the inclination to read.

On an oak table in that library there was a silver-framed black and white photograph of Carl Husk, Mariah Sweeney, and their former business partner, Howard Guffy. The picture was taken in Arizona during their first trip to the gold mine. In the photograph they are standing beside riding horses and pack mules at a trailhead in the desert. That was the trip during which Howard lost his life. Carl sometimes told the tale after dinner was finished and the guests had moved to the library to drink brandy. Things on the trip had gone fairly well, considering they were unfamiliar with the area, until the very end. At the last minute Mariah decided they needed a few more ore samples. She asked Howard to help her as Carl prepared the horses. Not long after that she came screaming down the trail with the news that Howard had slipped and fallen into the canyon. Carl rushed to the point and saw his friend sprawled on the sand below. Howard had fallen into an inaccessible place in the slickrock and could not be reached. They called and called. He did not move. He must be dead, Mariah lamented, poor Howard must be dead. No one could survive such a fall. Carl reluctantly agreed. The snow was beginning to fly by then, and so Carl and Mariah rode off into the desert, nearly losing their lives along the way and they would have, too, except that a Paiute Indian searching for his lost sheep had found them instead. When they returned six weeks later, Howard's body was gone, probably carried off by coyotes. No trace of him was ever found. Howard Guffy had been Carl's best friend—he had even saved Carl's life once in the service—and so Carl had named the mine after him in memory of the loss.

On this particular day Mariah and Carl were having a party to celebrate the fact that their company—Howard Guffy, Incorporated—would now be represented on the New York stock exchange. The fresh capital would be invested in a number of profitable ventures, including new consumer products, promising technologies, and the always lucrative pharmaceutical industry. Mariah had assembled a staff of well-educated financial advisers for this purpose. The finest citizens in Hawaii—the lieutenant governor, the mayor of Honolulu, the president of the chamber of commerce, a half-dozen retired celebrities—were in attendance. Over one hundred people had been invited and everyone had shown up. The high point of the evening would be the appearance of an aging music star from the mainland, who would undertake a personal performance of some of her most popular songs. This was after the private screening of a new film by a well-known production company. All of the events, of course, were being paid for by the new investors of the company, most of whom were the general public.

At the gatehouse there was a guard who was a native Hawaiian and who had grown up not far from the point. It was his job to check the invitations and electronically open the iron gate and call his supervisor if there was a problem. He hated the people he worked for, but he was always civil. He was a descendant of King Umi, and so he had to honor the family tradition, even if he was no monarch, only a part-time college student working for mainlanders. Late in the afternoon he noticed a man walking up the Queen Kaahumanu Highway from Kailua. The young man was dressed in plain clothes and was climbing the hill at a steady pace, neither fast nor slow. The guard concluded that the young man's automobile must have broken down and that he would need to call for a tow. When the stranger arrived at the gatehouse he asked if he could see Carl Husk. The guard explained in his normal brusque tone that Mr. Husk was busy with the party, and that the party was by invitation only. The man thought for a moment and asked politely if a note could be delivered to Mr. Husk. For some reason the guard liked and trusted the stranger and so, contrary to his normal procedure, he agreed to have someone come down and run the note up to the main house.

Half an hour passed. The two of them talked about nothing in particular as, one by one, the limousines and sports cars were waved onto the property. The stranger would only say that he had some important business with Mr. Husk. Suddenly there was the sound of feet running down the driveway. They stepped from the guard house and looked up the pavement and it was Carl Husk, racing toward them. Carl had the note in his hand. It read: "Do you remember the night you told me the story of William Upshur?—Guffy."

Carl and Howard embraced by the guardhouse—Carl lifting Howard off the ground—and the guard watched in mute surprise. The two whooped and hollered and as cars drove by on the road Carl yelled "Yes, there is a god!" and pointed to Howard. Carl and Howard eventually walked back to the house. The guard joined them, for he had just been relieved for afternoon grounds duty. Howard explained to them that he had only been stunned by the fall. A short time later an old desert rat named Ike Brody came upon him—having smelled the smoke of their smoldering fire—and took him back to the camp to recuperate. Howard had a few broken ribs and some bruises, but otherwise was fine except for one thing. He could not remember who he was or where he was from. This state had continued uninterrupted until a week ago. Howard had been working as a short-order cook in Kansas City and had heard a radio news broadcast about Howard Guffy Incorporated going public with a stock offering. At that moment it all came back to him, his entire life before the fall and every single thing except the fall. He could re- member nothing of the fall. His sister in Orange County had put up the money for his trip over to Hawaii.

Once at the main house Carl and Howard ran upstairs through the private entrance. The guard went off to patrol the grounds. When Mariah saw Howard, she involuntarily dropped into her bedroom chair with a horrified expression, but later regained her composure when she realized that Howard did not remember anything of the fall. Howard noticed that her face was drawn and tired and that several years of smok- ing, drinking, and tropical sun had begun to have their effect. He ap- peared as he had before, the eternal child of innocence. She listened to the story in amazement and insisted that they celebrate with a drink, or two, or three. The guests were watching the movie and so they would not be missed for the next hour or so. After Carl and Howard had con- sumed the better part of a bottle of hard liquor, she suggested that they show Howard the beautiful view of the ocean from the point.

It was a spectacular prospect that ranged for many miles up and down the coast. There was a pocket beach of sand two hundred feet below the rocks, and then the pale green of the lagoon, and then the white line of the waves beating on the reef. Beyond that was the sea, a blue so dark as to almost be purple. Far out to sea, on the horizon, were billowing clouds as a distant storm approached the island. The clouds had plunging canyons and immense peaks and were building even as they watched.

There was rain falling beneath them, but the thunder was not reaching the shore yet and on the point it was still a sunny day. They stood there on the edge of the world for some time, gazing out at the expansive view. Carl and Howard were standing with their arms around each other and Mariah was behind them. The two men were both so drunk they could not form intelligible sentences. Carl kept trying to say "That'll teach you to cheat at cards!" but he could not pronounce the l's or the t's and so it sounded like gibberish. Howard understood the joke anyway, and laughed heartily. Just when they were about to turn and go back to the house Mariah reached out and firmly pushed both men over the cliff.

A couple of seconds later there was a single thump, for they had fallen together.

She peered over the edge once, to confirm the result, and then turned to walk back to the house. No one had known she was gone and no one would ever know what she had done. It would be her little secret. Now the fortune would be all hers. She giggled. In a few minutes she would sound the alarm and then there would be a search. The bodies of the two grossly inebriated revelers would eventually be found at the base of the cliff and she would have to put on quite a dramatic show of grief. She would have to play the role of the tragic widow, at least for a few weeks.

She was smiling to herself and giggling now and then and skipping slightly on the stone path up to the very moment when she saw the guard standing at the edge of the forest.

AFTER A LENGTHY AND VERY PUBLIC TRIAL and a protracted appellate battle, the eyewitness testimony of the guard proved an insurmountable obstacle for the defense. Mariah Sweeney was ultimately convicted of two counts of second degree murder. After several years in prison, she was transferred to the state asylum, where she later died in a fire. The estate of Carl Husk was divided between the lawyers, an elementary schoolteacher named Florence Guffy in Orange County, California, and, as Carl Husk had directed in a minor proviso of his will, the Little Sisters of the Poor.

Spring's Progress

SPRING ON THE DESERT can be measured in the melting snow and the coming of small flowers in sunny places. Each morning the sun rises a minute or two earlier. The change in the balance of day and night becomes noticeable by mid-February. By March there are afternoons when it is genuinely hot, although winter still remains in the neighborhood. With the spring there comes a general revival. One is reminded of the Italian painters of the Renaissance, who began to create anew after their country had slumbered for ten centuries, or of the early Greek thinkers—Thales and Heraclitus and Pythagoras—who posed the first abstract questions at the dawn of philosophy. In such a spirit of freedom and discovery and fresh starts do the canyon waterfalls thunder and the wildflowers blossom and the warblers make music. The whole landscape is aroused from a sleep, a death, and forms itself again in beauty and power. A realignment takes place. All living things are moved by the impulse to grow, to propagate, to embrace that which sustains them. The air is no longer cold and sharp, but now is warm and gentle, like the touch of a lover. Even the rocks seem alive.

March is the month of the vernal equinox, but it is also a time of both forward and backward motion. The snow remains in the highlands, but below the desert is changing. Think of a day when you exercised vigorously in the outdoors, walked perhaps twenty miles over difficult terrain, and then slept long and deep. The next morning you awoke slowly, by degrees, feeling the life gradually flow back into your limbs. You lay in bed for a long time, half in slumber and half awake, as if emerging from the weightlessness of water. One moment you drifted back into the world of dreams and the next you vaguely considered the day to come. That is the desert landscape in March—a gradual awakening. The pasqueflowers are about, even if they must close their purple-pink blossoms on certain days, and the snowdrifts stubbornly linger where the sun does not reach. Some days the month is a journey back into January. Other days it is a preview of June.

April is the beginning of the waterfall season in the desert. The falls come as a pleasant surprise to those with conventional expectations of an arid landscape. Like all things in nature that are scarce, from true fishing stories to twenty-year-old virgins, their stature is enhanced by their rarity. The best are confined to the canyons, but nice waterfalls can sometimes be found in the higher elevations. The latter tend to be of the Rocky Mountain variety, with a flat step-drop of six or eight feet, and a resident water ouzel near each pool. The most dramatic plunges, though, are found in the lower canyons. Here the water often encounters a shelf of sediment that is a hundred or more feet in height. There is no other way but down, and away the stream goes, with sheer abandon and in what seems at times pure joy, singing and dancing all the way to its doom.

On whatever landscape they occur, the waterfalls peak during the height of the snowmelt. A few continue in diminished form through the summer months, but most are reduced to a slow trickle by the time the sunflowers blossom. Some are as narrow as a single braid hanging down the middle of the back. They tumble in a tight bundle of luminous threads and dissolve into a spectral mist of ruby-throated hummingbirds and darting cliff swallows. Others are as broad as a thick mane of blond hair shaken back over the shoulders. They are full of light and thunder. They bring to mind the classic locks of Helen, or the fabled tresses of a Nordic goddess, or the central metaphor of a medieval folktale. They are the stuff of photographers and artists. All about them are lush gardens from the fertile imagination of Coleridge. Still other waterfalls are as ragged as the uncombed tail of a dude horse. They fall in wild spurts, split and resplit over the rocks freely, and tumble about with no particular plan, changing by the hour and by the day according to their mood and the vagaries of current and wind.

Zion Canyon is known for its waterfalls. The most unique are the nameless ephemera that slide over the canyon rims during the month of May and then dissipate into the breeze before they reach the canyon bottom, some two thousand feet below. They take the plunge without hesitation, and hang suspended in midair for long moments like a loose piece of silk on a laundry line. Down lower is Upper Emerald Falls, which fogs the glasses of anyone who approaches within twenty feet. A secret cave or antechamber behind it allows people to pass into another universe, but only after they have been completely cleansed and baptized by the sacred waters. Sometimes the chief attendant is seen, a husky yellow-splotched tiger salamander. Nearby is Weeping Rock, which is a sort of a waterfall or, more accurately, a rock wall that continually rains.

A few hours away, near the town of Escalante, is Calf Creek Falls. The water here tumbles over a one hundred foot cliff of slickrock and in its vertical plunge forms a smooth column that resembles the marble shaft of a Greek temple. In the heat of the summer, the tiny oasis attracts everything from collared lizards to golden eagles to French-speaking tourists from eastern Canada. It is a fitting place to contemplate the impermanence of rock and the permanence of water, or the reverse (both being equally true). Farther to the east is the legendary Bridal Veil Falls near Telluride, Colorado. The falls is the tallest in the Southwest—three hundred and sixty-five feet—and sits like a resident wizard or wise man at the head of its own box canyon. It roars profundities all through June and July. In the winter months climbers make the pilgrimage and try to see who will be the first to die on the slippery ice.

In the Grand Canyon the falls are more remote. A twenty-mile trek on the Tanner Trail leads to the Great Falls, which are rendered even more striking by the mineralized turquoise blue color of the Little Colorado. Follow the North Kaibab Trail for a few dusty hours and you will reach Roaring Springs, which produces its own waterfall—a translucent fine curtain of water that is ever expended and ever renewed. Far to the west in the wilderness beyond Bridger's Knoll is Deer Creek Falls, as lovely as the neck of a swan and seen only by those willing to hike a blistered distance through the desert, and along switchbacks that would make a tarantula nervous. Here one can have a conversation with a chuckwalla or listen to the stories of a kingfisher.

The finest of them all is Havasu Falls. Fed by the springs and snow-fields of the Coconino Plateau, Havasu Creek runs for many smooth miles between two grassy banks. Quite suddenly in the midst of a sun-washed canyon it drops over a sculpted ledge and falls the height of two fully grown cottonwood trees into a lovely turquoise pool. At the bottom people must shout to be heard, even during the dry days of August. Most of those who make it that far (ten miles) immediately remove their clothing and go for a swim, occasionally joined by the local reptiles and amphibians. Looking upward from the pool, the white cascading falls resemble the tail of a comet. Swimming beneath the surface in the turbulent backwash, one can feel the power of the element that shaped the canyon. Every so often a solid mass of water goes over the ledge in a single piece and falls with a resounding crash onto the sacrificial victims below, only adding to the fun.

Havasu is also a fine place to look for flowers in the spring, for the season in the desert proceeds from the canyon bottoms upward. Some years sego lilies and lavender phacelia and blue flax appear in the lower reaches of Havasu as early as February. After many tedious months of winter, even the dandelion is appreciated, its vivid flowers brightening the most desolate slope. By degrees the violets appear among the mosses, the flowers the same color as the lid of the human eye. Red shooting stars briefly come and go. Shortly they are followed by small buttercups, each as pale and sad as a woman who dies unloved. By late March the yellow brittlebush are in blossom, filling whole hillsides, and the fragrant cliffrose shortly follows. Beavertail cactus, so prevalent in the Mojave, are found in Havasu, and produce delicate blossoms in the color of a prom night blush. Later come the globemallow, as red as any of Monet's poppies, and the yellow beeplant, which can fill an entire basin with color. In the sandy stretches along the river grows the evening primrose, whose large white flowers, like some romances, open at sunset and wilt by noon of the following day. In upper Havasu the peach orchards of the Havasupai blossom in April like something from a Van Gogh painting, had Van Gogh grown up in sunny Arizona instead of the somber Netherlands.

The desert birds begin singing in April. Their spring melodies fill the canyons and echo mellifluously from the sandstone amphitheaters of Capitol Reef to the travertine caverns and canopies of the Grand Canyon. Whole books can be written about them, and have. Two stand out in their grace and song. The first is that popular vocalist of the high plains, the yellow-throated meadowlark. I have heard his song on the high prairie of Island of the Sky, along the entire length of the Hole in the Rock road, and on isolated grasslands across the desert—places such as Castle Valley or even Monument Valley. The song goes something like this "*Oh yes, I am a pretty little bird!*" The song of the meadowlark is so cheerful it can even lift the hearts of a group of mourners standing over an open grave.

The other renowned soloist of the desert is the poor-will, a bird that is rarely if ever seen but is occasionally heard at dusk and dawn. The poor-will, or nightjar, is wholly nocturnal, living with the great horned owl and the ghost-faced bat and the sphinx moth during the dark hours. It has traded the muse of the sun for that of the moon and the stars. It looks somewhat like an overgrown sparrow, but does not have the bulk or length of a meadowlark. Poor-wills are found throughout Zion in places like Crystal Spring and the Court of the Patriarchs and on the Kolob Terrace. Long ago and far away a poet fated to never see his twenty-seventh spring composed an ode to the English nightingale. The Southwestern poor-will has yet to find its Keats, though the bird is certainly deserving of such an honor. The plaintive song—*poor-will, poor-will, poor-will*—haunts the desert woodlands on warm nights, especially if a full moon is on the rise. If you are like me, you sometimes half-wish at those moments for Keats' glass beaker, so as to drink the liquid song and "leave the world unseen/and with thee fade far away into the forest dim."

The poet laureate who a century later wrote that "April is the cruelest month" never visited the desert, never saw a hedgehog cactus in blossom, never stood beside Havasu Falls, never listened to the song of the hermit thrush. Spring on the desert is more a verb than a noun or an adjective. It is a season of restless motion and continual change. It has the power of a great book, a beautiful woman, a moving song, a masterful canvas, a riveting theatrical performance. One is reminded of childhood, of adolescence, of youth and romance. There are days when the old feel young again, and the young feel as though they will never be old. The thought of autumn or winter is just that, a thought. There are no limits. Everything is a possibility. Everyone is on a honeymoon, and the desert is the lover of choice. Revolution is in the air, even if it is as modest a rebellion as a tadpole climbing up on a rock to have a look around.

The Story of Diego

IN A STONE HOUSE IN THE DESERT there lived a man. He was about fifty years of age, sturdily built, and with hair and a beard that had gone as gray as a fox. He was an early riser and often took morning walks. In the middle of the night sometimes he would climb a wooden ladder to the roof and consider the stars. He was no ordinary dreamer, for he would look beyond the desert, beyond the curving margins of the earth on which he had been born and would die and beyond the moon that waxed and waned each month to that other world of fixed suns and stars whose bounds even science can not discern. He lived out there a lot, on the dark shadowy edges of time and space near what seemed to be a kind of radiance. Sometimes his lips would move as he silently conversed with someone or something, for there was no person beside him, and even the deer walking by on their way to the apple orchard would regard him with some curiosity.

They say he was called Diego, although the story does not come down with his family name. Much of his time was devoted to reading works of philosophy and history. Over the years he gradually neglected almost everything else, even the management of his garden, for he grew his own vegetables and fruits. His neighbors, who were few, always smiled at the mention of his name. He was quite distinct in his habits, but he also struck local observers, even the skeptics, as being completely harmless. To the children he was a character who had escaped from their own imaginations. Eventually he sold half his land so that he could buy more books. He spent whole days and weeks reading works that he ordered and that would arrive in boxes at the post office.

After seven years of study he decided that he should go out into the world as a knight of old, and do good deeds. He would be noble and virtuous. He would listen to grievances and resolve wrongs. He would stand up to the powerful and reform abuses and he would rescue the meek from the unjust. He would, especially, defend the honor of women. He put an ad in the paper down in the valley and asked for a squire. He was a bit crazy, but there are a lot of crazy people in the world, and nine people answered his ad, for the job paid three hundred dollars a month. That was a lot of money in those days.

He interviewed them all closely, sometimes asking them questions from his books. These were books not read much anymore, tracts and memoirs and chronicles that dated back to the dark gilded age of people such as Thomas Beckett and Geoffrey Chaucer, when English was a simpler language and the world was a very different place, at least on the surface. He tried in these meetings to determine if the person would be willing to serve a higher end, or whether they would forever be prisoners of their own vanity. He would inquire of them what they thought was required of a good knight and what they believed the function of chivalry was. He would test their knowledge of history, particularly of the crusades and Richard the Lion-Hearted and the quest for the holy grail. Most were perplexed at the questions and some were amused. No one was alarmed, for he carried with him a presence of kindness and understanding. Standing beside him was like standing beside a very old tree that, once struck by lightning, now grows at a peculiar angle. Birds sang from the branches and of course he cast a shadow as other trees.

None of these people worked out for various reasons.

Diego was in despair at finding a squire when a young woman from the local newspaper showed up to interview him. This young woman, whose name was Selena, was fascinated by Diego in the same way a botanist is drawn to an unusual new flower or a geologist to a rock he or she does not understand. She agreed to go out with him through the countryside. She would be his squire. This was the modern world, after all, and a woman could be a squire as well as a man. She thought the story might make a good book.

Diego said that his first task was to complete a mission of courage to prove his worthiness as a knight.

And so one day they set out with Diego's horse, Pegasus. The horse did not carry a riding saddle. He wore a pack saddle in which Diego kept his books and their personal items.

They had not gone far when they came upon a robbery that was taking place. This was about a hundred years ago, before there were automobiles and the desert was still a wild place. Four men had stopped a wagon and were demanding all the valuables of a brother and two sisters who were on their way home from a shopping trip to town. After robbing the trio they expressed their intention to take the sisters with them, as well.

Diego stepped forward from the trees with a flourish—he knew no other way—and told the men they could only have the women over his dead body. He had no weapon other than his walking stick.

The tallest of the robbers asked Diego if he had lost his mind.

Diego replied that he was no more crazy than anyone else in this world.

The man then struck Diego in the head with his fist. When Diego awoke the robbers were gone. They had been afraid they killed Diego. Murder was not their intent and so they had panicked and left. In other words, Diego had succeeded in defending the virtue of two young women.

Diego was now a knight and that evening he and Selena celebrated with the three strangers, whose names were Olive, Lillian, and Trevor. The three lived with their parents Seneca and Amelia Gould on a small farm along a permanent river of the desert. By morning Trevor, who had fallen in love with Selena, told his parents that he wanted to be a squire, too, and so they gave their blessings and he joined them. He was nineteen and had begun to be rather difficult to have around the house. Diego impressed both parents as a man, however peculiar, who would be a trustworthy chaperone for their son's first great adventure.

Eventually the authorities in a certain county took an interest in him, for Diego seemed to pose a threat to their authority, pursuing as he did a code that was not represented in their laws and doing all that he could to protect the poor from neglect. Diego's pronouncements sometimes embarrassed them, exposing as they did corruption and scandal and the waste of resources that could be used for the less fortunate.

Diego was ultimately brought before a judge named Carlisle Grant in the town of Rock City on a charge of vagrancy. A search of the records determined only that he had been given a section of land for his service as a naval officer during the last war, by a grateful nation. Nothing was known of his former rank or particular exploits, because the government records office in San Francisco had been lost in the fire following the earthquake.

The judge listened to Diego in his chambers for about three minutes and ordered a sanity test.

The doctor pronounced him sane according to the tests they used in those days, even though he seemed to have this peculiar conviction that he was a knight. Diego also seemed to know more about medicine than the doctor did, and lectured with such helpful insight on certain maladies that the physician began to take notes.

He was brought before the judge again.

The judge asked what seemed to him the most germane question. "Do you know who you are?"

"Sir, I know who I am. My peers are in these books. Do you know who you are?"

"Don't take that insolent tone with me."

"I mean no sport sir. Let me explain."

They had some further words and over the course of the next hour, in front of a courtroom of restless citizenry awaiting all manner of tribunals, Diego argued the judge into exhaustion on the subject of higher laws, citing examples as remote as the story of Antigone and Creon and as recent as the report of a hermit from Massachusetts, the author of an essay on civil disobedience, who had refused to pay a poll tax because it would support the Mexican War. Judge Grant finally ordered Diego released on the promise that he never return to his jurisdiction.

Diego, Selena, and Trevor then proceeded north into the mining camps and after liberating several foreign workers from unpleasant circumstances then wandered around the southwest in a leisurely circle of one thousand miles performing various miracles and rescues before returning to his stone house. Diego, whose mind was ever active—picture the reflections of sunlit water on the ceiling of a grotto—then proceeded to commence with the recomposition of the three lost books of Pythagoras (*On Education*, *On Statecraft*, and *On Nature*), which had been destroyed along with noted works of Sophocles, Aeschylus, and others by the conflagration at the library of Alexandria in 415 A.D. The last that history records of Diego is that he went off to become the governor of an experimental society based on the writings of Sir Thomas More on an island in the Micronesian archipelago, and that the local paper refused to print his long descriptive letters because they asserted that no place that perfect—the mild climate, the exquisite scenery, the happy and healthy people—could exist on earth.

Selena and Trevor remained at his stone house in the desert for the rest of their lives and maintained a school for the training of knights. Years later, on her deathbed, Selena confessed to her eldest daughter Almira that Diego had once told her that his journey into knighthood had all been a dream to escape his sorrow from what had happened in the war.

Summer

FOR SOME TIME NOW in the open places and on the south-facing slopes the desert has been growing dry and hard to the touch. In recent days even the canyon shadows have lost their former dampness. At the bottom of what were once canyon streams, where even last week I could touch ground that was cool and wet, there is now only warm sand. On the slickrock above, the water that had gathered in natural potholes has vanished. All that remains are concentric rings, each telling of a slow retreat beneath the sun. A universe collapsed here, taking with it whole stars and galaxies, not to mention fairy shrimp and filamentous algae. Scattered around these basins—some as small as a desert tortoise, others the size of the shadow beneath a pinyon pine— are the withered skeletons of dragonflies and honeybees. Occasionally you find, at a further distance, the bones of some small mammal that died of thirst.

The spring flowers, too, have come and gone. It will be another year before I see the lavender blossoms of the hedgehog cactus above the Pariah dry wash again, or the scarlet flowers of the claret-cup cactus at Imperial Point. The lemon colored blossoms of the prickly pear cactus have now been replaced by dark red fruit. The flat green pads have changed as well, shrunken somewhat, and are no longer as plump as they were two months ago, after the spring rains. For the next several months, each plant will have to live upon whatever water it has saved.

On a deer path near Bridger's Knoll there is a hillside on which the cliffrose flourish in early June. They have lost their blossoms now, and their lovely scent no longer sweetens the breeze. The honeybees all have gone elsewhere in their search for pollen. On the high pastures of the mesas the bunch grass is dried and yellow now, and the sunburned ground is the color of old potsherds. The mariposa lily is gone, as well as that queen of lilies, the yucca.

They are all gone.

The only flowers that remain are in places like Zion Canyon and Escalante Canyon, hanging gardens of yellow columbine and red monkey flowers and green moss and delicate ferns that drip water all through July, thanks to the eternal springs of the underworld.

That's where people go, this time of year. To the river canyons, hiking and rafting or kayaking, or up into the mountains where the snow banks linger and the golden eagles circle and the collared pikas chirp back and forth.

But here, in the middle of the desert, a solemn heat is upon the land. You can feel the landscape contract, guarding its life until the drenching rains of fall, and the snows. The snakes and lizards are scarce these days, as they wait for relief in the shadows among the rocks. All day the leopard frogs cling, half-submerged, to the cattails in what water remains in the canyons. Even at night, the rocks do not fully cool, but stay warm, radiating back the heat of the sun. When you touch them it is almost as though you are touching the skin of a living animal.

The clouds of the summer desert are magnificent. Each day they begin forming over the mountains around the time the birds stop singing. At first they are mere suggestions, scattered here and there like the feathered seeds of a cottonwood drifting across the sky. But gradually they gather in small groups, and begin to darken in places. Patterns begin to emerge, and shapes to form. By noon they are massive, with thick bases and plunging grayish-purple canyons and brilliant white peaks trailing banners. The sky around them is shades of blue, vast luminous chunks of lapis lazuli and turquoise. The clouds rise above the desert with the stark power of a metaphor. Sometimes you see that they are raining in the peaks, with purple-black columns that drench the deer meadows and elk forests. You hear their thunder and see their lightning. In the lower desert the summer rains fall only as virga, wispy strands as fine as a child's first hair, rain that falls but never reaches the desert floor.

Once in a while, though, the distant rain does come to visit, pouring down a slot canyon in a violent wave that carries away everything but the canyon itself. Far away, in a city like Paris, people sitting on bamboo chairs at outdoor cafes read a day or two later of how nine of their countrymen and women perished in a place called northern Arizona during a summer flash flood. They wonder at the irony of it—drowning in the desert—and try to imagine the panic of being trapped with the approaching roar and the swollen battered bodies floating into Lake Powell and the children of the one couple waiting in the motel room in Page for the mother and father who would never return.

At midday, the heat beneath the sun becomes unpleasant. At times it is nauseating. At other times it is more deadly than a pit viper.

Once, while hiking in Canyonlands, I failed to bring sufficient water on a long summer walk. It was a hike of considerable distance and difficulty and, halfway back, I realized my error. After another mile, there was no alternative. I had no choice. My body made the decision for me. The spirit was defeated, the mind was overruled, the pride was forgotten. I crawled under a juniper like a coyote and waited for the sun to go down. Somewhere in one of his sonnets Shakespeare writes about being "destroyed by that which nourished me." That is how I felt that afternoon, as I saw the scapula of a mule deer grow flesh on it, and go off running as a young doe. A few minutes later I saw my leg bones on the floor of the desert, and a ring-tailed cat smelling them. And then I saw myself as a newborn infant again, and saw all that would happen to me, and even glimpsed my cranium as part of a crumbling sandstone ledge ages hence, and was at peace with the whole thing. Finally evening came and I was able to return from my journey.

Others have not been so fortunate. So you walk across the desert in the summer with a sense of respect. You begin to grasp how life survives here, and how you can carry those lessons away back into your own life, for each is a valuable truth.

The silence in the summer on the desert, with people gone, is immense. It spreads to the horizons. Whole days go by and there is not a sound. A country church in deep prayer would seem noisy by comparison. A college library would seem an endless clutter of idle whispers and pages turning. The silence in the desert is something else entirely. It is like the solemn quiet after someone takes their last breath, or the surprised hush when some penetrating truth is revealed. Only in the desert can we hear that which is the repudiation of sound, the harmony which expresses itself most perfectly in silence.

The best time on the desert in the summer is the morning. Gradually an otherworldly radiance makes its presence known in the east. The sky becomes the color of an opal. The wrinkled mountains assert themselves. Canyons emerge from the shadows. Peaks sharpen themselves against the hard blue sky. A distant cloud turns as red as a spark from a campfire, a cactus blossom, a horseshoe taken from the forge. The last somewhat mild breeze of night stirs. No sounds, no birds, no crickets even, because this is the summer on the desert. And then there is the sudden blinding nuclear flash. Everything is bleached white. But for those brief moments— a sprinkling of stars to the west, a luminous miracle about to occur in the east, a shadowland modulating toward the spectrum—the desert, even in August, is pure revelation.

IN A CANYON IN SOUTHERN UTAH I walk among the cottonwoods. It is late summer. The antlers of the deer have hardened. The snakes have shed their third skins. The baby mountain lions are no longer babies. Somewhere a second hay cutting is taking place. Houseboats fill Lake Powell. People flock to the South Rim.

The rocks in the canyon are as hot as the rocks near a campfire. They are too hot to touch. I am looking for a favorite pool, beneath a place where there is a wonderful waterfall in the spring. When I reach the pool it is empty of water. There is another possible pool half a mile further down the canyon, but I will not walk any further. For one thing, I do not have the water in my pack for another mile.

Three cottonwoods grow in this place, their heart-shaped leaves hanging, their deep roots tapping the deeper stream, beneath the sand and rock. I climb a tree, first one fork, and then another, and find a comfortable place among the branches. I feel as a child must in the arms of its mother. I will stay here cradled in the shade until the sun is a little further to the west, and then I will walk back to where I will sleep for the night.

There is a canyon wren singing in the tree, and I listen.

Summer is composed of such moments, the solstice light falling like a welcome gift and everywhere a sense of calm. Somewhere a phone rings, a letter is delivered, a person comes to the door, but they will not find me, or you, not today.

The Heart of the Matter

IT WAS SEPTEMBER OF 1939 and three men were riding across the Kaibab Plateau in northern Arizona. They had left before dawn, when the air was cold and their breath rose in white wreaths into the hayloft of the barn. They had ridden for half a day, stopping only to tighten cinch straps and adjust diamond hitches, and they were a mile from a place called Dry Park. The trail cut back and forth across the lightly timbered slope, pushing upward through rust-colored patches of fireweed, and then flattened out in a line as straight as a length of rope. The park was in sight now—a saddle of sage and grass—and it was nearly noon and they were shedding jackets and unbuttoning wool shirts. The sun sat alone at the center of the sky. The word cloud would not be heard that day. A breeze stirred every few minutes, liberating the last of the golden willow leaves along the creek, but generally it was quiet enough to hear the bees in the asters.

The man in front, who rode a buckskin the size of a small draft horse, was the outfitter Ward Rowland. He owned the Red Mountain Cattle Ranch near Jacob Lake and he held the forest service permit for the hunting camp. His hair was gray but he had a young face. Behind him was Guy Barnes, an executive with U.S. Steel in Pittsburgh. Guy was trying to find a mule deer similar to the one he had killed on the Gros Ventre the year before. His horse, a claybank mare, had a cape of sweat from the load. The last rider was Wulf Angstrom, a nineteen-year-old wrangler. Wulf had hitchhiked up from Flagstaff to work for the summer on the ranch and was helping out with the hunting season. Wulf rode a strawberry roan named Pontiac and led three pack horses and one pack mule. He was a natural rider and rode square in the saddle with his shoulders back, and never moved but in rhythm with the horse.

The men stopped in the timber at the head of Quaking Aspen Canyon for a quick lunch of fresh homemade bread and Swiss cheese and then rode for two more hours. They finally made camp on the edge of Blodgett Pasture near the North Rim of the Grand Canyon. The camp was in a grove of ponderosa pine. There was blowdown for firewood and a springhead in the rocks where some of the frost-burned ferns still held a bit of summer's green. Ward and Guy slept in one canvas wall tent and Wulf stayed in the other, which was also the cook tent. There was a cot in his tent beside a folding table with a kerosene lantern and that night after the others retired Wulf stayed up for awhile and read a short story by Arthur Conan Doyle entitled "The Lord of Chateau Noir." The story was better than the first two—"The King of the Foxes" and "The Bully of Brocas Court."

Occasionally he removed the bookmark, which was a postcard of a city scene in Florence, Italy. The postcard was lightly scented with an oil made in Greece from crushed orange blossoms. It was written in a surgically precise but flowing script,

Dear Wulf—After finals in London, Emily and I flew to Paris and played around, amusing people with our crude attempts at French. Down to Nice to see the zinc-blue Mediterranean & along the coast by train to Genoa, which was a sunny Renaissance painting. To Florence from there to view some of the most striking art and architecture yet, then up to Venice, which does seem to be sinking, but was still lovely in its baroque romance, the canals winding like gnarled roots through the city. Scowling brownshirts everywhere, so we left New Rome. Now visiting Lyon. x, Bridgette. PS today is Bastille Day! PPS we arrive 9-18 aboard the Brittania at pier 54—will you be there?

The next day Wulf remained in camp building a corral and cutting wood. High clouds blew in during the afternoon and gradually thickened. The air took on the chill of a freezer and all of the shadows left the earth. Ward and Guy returned at dusk with the skull cap and spreading antlers of a mature, if undistinguished, nontypical buck. Guy still had a bear permit, and so the hunt would go on. After dinner the three men sat around the campfire and Guy related his Hugh Purvis stories, Purvis a colorful former colleague and part-time bootlegger from the Twenties who had disappeared along with his fishing boat *The Queen*

Conch off Key West during the Matecumbe hurricane in 1933. The accounts were all bawdy and ended with lines like "It was so hard a bird could sit on it." Ward brought up the *Wehrmacht* to change the subject and Guy said he had been warning about the National Socialists ever since they seized the Rhineland in 1936 and that there would be a special place in the rock quarries of the afterlife for Neville Chamberlain and all the spineless diplomats like him.

Guy and Ward hunted the next day near Fossil Ridge without any luck. It seemed the game was drifting back into Grand Canyon National Park. At the campfire that night—the flames rising and falling as the breezes came and went—the conversation turned to women and Guy asked Wulf if he had a sweetheart yet. Wulf told them about his high school classmate Bridgette Fourtier, who was in Europe with her new best friend from college Emily Butler, and he mentioned how much he would like to be there to greet her in New York, but that he couldn't afford the train fare.

"How much would that be?" asked Guy.

"Well, it's a hundred dollars for the southern prairie express."

There was a silence then, Guy and Ward exchanging looks, and after Guy retired for the evening Ward walked over to the cook tent and sat down at the card table with a flask of Scotch, two silver cups and a proposition. Ward and Guy had ridden into Grand Canyon National Park that day—not far, but far enough—and had located those mythic bucks that Ward had discovered on his reconnaissance in August. The bucks were all gathered at a place called Big Spring Canyon. The offer was in the form of an exchange—two hundred dollars for one of those deer.

Wulf pondered his response, weighing the knowledge that a crime was being suggested against the fact that Ward was the man who had saved his father's life. It was Second Lieutenant Ward Rowland who had carried Corporal Leif Angstrom, unconscious, to high ground after their position had been shelled with mustard gas. This was during the battle in Bois de Belleau, Louis XIV's private hunting preserve north of Paris and the last line of defense against the Germans. After the battle the Germans had called the Marines *Teufelhunde*—Devil Dogs—and the French Premier Clemenceau had opened the brothels of his capital to the men who had saved it.

"But what about rangers?"

"The nearest cabin is at Bright Angel. That's twenty miles from here. He's patrolling Cape Royal."

"You know that for sure?"

"I know that for a fact."

"So …?"

"So no one will ever know. We'll bury the other rack and within three days the bears will scatter the new carcass. Just another deer gone back into the ground and one more legal buck—four quarters and one set of antlers—coming down the trail to the meat locker."

"What if I get caught?"

"Guy would pay the fine."

There was a silence and Wulf said he needed to sleep on it and his boss stood up to leave.

"You're a good man, Wulf. You're a lot like your father. You know what it's all about at the end of the day."

"What's that?"

"It's about friendship and loyalty and the rest of the world be damned."

Wulf left before sunrise the next morning, riding Pontiac along the game trail south toward the park. Within a few miles he sensed that he was approaching the boundary. Although there was no marker, he knew the moment that he passed from the national forest to the national park. Everything changed, and not just inside him. He had a crude but accurate map and followed Ward's directions. The trail led upward and after awhile he saw a light coming through the ponderosas and suddenly he emerged on the rim of the Grand Canyon. He stopped for a moment, watching the morning abyss fill with sunlight. A bit of the distant river was visible down in the rocks and far to the south on the horizon he could make out the San Francisco Peaks near Flagstaff. To the west he could see part of the browned scorched desert near the Nevada border.

It was a hard view to ride away from.

As he approached the second park—the first presenting a stalking problem with the wind and the position of the animals—he dismounted and tied the horse off and moved forward quietly through the trees. He crept to the edge of the park and stopped behind a deadfall where blood-red berries sparkled near the ground. The woods were still, but things moved here and there and made sounds—a thrush flitted about in a thicket of wild rose, a family of magpies talked back and forth in a tangled spruce, a Kaibab squirrel jumped from branch to branch. He lifted his head slowly, cautiously, like a coyote, and stopped when his eyes showed. He caught some movement far out on the yellow sun-bleached grass. There were dark bucks, two of them, with thick necks and heavy racks. They had moved away from the scattered band of does and were locking antlers. It was preliminary jousting—the rut was still two months off—but they were distracted and unsuspecting. This was a sanctuary, after all, and no one hunted deer here, except for mountain lions.

Wulf made his plan and moved to a place where he had a clear shot. He eased the safety off, took a deep breath and settled the iron post of the two-seventy low on the chest of the buck to the right. It was a finely made hunting rifle with a blued octagon barrel and a black walnut stock that fit smoothly against his cheek. When he fired the buck did not move, but his opponent stood back and looked around. The sun was at Wulf's back and the wind was in his face. The other buck could not see or smell him. Sensing that something was wrong, the other buck turned and followed the already departing does into the forest. A moment later, the buck that had been shot collapsed in a slow series of movements. He fell like a ponderosa in the forest that a logger has worked on with an axe, that gradually angles off center, inch by teetering inch, and then topples with a rush all at once, the air vibrating from the sudden passage.

When the death throes had ceased Wulf walked over and knelt beside the deer, appalled at what he had done. The buck was spread out on his side, with a gallon of blood on his neck and chest and his eyes fixed on a point deep inside himself. The first flies had already found his tongue.

Wulf worked quickly. He unfolded his bone saw and separated the crown of the head from the rest of the body, and then drew out his skinning knife and opened the abdomen so that the bears could make quicker work of the evidence. The antlers he tied upside down to the saddle, Pontiac standing still and seeming to understand just then the importance of being silent and cooperative. As Wulf walked back to camp with the lead rope in hand, it began to snow—not a lot, but enough to hurry his pace. Wulf could see that tracks were something to be avoided in such a situation.

Back he went, along a route that had been unfamiliar at first but was familiar now.

Wulf was uncommonly quiet that night at the campfire, and sat motionless as if stunned by a blow. Finally Guy raised his eyebrows to Ward in a silent request. Ward thought for a moment, actually several minutes, and then related the account of a Marine runner at Belleau Wood—Private Paul LaBarge of Mandan, North Dakota—who accidentally stumbled into a German position and somehow convinced their commanding officer, a captain named Gerhard Boldt, that they were about to be overrun by a superior force and should immediately surrender to him. LaBarge then returned to brigade headquarters with eighty-two German soldiers as his prisoners (LaBarge armed with a military police revolver). The German soldiers all lived to see the end of the war, unlike their comrades in the trenches. Private LaBarge received a field commission and later became governor of his state.

The moral—that deception can be a virtue—did not escape Wulf, but he was still conflicted, for his father was a Lutheran minister with a preference for the Gospel of Mark. Wulf did not sleep well in his tent that night. At one point he fell off the cot from a bad dream, awakening with no sense of where or who he was, his heart pounding and his forehead wet with a fevered sweat.

The next day the snow fell. It was a dense wet snow that weighted the branches of the spruce and fir and dropped onto the horses and men. Sometimes it went down their necks, and they cursed, playfully. The birds were on the move now, heading out of the high country, and the men heard their feathered wings beating overhead, and their voices on the wind. Along the trail the cinnamon trunks of the ponderosas stood dark and still against the whitened ground. The sun came out before the end of the day and the skies cleared. As the last fast clouds flamed red the hunting party made a bivouac near Little Mountain. In the morning the leather of the tack was frozen stiff and they had to warm the bridle bits in their hands before putting them in the horses' mouths. The country down lower, below the snow line, was different now. It looked old and tired, with no life in it, lying ready for another winter, lying poor and quiet against a cold blue sky.

The men didn't say much on the trail, or when they unpacked the horses at the ranch corral, or when they parted at the train station in

Flagstaff, Guy heading west to a business meeting with a military ship-
builder in San Francisco and Wulf traveling east on the prairie express.

All across America he tried not to think about what he had done.

Three days later, on the crowded docks at pier 54 in New York City,
Wulf saw Emily Butler first. She came down the walkway alone, which
was odd, and took him aside, her hand tightly grasping his elbow. She
told him with a tense face and a fixed stare that avoided his gaze that
Bridgette had become attached to another man, a young army pilot
named C. J. Polk, in London and on the passage over from England.
Bridgette couldn't see him again.

"That fast?" asked Wulf, pushing his cowboy hat back on his head.

Emily turned away, knowing that love has nothing to with the application of reason. The passage over the Atlantic had been perilous, if
swift, and especially so after the passengers had learned by shortwave
radio that the liner *Athenia* had been torpedoed off Ireland before the
British fleet had secured the western Hebrides. At such uncertain moments, when death and life are only dictionary words, the unexpected
holds reign. Despite Emily's entreaties, Wulf insisted on seeing Bridgette
again. He subsequently made such a scene, twice punching the "fancy
pants" as he called him, that he was arrested by the port authority police
and taken away in handcuffs to a detention cell where he was locked up
with the vagrants and the drunks for the night.

He left New York City the next day, promising the authorities never
to return after paying the ten dollar fine with one of the bills he had hidden in his right sock (the cash in his wallet having been misplaced by the
property clerk).

ii.

THAT WINTER HE STAYED AT HOME in Flagstaff and worked nights
as a stacker at the grocery store, his father Leif imploring him to enroll
in an officer training program at the university in case Roosevelt insti-
tuted a draft. But Wulf did not want to see so fair or foul a creature as
Bridgette again, and so he left the application unopened on his desk and
spent what free time he had at the movies (*Stagecoach, Gone with the
Wind, Mr. Smith Goes to Washington*) or reading the new titles from the

Book of the Month Club (Sandburg's study of Lincoln, Steinbeck's story of the Joads) or listening to his collection of Louis Armstrong records. Finally the Selective Service Act became law and Wulf hitchhiked to Phoenix and joined the 163rd Infantry Regiment of the Arizona National Guard. He hoped to avoid active duty not because he was reluctant to serve overseas but because his mother and maternal grandparents had been Quakers and he wanted to honor what little remained of their memory in his life.

For a year everything was as fine as it can be when one holds the rank of private first class. The soldiers lived in barracks along the Salt River east of town and trained on the desert and in the mountains. Most of the time they drilled and exercised and cleaned their equipment. Weekends were spent along Van Buren Street, primarily at dances. A few of the men went into the mountains and tried this new sport called skiing. Wulf tried once, spraining his knee on a deadfall buried under the snow. In January 1943 a regular army officer they had never seen before told them that their unit had been activated and that he was their new commanding officer. His name was Philip Moss and he proudly wore the gold oak leafs of a West Point major and he would be the first of three commanding officers. Early in June the 163rd steamed across the Atlantic—the lights on the transports blacked out at night and a covey of destroyers surrounding them. They disembarked in North Africa at a hot and dismal port where everything was the color of sand and the people wore light cotton turbans to protect themselves from the desert sun. The town was called Oran and it was not as lovely as Casablanca in Morocco, where they had stopped briefly to refuel and which had reminded Wulf of Phoenix if Phoenix was two thousand years old and had grown up beside a lovely blue ocean. No one liked Algeria—it was about like travelling by time machine back to the days of Hannibal—and everyone was relieved that Rommel's tanks had finally run out of diesel fuel in Tunisia.

Two weeks later Wulf took part in the invasion of Sicily, and on that antique island he fought—a lean and darkly tanned sergeant now—through white-washed towns with strange names such as Vizzini and Riesa and San Stefano. Here he saw for the first time in his life people so impoverished by war that they literally had no possessions, other than what they could find on the dead. That fall the 163rd landed in southern

Italy, where they made winter camp and took on replacements, and in late January—spring coming early in the Mediterranean—Wulf made an assault with his regiment at a nowhere place called Anzio. By this time Wulf had learned not to make many close friends, because people were being killed around him at every hour of the day and night, and sometimes in the most unlikely ways—a buried landmine, a booby-trapped battle trophy, a bullet coming from nowhere during a march.

The most unlikely event of the war occurred one foggy morning at Anzio when Wulf found himself alone with a freckle-faced German soldier about the age of seventeen in a trench during a shelling. The German could have shot him, but instead raised his weapon to the sky and spoke broken English: "Wouldn't you agree this is madness? And that the real enemies are the people who put us here?" They both agreed not to kill each other and to disband in opposite directions when the shelling stopped. A month later Wulf would see the soldier in a line of prisoners. They would wave and smile—two friends who would forever be strangers—and everyone on either side who witnessed this passing exchange would wonder about it all of their lives.

The last year of the war was spent working north behind armored units through eastern France—St. Maxime, Loriol, Lyon, Grenoble, Rambervillers. The fighting was so rapid and often disorganized that at one point they received no mail for a month. A week before Christmas in 1944 the 163rd crossed the pontoon bridge into Germany, eventually capturing Nuremberg and Munich, and on April 30, 1945 they were assigned the task of liberating the concentration camp at Ravensburg, which had been in operation since 1933. This was the same day the German chancellor shot himself in the mouth with a pistol at his bunker in Berlin. Wulf was a captain by then and was in temporary command of a battalion because all of the field grade officers had been killed by a mortar round that fell on their tent while dessert was being served. The first thing that Wulf saw on entering the camp was thirty-nine railway cars filled with bodies. From there it only got worse and soon his men became nearly uncontrollable. When Wulf went into the camp headquarters to supervise the preservation of documents for the war crimes tribunal, a replacement squad leader, enraged by what he had seen, executed the twenty-seven SS soldiers who had surrendered under a white flag. This happened in a single burst of machine gun fire, and literally in the time it takes to read this sentence.

Three weeks later Wulf was summoned to the temporary field post of General Patton, the commander of the Third Army. Patton's office was located in the bombed out ruins of a Catholic cathedral at Ingolstadt, Germany. The church had been built in the early thirteenth century during the reign of Frederick the Second. The office was the only room in the building that was still covered by a portion of the roof. It was located just off the choir box in the upper chapel and had a worn wooden floor and a vaulted Gothic ceiling. Ribbed stone arches rose from each corner. Set into a recessed portal on the north wall were life-sized marble sculptures of Abraham, Isaac, Moses, Samuel, and King David. None of the figures had received any damage during the recent battle that had taken place in the town.

Patton was a lean muscular man of about sixty winters with short white hair on the sides of his head. He wore his trousers tucked into his boots and a campaign jacket with three silver stars on either shoulder. Patton was seated on a wooden box behind a desk made of an unhinged door resting on two shipping crates. The desk had two wire baskets on it. One was marked "in" and the other was marked "out" and both were full of documents. The only other object on the desk was a buckled leather map case that had formerly belonged to a German field marshal in North Africa.

Patton removed Wulf's bulky service record from the "in" box and told Wulf to stand at ease. Patton opened the file. He asked Wulf a few questions about Sicily. He was particularly interested in a series of running battles across the Salso River valley near Licata. Patton had commanded the Seventh Army during the campaign, and was as familiar as a geographer with the island. The general read aloud from a citation which described an action that took place in the early afternoon of July 14, 1943:

> *With complete disregard for his own personal safety, Sergeant Wulf Angstrom did then mount a burning enemy tank and employ its machine gun against an advancing line of German infantry supported by an enemy half-track. Despite numerous shrapnel wounds from rifle-fired grenades, he continued firing to protect the advance of his platoon and in so doing killed or wounded thirty-one Germans. As a result, American forces were later that*

day able to liberate the town of Licata, Sicily with minimal casualties.
His actions were in keeping with the highest traditions of military service.
    Sergeant Angstrom is here awarded the Medal of Honor for conspicuous
gallantry above and beyond the call of duty. By order of Lieutenant General
Dwight D. Eisenhower, Supreme Commander of Allied Expeditionary
Forces, Harry S. Stimson, Secretary of War, and Franklin D. Roosevelt,
President of the United States.

When he had finished reading from the citation Patton stood up and
walked over to the open glass window, his hands clasped together loosely
in the small of his back. He was a tall man, and he held himself as
straight as a flagpole. Outside was an apple orchard. Most of the trees
were still standing, although a few had been damaged by flying debris.
It was a bright spring day, and thrushes were hunting for earthworms in
the grass beneath the trees. Honeybees buzzed among the columbine.
Squirrels chased one another among the forking branches. Farther in the
distance a convoy of diesel trucks could be heard laboring up a hill on
the road out of town. The general considered the scene for a full minute
in silence and then, without turning, related a story about something
that had happened when he was a young captain serving under Pershing
in Mexico. It was an occurrence from long ago that only he and a few
other people knew about. He told the story simply, as one soldier does
to another soldier, and did not embellish or editorialize. He merely related the sequence of events as he remembered them.

    Patton then walked back over to the desk. He took the file with the
court-martial charges brought against Wulf by some new officer from
the states—twenty-seven meticulously documented counts of derelic-
tion of duty—and threw them into the fireplace. He said that Wulf had
done the best he could under the circumstances and that no one on
Earth would ever bother him again about what had happened.

iii.

WULF SPENT THE NEXT WINTER wandering around his father's house
in Flagstaff like a ghost. On a good day he would be able to control the
shaking in his hands. On a bad day he would hear a sudden noise—an
airplane buzzing low overhead, a car door slamming, a tea kettle

whistling—and he would drop to the floor, crawling for cover and struggling to find his breath. Sometimes he spent the entire day in bed, reading books and listening to records. At night he kept the curtains drawn, having more than once seen the inattentive killed by snipers.

Every morning at seven-thirty his father closed his briefcase and walked the twelve blocks to work. When he returned home in the evening he sat in his easy chair by the radio and read the newspaper. His favorite program was Edward R. Murrow's daily review of the news. The two men, father and son, rarely talked, except to exchange pleasantries or discuss the weekly grocery list. For about a week around Christmas they debated the possibility of adopting a dog from the pound, but then finally decided against it. Wulf preferred not to venture outside during the daylight hours, and consequently would not be able to walk the dog.

This state of affairs went on for six months.

On the first day of spring Ward Rowland called from the ranch and asked Wulf to come up for the calving season. He was short on experienced hands, and could use the help. Wulf worked at Red Mountain that summer, helping with the cattle through the roundup, but left before the fall hunt. When they were out patrolling the range, Ward often joined Wulf, who still preferred to ride the big roan named Pontiac. Ward told Wulf some things about his father in Europe that Wulf had never known. These revelations helped him to find his way to at least a partial equilibrium.

That fall, to the surprise of everyone in Flagstaff, Wulf enrolled in classes at the university. At first it was a struggle to sit through a class but gradually he became more comfortable and in August of 1950 he graduated with a degree in history. Three years later he received a law degree and joined a respected practice at the state capital. There he specialized in business law and especially the law of contracts. He enjoyed the work and, especially, the panoramic view from his office in the new Southern Desert Office Building designed by Frank Lloyd Wright. Things went well for him, as they sometimes do, and in 1957 he was made a full partner. In 1959, when a seventy-four-year-old judge named Dale Paradis on the circuit court suddenly had a stroke, Governor Ron Lavender was told by his bright young aides that Wulf Angstrum was a man everyone liked and respected. Calls were made, records were scanned, a brief friendly interview was conducted in the governor's office, and Wulf found himself back in Flagstaff at the age of thirty-nine wearing the black robes of a state judge.

iv.

LIFE MOVES AS SLOWLY as a low autumnal river sometimes, drifting idly in quiet eddies and swirling aimlessly in lost backwaters. Whole months and years pass by, and little is done or even set out to be done. Projects are postponed, excuses are made, goals are forgotten, paddles are lifted from the water, and the days are spent as comfortably, if unprofitably, as in the proverbial dream. Other times the current plunges forward. Difficult rapids are faced. Exhausting portages are made. Long dangerous stretches over open water are traversed. At such times a person who has scornfully renounced travel for years may suddenly embark upon a world adventure. Or someone who has always sworn they could not draw a straight line may take up painting. Or a skeptic who has lived alone, and often made light of romance, may wonder in disbelief how anyone could exist without this thing called love.

Such was the case for Wulf in the spring of 1960.

It was Memorial Day and he had gone to the cemetery, as was his custom each year, to visit the graves of his parents. As he drove into the park he noticed a woman in the distance standing by a headstone. He paid little attention to her, and drove on to where the road ended. At the gravesite he placed a mixed bunch of carnations beside the marble pillar. Scattered white and gray clouds floated slowly across the sky, and a light fell from the sky that was alternately bright and overcast. Around him, silence and peace reigned. He stood there awhile, regarding the earth, and then gazed at the clouds navigating across the heavens. It was one of those moments when Wulf felt close to the wall that separated him from everything that he would never know. The practice of law had taught him much about people and their virtues and shortcomings, but most of all, he had learned how little we understand about ourselves and why we are here. When he looked at his own journey, he saw only a solitary shadow on the grass.

Some time later, as he was driving out, the woman was still there. For some reason, he stopped his car in the middle of the road and stared in her direction.

When she looked his way he realized who it was.

He turned off the car engine and walked across the grass. She was looking at him and he stopped when they were about ten feet apart. Both were motionless. Their faces were blank with surprise and remembrance. A cloud passed overhead, shading the grass on which they stood, and then they were in the sunlight again. He said hello to her in the gentle tone of voice one reserves for family and friends. Nothing in his spirit had changed since he had last seen her. It was not a matter of regret or forgiveness, only of a shared affection that is never lost and bears with it a simple grace.

She had come to pay respects to her younger brother Lamar Fourtier. Wulf could see from the inscription on the headstone that he had been a paratrooper at St. Mere-Eglise.

"You know," she said, "the funny thing is I had a dream about you the other night."

"And?"

"I can't remember. Something about you and Lamar. But it was one of those strong dreams, you know."

A flock of sparrows flew by, singing on the wind. They watched them until they passed out of sight.

"It's been a long time," he said.

She said nothing for awhile, and he waited.

"I heard you were a judge now. I could have looked you up, but ..."

"But?"

"Well, like you said, it's been a long time."

"How is your husband?"

She made a quizzical face.

"I thought ..."

"You didn't know?"

He shook his head.

"He died in January 1942. It was the same commercial plane crash that killed Carole Lombard. You remember—"

"—I remember hearing about the crash, and Clark Gable driving up there, but I had no idea ..."

"He was on his way to the South Pacific. He had resigned his position as an instructor pilot in Iowa. I begged him not to go. But you know how it was back then."

Wulf asked her to join him for lunch and they drove into town on old Route 66. As they conversed in the car, catching up on twenty years, he studied her closely from the side, in profile, and saw that everything about her—the dress, the hairstyle, the manner of speech—was frozen in the year 1942. Bridgette had physically not aged at all, except that her long anthracite hair now had a few strands of gray. Other than that, she could have still been standing on that pier in New York in 1939, a lovely young woman of nineteen. She was holding like an island against the stream of time.

Over lunch he learned that she now lived in Phoenix and worked as an executive assistant to a college president, and that she had never re-married. The conversation wandered across the years, pausing here and there and touching on matters personal and historical. On the busy sidewalk outside the restaurant they exchanged phone numbers and addresses and promised to see one another again. In the weeks and months that followed a courtship of sorts ensued—letters and calls and exchanged gifts and visits back and forth—and a year later they were married in a chapel near Chinle on the Navajo Reservation. It was an impulsive decision. They were driving by the wood-frame church on a Saturday morning and the minister was outside working in his flower garden. They waved to the minister, and he waved back.

"Hey, if we ever get married," Wulf joked, as Bobby Darin sang *Volare* on the radio, "let's get married in a place like that."

"Well, alright then, let's do it!" she exclaimed, turning down the radio.

"You mean right now?"

She nodded her head.

Two years later, in 1963, they adopted two children, Rosemary and Owen. Rose was seven and Owen was nine and their parents had drowned in a boating accident off the coast of San Diego. This was for awhile a happy time for Bridgette and Wulf. Bridgette stayed at home with the children, and Wulf worked tirelessly at the courthouse. Summer vacations were usually spent in California, because everyone loved the ocean. The marriage was good, or at least as good as a marriage can be when it comes that late in life. Because of their age, both had the advantage of maturity and experience, but they also had to contend with the fact that they were very independent people. The result was more a loose partnership of affectionate comrades than a passionate union of two lovers.

When Rose was diagnosed with juvenile diabetes in 1967, Wulf did not think much about it—treatments at the time allowed for children to lead a fairly normal life—but three years later Rose died of an infection during one of her lengthy hospital stays. Bridgette was for some time inconsolable, and spent an entire month in her daughter's room, refusing to leave and keeping the curtains drawn at all times. A psychiatrist suggested a well-known institution and a program of electroshock therapy, but Wulf would not hear of it. Eventually she began to spend more time with Owen, who now received all of his mother's affection.

Wulf devoted himself to his legal work, and, increasingly, to the party that controlled all three branches of state government.

Eventually, his travail and planning were rewarded, and in 1972 Wulf was appointed to the Arizona Supreme Court. A popular war hero and friendly conservative, Wulf was by wide agreement the ideal person for the position. Moderates and liberals respected him, and hard-liners could trust him to render decisions consistent with their views. For his part, Wulf enjoyed the opportunity to have a beneficial influence on his province of the world. At first his rulings were in keeping with his past record, but within a year he moved more toward the center, as when he wrote in a minority opinion that life begins when the fetus can live outside the womb. A few observers were surprised, but no one was alarmed. Wulf was merely responding to the philosophical freedom of a lifetime appointment.

At home, Owen flourished in his collegiate studies and athletic pursuits. After graduating with a degree in architecture, he moved to Santa Monica. Here he joined a firm that specialized in constructing residential homes, especially in the hills around Malibu. Everything went reasonably well in this way for the Angstrom family for about a decade. Bridgette became involved in community activities, especially in fundraising for the university hospital, and Wulf continued to work on the highest tribunal. The husband and wife enjoyed a fairly active social life, as well, although they were not as visible around town as other members of the court. For them the most important things were the small things, and most of those were found at home.

Everything changed one Sunday night in June of 1984. It was a pleasant summer evening and Wulf and Bridgette were in the family room watching a segment of *Sixty Minutes* commemorating the Normandy invasion. Network anchor Walter Cronkite was interviewing a former German general named Baldur von Schreubner through a translator and the general was explaining that the unusual storm had worked to the Allied's advantage, because it grounded the *Luftwaffe*. Otherwise, he observed, the invasion would have had a different outcome.

When the phone rang Wulf walked into the other room to take the call, which was on his private line.

"Is this Wulf Angstrom, the father of Owen Leif Angstrom?"

The man had the accent of someone from Pakistan or India.

"Yes."

"This is Dr. ―――― from ―――― hospital."

Wulf didn't catch the name of the doctor or the hospital. Something in the doctor's voice came to him as a warning.

"I have some difficult news for you."

Wulf sat down in a chair with his hand on his forehead and listened.

It turned out that Owen had committed suicide after learning that he had tested positive for the virus that causes AIDS. His roommate Stuart Gregg had found the body in his room and called the police. Owen had left a short note explaining everything. He had overdosed with prescription painkillers he had purchased from a stranger on the beach.

At the funeral Wulf could not speak. He sat mute in the first pew in front of the casket and had one of his colleagues read a lengthy statement, which chronicled the love of a father for his son. In the weeks that followed his hair turned white, and his face sagged with the weight of an inexpressible grief. Bridgette remained at home under the supervision of her doctor. Six months later she died of a heart attack while shopping for Christmas gifts at the mall.

After the death of his son and wife Wulf's politics, much to the everlasting horror of the Republican party, took an unexpected turn to the left. Within the year, for example, he tried to engineer a ruling that would have allowed same-gender couples to form civil unions in Arizona. This would have made it the only state with that provision in the law. His attempt failed—the other conservative justices privately thought that he had lost his mind—but elsewhere he was successful. He fought the excesses of the health care industry. He championed the rights of endangered species. He reflexively sided with Native Americans on every single issue that came before the court. He received the William O. Douglas Award, and the Frederick Douglas Award, and the Cesar Chavez Award. He was vilified by every conservative talk show host from New York to Los Angeles. He became, in short, a new person. He had been wild in his youth. He had been conservative in his middle years. And now he was going to be wild at the end.

v.

TO BE HONEST, WULF DISTRUSTED PHYSICIANS. He knew that doctors can accidentally make some conditions worse, and that very often even experts can not agree on a diagnosis until an autopsy proves or disproves this theory or that theory. He had seen malpractice suits argued before his various courts, and he had listened for hours to testimony pro and con and viewed slides and videotapes and was familiar with all the miracles and catastrophes of medicine. As a result, Wulf, even more than most men, avoided doctors. When he did feel a pain, he ignored it. Over time, he had learned, a pain usually departs as mysteriously as it arrived.

In the years following his wife's death, though, Wulf began to notice some unusual changes in his body. The symptoms at first seemed of the ephemeral variety, but gradually they began to assert their unwelcome presence in sometimes unsettling ways. The persistent abdominal pains—at times severe—he rationalized as ordinary indigestion. The occasional spots of blood, he reasoned, were probably the result of a minor nuisance found in many people of his age. When his wife was alive she had implored him to see an internist for a common, if unpleasant, procedure that many people undergo every other year. His response had always been in the form of a joke: "Sure they can do that to me. Right after they peel my cold hard dead fingers from my empty rifle." Now, in the middle of the night when he was alone with his pain, Wulf wondered if Bridgette had been right, and that perhaps he had waited too long.

Finally, nature gave him no choice. For one entire weekend in the spring of 1989 Wulf could not sleep because of the pain in his hip. At work on Monday morning he collapsed in the hallway outside his office from a particularly violent spasm. Law clerks and secretaries swarmed around him, and helped him to his desk. He waved them off, claiming it was a piece of shrapnel in his leg that sometimes "acted up." That afternoon, though, he saw his wife's internist. After a brief examination she drove him to the hospital emergency room. Every diagnostic test known to science was given, and the results were scrutinized by the best minds on the permanent staff. The surgeon's report from the exploratory operation undertaken the next morning noted "a primary, necrotic, and deeply ulcerated carcinoma arising in the cecum near the ileo-cecal valve and exhibiting transmural invasion into the pericolic fat, with extensive lymphatic and vascular involvement, including metastases in six of seventeen lymph nodes." The tumor in the colon was judged to be inoperable because of its size and location, and the examination of the liver and pancreas revealed that death would not be long in coming.

It was now September of 1989 and Wulf had been moved from the university research hospital in Phoenix to a comfortable hospice near Flagstaff. The hospice was, in fact, located on a former cattle ranch just outside of town, the owner having found health care more reliable than beef cattle. Wulf had a second floor room in what had been the main lodge. The room had a view of the San Francisco Peaks seventeen miles to the north. He could make out each of the individual peaks, beginning with Agassiz, and could note the progress of autumn along their slopes. Although the aspen groves up higher had turned golden, those down lower held on to summer's green. Above them towered Humphreys Peak, at 12,633 feet the tallest peak in the Southwest. He had climbed it once as a boy, and could mark now the route of his long-ago ascent with a pair of binoculars.

In the first few days, sitting on the porch in his wheelchair, he occasionally thought back to two cases from his early days on the court. The first was a suit by the Hopi and Navajo to block a ski resort expansion on some state-owned land in the San Francisco Peaks. The second was a case several years later in which the same company tried again to expand. In the initial proceeding the plaintiffs prevailed on a technicality—the application for rezoning had been made improperly. In the second instance he wrote the majority decision against the Indians, stating that anything could be done on state land that comported with the law. He found no legal basis for their argument that the mountains were sacred and shouldn't be defiled.

He regretted those decisions, and wished that he could go back and change what he had done, but that was all long ago. He was a fragment of his former self now, just another terminal patient dying on a shaded porch at the far end of life. His world had shrunken to this—a chair facing north so that he could watch the clouds over the mountains. Each morning the clouds began forming around ten o'clock. By noon there was usually a rainstorm, sometimes with far away thunder and lightning, and then the clouds would dissipate overnight. In the morning the whole thing would start again. It was the most ancient form of entertainment in the world. Beyond the mountains, somewhere to the north, was the canyon, and at the bottom of the canyon was the river that had been flowing over the rocks for all time. Just knowing the canyon and the river were out there, in a sun-washed sanctuary somewhere over the horizon, gave Wulf a sense of contentment. It was as beautiful and remote as the idea of an afterlife.

Although Wulf lamented that he had no family to visit him, and that he had been forgotten by his colleagues, he was determined not to show any sadness or self-pity. All his life he had been governed by the simple maxims of Zeno and Aurelius, and he was not going to change now. He was an old soldier and he knew that the door to death is always standing open beside you and that the only thing that matters is whether you were alive—in the fullest sense of that word—today. He was grateful at least for this much—he would see it approaching. He would know its shape and form and even its approximate time of arrival. He would look at it clearly and without fear or anger or guilt. He could have died a hundred different ways before, and now it would happen this way. The souls he pitied most were those who had left abruptly, when they were young, before they could understand what was occurring, or make peace with it.

For two weeks he lived this way, obediently taking his medicine, which was primarily pain medicine, and curiously waiting for the next stage of development, whatever that was. At first he rose from bed every morning and traveled by electric wheelchair to the porch or to the day room. Gradually, though, the pain of climbing into the wheelchair became too much. He found that if he took his medicine and lay very still in the bed, he could be without too much discomfort in his right hip and right leg. Most of the time he looked out the window at the San Francisco Peaks and pondered his situation. His mood was fairly stable, although he had pangs of despair and moments of hope. Everyone, for example, had heard of miraculous recoveries, and of tumors that suddenly disappeared. But all of that seemed unlikely. Every day or so another person in the hospice would expire, and they would wheel him or her out on a gurney, and they would be replaced by another person. It was a dying house, the hospice, a bridge between the worlds, a final weigh station before eternity, an aperture into the unknown.

On the fifteenth day of his stay the head nurse, Garnet Paige, came in and sat at the foot of his bed. She was a slightly built woman with oversized glasses that made her narrow face appear even smaller. She spoke in a soft voice that was accustomed to the sharp presence of tragedy and she asked him for a favor and he listened politely.

The next morning Garnet brought in a girl of around nineteen summers named Minerva Rivers. She was of the height of a female basketball player, and she had thick blond hair blocked off in the popular Madonna style. A year before Minerva had been responsible for an alcohol-related car accident that had injured three of her friends. Her father, a prominent land developer, had negotiated through an intermediary with the county prosecutor. In the end his daughter had been sentenced to twelve months of full-time volunteer work at the hospice, a ten thousand dollar fine, and five years of probation. Some in town thought the sentence was too severe. Others thought it was too lenient. The mother of Andromeda Romano, the girl who had been paralyzed from the waist down for life, thought it was just about right. So did the mothers of Gaia Schoenfeld and Jade Castaneda, the other two girls who had been seriously injured.

After Garnet left, there was a silence in the room that extended for five very long minutes. Minerva was angry and confused by what was happening, and Wulf was afraid of losing the fragile grip he had on himself and his circumstances. Minerva was, he could see at a glance, a spoiled and self-indulgent daughter of the local gentry. If she had a religion, its chief artifact was a vanity mirror. If she had a credo, it was that perpetual motion, even a stationary kind of gyroscopic spinning, was progress. The prospects of her ever serving a cause higher than her self-interest were at the moment nonexistent.

Finally someone had to say something.

"I'm sorry you have to be here," he said.

She didn't respond. She saw a bed-ridden elder whose presence reminded her of death and the injustices of life. She hated him for reminding her of the fact that she, too, had been born against her will on this god-forsaken planet and that, like everyone else since the beginning of time, she had been unfairly given a death sentence.

A half an hour passed, Minerva staring out the window at the mountains, and finally she spoke.

"What is it like?"

He did not speak spontaneously about his affliction, and always framed his answers with care.

"Sometimes the pain is so bad I want to die." He paused. "But other times the strange thing is I feel alright and I want to keep on living."

Another hour passed.

Lunch was served on trays and they ate together—Minerva at a circular table beside the window and Wulf on a plastic tray in bed. At one point, when he asked her for more water in order to take his pills, it became clear that she was afraid to touch him.

"Don't worry," he assured her, "It's not contagious. It's in my genes."

After lunch there was a conflict over the television, Wulf refusing to have the thing on because it would interfere with his afternoon reading of the Bible, a book in which he had recently acquired a renewed interest. His goal was to re-read the entire Bible, every word of it, before he died. He had finished Genesis, Exodus, and Leviticus and was beginning the fourth book of Moses. Secretly, he hoped that if he read very slowly it would prolong his life that much longer. After all, how could a benevolent and merciful deity take the life of a suffering soul who was devoted to the supreme work celebrating his wisdom and love?

Minerva sulked in a corner of the room, reading a stack of month-old fashion magazines she had gathered from the waiting room.

The next morning Wulf suggested the following compromise—Minerva could watch television every other hour. The other hour she would either have to read a book—no magazines—or talk with him. And the choice of programming would be entirely his, because it was his room.

The programs he selected were from an obscure cable channel: *I Love Lucy, The Real McCoys, The Andy Griffith Show, The Lone Ranger, The Honeymooners.* Wulf enjoyed them because they reminded him of a more pleasant time in his life. Minerva was incredulous at the vintage black and white images.

The shows had been popular when his children were little, and Wulf began to idly recount various episodes from that era—the funny things that children do, the happy moments of parenting, historical events of the period. Gradually he opened up more and more, telling stories from other chapters of his life. Soon an entire biography was pouring forth. The accounts were not related in any regular order. They were haphazard, jumping from decade to decade, from youth to adulthood and back again, connected sometimes only by vague associations, gossamers and threads as fine as a single first name repeated again or the season of the year. Wulf enjoyed freely opening up to someone. It was a relief to get rid of these things. Everyone carries such memories, and they are a burden, as heavy in the pack as rocks.

At first Minerva only feigned interest, but soon she began to listen with sincere attentiveness. The stories were unlike anything she had ever heard before. She learned about the distraught ex-husband, a police officer, who shot his ex-wife to death in open court, and the young lawyer who tried to bribe Wulf with a briefcase full of stock certificates, and the time an affluent air traffic controller suddenly admitted on the witness stand that he was, in fact, the bank robber who had stolen $40,000 from eight banks over a ten month period. And there were stories from the war, as well, things he had avoided thinking about for half a century. He even admitted the truth about the SS guards at Ravensburg—that he had sensed what the replacement sergeant was probably going to do, and had left the area so as to not interfere.

"The only other person I ever told that to was my wife."

"What did she say?"

"She said a quick death was too merciful."

"Judge Angstrom, what do you think my life will be like?" she asked.

"I think … that you will go to college and find a career that you love and eventually marry a good man and have children."

He didn't tell her the rest because he liked so much that innocent look on her face.

She was quiet, thinking of how it might be, and he interrupted her thinking, "Who knows? Maybe you'll become a lawyer."

She reflexively made a sour face and then, as she imagined that future, she began to smile.

Each day Wulf was becoming weaker. At times, when he was sleeping, it was hard to determine if he was alive or dead, and Minerva would walk over to make sure he was still breathing. By degrees Wulf was entering a twilight realm between the worlds, and was slipping back and forth before the final crossing.

When Minerva finally inquired as to the prognosis, the head nurse just shook her head.

The next morning Wulf was awake and alert, and she asked him if he had any more really good stories. She had grown to enjoy the gruff old man, and was afraid that once his stories were gone he would go away. She could see that he was like the white-barked aspen trees outside the window that were shedding their golden leaves to the wind. She could see that one day soon his branches, like those of the aspen, would be empty.

He said he did have one more story to tell her. It was something he had never told anyone—not even his wife.

When he finished the account there was a silence. He motioned for some water and then asked, in a voice weakened by fatigue and pain, a voice that, in fact, had become a faint whisper, "Well, what do you think?"

She paused for a moment, staring out the window at a passing cloud moving from west to east above the San Francisco Peaks. After awhile the cloud passed from view—such extended silences were common in the room—and she sighed and said that she thought it didn't really matter.

It was, after all, a long time ago, and the only thing that mattered is what happened after.

Wulf said nothing in response and she turned to look at him.

She saw then that he was no longer awake. His eyes were closed and his mouth was slightly agape and he was breathing irregularly.

She walked over to him and took his right hand in both of her hands. After a moment she gave him a kiss on the forehead.

Two hours later, after a series of violent shudders, he stopped breathing.

She would always wonder if he had heard what she had said.

A Rumor of Autumn

IN THE DESERT autumn comes first to the mountains.

It begins with a change of color in the high country. Fresh snow dusts the crags. In places the tundra—a deep sod of moss campion and dwarf flowers—presents the reddish earth tones of a Ganado rug. Elsewhere, the arctic meadows take on the faded hues of an old riding saddle. Golden leaves, wherever the dwarf willows grow, fill the alpine depressions. Isolated stands of bristlecone and spruce still hold their olive green, but all around the colors warm toward burgundy and honey. Even if I am far out in the desert—perched hawk-like on the Palisades of the Grand Canyon or roaming the desiccated flats of the White Rim—I can glance up at the nearby San Francisco Peaks or the La Sal Mountains and note the change.

The message is clear, even to the water-skiers etching the blue enameled surface of Lake Powell. One season is ending. Another is beginning.

Soon after the first hard frost the leaves of the quaking aspen grow as luminous as lemons. This transformation takes place in some years over a period of weeks and other times over the course of a single weekend. Quite often a grove is half-green and half-yellow, like a person whose hair has begun to lose its pigment at the temples. The colors of the aspen can range from peach to maroon to cadmium, and everything in between. They are uniform only in their brilliance. There are aspens down lower, too, and you find them in unusual places. How they came to live there remains a mystery. In Kane Gulch on Cedar Mesa, for example, there are several dozen aspen along the streambed about a mile west of the state road. These are beautiful trees, standing tall and immaculate in their fine powdery white bark, but they seem strangely out of place. They are incongruous visitors from a higher realm. There are no blue columbine or bracken fern here, only prickly pear cactus and barbed yucca. When you see them at such an unlikely elevation, you pause. Your face registers the same surprise it would if you saw black and white tuxedos and designer

145

gowns at the local bowling alley. You stop, and think to yourself—what in the name of Linnaeus are they doing here?

The sounds of autumn in the desert mountains are muted, soft. Gone are the loud songbirds of spring, and the chanting leopard frogs and spotted toads. The thunderstorms of June and July are a distant memory. So are the crashing waterfalls. Whole days pass and there is not a wind. Not even a breeze. Occasionally a sleepy hermit thrush calls out, forgetting the season. Pine squirrels chatter back and forth. Grouse whirr and elk bugle. Black bears move with brusk authority through the acorn patches. Ravens cry out. Somewhere a man applies an axe to a fallen tree. Another stalks a deer with arrow notched, trying unsuccessfully not to disturb the parchment-like leaves.

At times a vast unbounded stillness fills the groves, as if the earth is drawing a well-deserved sigh at the conclusion of her creative labors. On certain afternoons on certain slopes you can sit motionless beneath an aspen tree, breathless and invisible, and actually move inside the autumnal silence, pass into a place where the wheels do not turn, at least in a way that can be measured by any instrument of man. For a day, perhaps, or an hour, or a minute, the smooth celestial sphere of the earth is poised, as an apple thrown into the air hesitates for a moment before it falls back down. Time is suspended. Growth has stopped. Seeds and berries hang full and ripe. There is the collective sense, across the mountains, of spent fertility and of loss, but also of contentment and fruition.

Down on the desert the changes are more subtle than in the highlands, but it is nonetheless evident that a monumental transformation is taking place. The primary color of fall on the low desert is yellow, and it is found plentifully among the leaves of the Fremont cottonwood. These are large spreading trees with enormous trunks and whitish-gray corrugated bark. An entire cattle herd can find shade beneath them. A flock of one hundred migrating thrushes can comfortably roost for the night in the branches. They are an icon of the Southwest. My favorites are along the Virgin River in Zion Canyon. When the groves peak in late October the oil painters fill the valley, and spread out near and far with palettes and brushes and easels. Another famous spot is Canyon de Chelly, on the trail to the White House Ruins. Escalante Canyon has some striking groves, as does White Canyon in Natural Bridges. Elsewhere, there are always a few late-blooming sunflowers, which seem capable of flowering with no water at all, and petite desert marigolds, with their delicate blossoms that seem fashioned from Yeats' hammered gold. Rabbitbrush grows everywhere, and its ragged free-spirited blossoms are the yellow from which all other yellows are made.

The light in the fall is unique to the time of year. It falls upon the desert as if filtered through stained glass. It is less intense than the light of midsummer, and quite distinct from the light of spring. It carries with it a quality of celebration as well as a quiet warning. There are fleeting shadows in its depths, as well as tapestries of darkness. Vergil knew this light, and the Chinese poets of the T'ang dynasty, and Wordsworth in his lyric to the solitary reaper. So did Shakespeare, when he composed that sonnet that begins "That time of year thou may'est in me behold."

One of the finest places to observe the autumn light on the desert is along the Book Cliffs west of Grand Junction. Here, late in the afternoon, the blue shadows begin to slowly form among the eroded shale cliffs. What had been a confused terrain flattened by midday glare now becomes, in the last light of day, an extended shelf of singular loveliness. The cliffs awaken from their slumbers. Strong lines appear. Bold shapes assert themselves. Mysterious chasms retreat. Ridge lines are resolved. Shadows form everywhere, and each with a kind of opaque density. The entire countryside is simplified, as if by the graceful hand of an artist. Add a few longhorn cattle standing at ease on the sage desert in the foreground, and you have a scene from the imagination of Maynard Dixon, a mural-sized masterpiece the artist never painted, perhaps only idly conjured, and wishes now, in the afterlife, he could somehow undertake.

Some autumn days are as warm as summer. If you are working in the fields, hefting ninety-pound hay bales onto a flatbed truck, or harvesting peaches in the orchards, hauling a bushel basket among the honeybees and hornets, you know about the heat. Step out of the shade for more than half an hour and you will become as sunburned as on the Fourth of July. The fishermen know about the heat as well, for the canyon streams are low and slow and the trout are sluggish, floating indifferently at the bottom of the deepest pools. On other days the frost makes its presence known wherever water gathers—ice as clear as glass, with flattened bubbles and summer insects and fallen aspen leaves trapped inside. On those days the garter snakes seek out the rocks and join the collared lizards to warm themselves in the sun. Up at the Green River Overlook the white-haired retirees from Oregon en route to Organ Pipe notice that their breath forms clouds in the air and that bringing a wool sweater was a good idea after all.

If you take a stringed instrument—a mandolin or a guitar—into the desert in the autumn you will inevitably begin to finger the minor chords. G minor and D minor seem particularly fitting. The melodies tend to wander a descending path, drawn to the lower range of notes and eventually to the bass strings. Occasionally an augmented or a diminished chord will find its way into the improvisation, as well, bringing a bit of the mild discord that is always just below the pleasant surface of the fall. The best place for making music is some nameless side canyon where the acoustics are resonant. The birds will look at you curiously, but they will understand, for they sang too, once, in the long-ago spring.

As early as late August the heavens begin to change. One by one various planets make their appearance shortly after sundown, depending on the year, including such legendary giants as Jupiter and Saturn. The Pleiades, so lovely with binoculars, become visible to the east soon after dusk, as do Aldebaran and Sirius. Rigel and Betelgeuse form the belt and sword of Orion, which rises now before midnight. In gazing at the stars we are not that far removed from the biblical shepherds. There it is, after all the universe. Our place of origin, our final resting place. The greatest desert of them all, with bleak expanses that go on for light years and black canyons into which whole stars fall and empty gulfs that can swallow a spiral galaxy. It can be frightening, it can be comforting, but, most importantly, it is always there. It is enough sometimes to turn a grown man into a boy again, struck full of wonder at the beauty and enormity of it all.

Autumn is the season of the harvest, in the desert as elsewhere. In ancient times the cliff dwellers and pueblo builders gathered a rich bounty. On the low desert they found cactus and yucca fruit, mariposa lily bulbs and sunflower seeds. Higher ground offered acorns and wild onion roots, chokecherries and wild currants, snowberries and pinyon nuts. Later came corn and beans from South America, and then peaches and pears, apricots and apples from the Spanish. Of all the natural products of the desert, the finest by far is the nut of the pinyon pine. Its texture is not unlike that of a walnut, but the taste is something else entirely, with none of the dense woody oil of the peanut or the cashew. The nut tastes, for lack of a better comparison, like the landscape itself. It contains a bit of the mule deer that slept one afternoon in the shadow of its branches, and the brush of the wild turkey's extended wing as it flew off, and the song of the coyote calling up the new moon. It tastes of blinding hot July afternoons and bitter cold January midnights, of driving hailstorms and drifting virga and sudden thunderstorms and the ozone tang of lightning. It brings the flavor of the desert to your tongue—the big skies, lonesome winds, scattered clouds, wandering canyons and far-off mountains. Even as you sit beside the fireplace in the depths of a blizzard, arranging slides over a light table and listening to a Muddy Waters tape, a handful of pinyon nuts from a ceramic dish can instantly transport you back to your true home, the desert.

I have seen the pinyon as far north as the Gates of Ladore near the Wyoming border and as far south as the Growler Mountains in southern Arizona, as far east as the Walter Ufer country around Taos and as far west as the Alabama Hills beneath Mount Whitney. It is an odd-shaped tree, formed more like an alder or a cottonwood than a conifer. It generally prefers a dry rocky soil facing south. There are lovely specimens along the canyon trails in the Needles, and along the Escalante Canyon, and down in Grand Gulch. Cedar Mesa is covered with them, as is the Kaiparowits Plateau.

Wildlife love the nuts. Even gray foxes eat them. Stripped from the cones by the hand of a pine squirrel or by the hand of a Monument Valley sheepherder, they are a meal by themselves. A pound of pinyon nuts has three thousand calories. Of the nine amino acids essential to human life, seven are found in pinyon nuts. A total of twenty amino acids are found in pinyon nuts, making them comparable in nutrition to an elk tenderloin. They are also rich in potassium. The old people used the pitch to cement turquoise stones to silverwork, to repair leaky water jugs, to smoke hides, and to make a dye for clothing. The pinyon is the symbolic tree of the high desert.

One day in late November or early December a heavy snow falls and covers the mountains and the desert. Rafts of ice fill the Green, the San

Juan, and the Colorado. A cold, mean wind blows across the land. Withered stalks of fireweed empty their feathered seeds to the wind. Sparrows,
even ravens, huddle in the junipers. The normally blue sky is as gray and
bleak as the perpetual cloud over a Midwestern factory town. The mule
deer, already on their winter range, find it difficult to move through the
drifts. They are watched attentively by the coyotes. At a farther distance,
resting in the rocky solitudes, the mountain lions also take note. The solstice may not appear on the calendar for another few weeks, but everyone realizes, from the yawning hoteliers and storekeepers of downtown
Monticello to the pregnant mother bear lumbering toward her den in
the Blue Mountains, that winter has arrived.

Land's End

IT HAD NEVER BEEN WHAT SHE HAD DONE so much as what she was going to do. In high school, she had qualified for the state championships her sophomore year. Her event was the one hundred meter butterfly. The record she set in that event, competing against girls older and more experienced, seemed impossible. There were rumors of national competition, and possibly of the Olympics, until she sustained a broken meniscus and a torn anterior cruciate ligament in a drama class. Then there was college at Logan with a major in French Literature. After that came three years in the screenplay program at Irvine, followed by a documentary on a Navajo rug weaver that was nominated for an Oscar. Later that same year, at the age of twenty-six, Caron Meany was offered a job as Deputy Director of the Utah Film Commission.

On the surface, it seemed an ideal transitional position. The benefits were excellent and there would be an opportunity to work with directors and actors whose names were familiar to everyone in the world. As location manager, she would be responsible for finding the best landscapes in the state for a particular film. Whether it was a traditional western, or a contemporary drama, or an off-beat romance, she would know exactly where to go. As a result, she would be able to frequently travel to the places in the desert she loved—Coral Pink Sand Dunes, Old Pariah, Goblin Valley, and other spots less well known. All the while, she would work on the screenplays that would gain her the recognition she had dreamed about since she was a girl growing up poor in Escalante with her widowed mother and three sisters.

One thing did not lead to another, though, as sometimes occurs, and she now found herself at the age of forty-two reluctantly admitting that the success for which she had toiled half her years would probably never come. Events large and small had just not cooperated. First came the exodus of American filmmakers to Canada. Then came the layoffs in the state film office. As a result of this last development her savings, including

her retirement funds, were gone. To compound matters, she had con-
tracted breast cancer about a year before, and had undergone a painful
and disfigurative surgery. In the past month, her two best screenplays had
been rejected by the only production company that had shown any
serious interest. *European House Swap* was a light comedy about a family
in Milwaukee that trades their suburban home for the month of August
with a French family that lives in a country house near Marseilles. *Blue
Highway* was a bawdy road farce about two teenage brothers who fly to
Las Vegas to pick up their dead grandfather's RV and drive it home across
the country to Indianapolis. Everyone agreed the characters and stories
were brilliant, but no one would make the commitment. Even filming
in Canada with unknown actors on a skeletal budget, the projects represented too much of a risk, or so it had been explained to her.

Then, three days ago, she had discovered through a friend in the business that the film company had secretly taken her ideas and given them
to other screenwriters to develop. Her lawyer had explained the situation
to her—yes, she could fight and, yes, she would likely prevail in a jury
trial, but they would keep appealing for years, and one-third of the settle-
ment would go to him, and the mere fact that she had litigated would
have a career-ending effect.

And so she had driven the three hundred miles from her home on the
Wasatch Front to southern Utah in order to end her life. She had put her
papers in order, had left a note taped to her computer screen, and had
walked out the back door with just enough money for gas. She was going
to make it appear to be an accident—a fall while taking photographs.
One year earlier, anticipating such a situation, she had revised her will so
that her insurance money, about one hundred thousand dollars, would
go to establish an annual scholarship for young women students at her
undergraduate alma mater. It was all perfectly insane, of course, but she
had stopping caring about the distinctions between rational and irra-
tional long ago. What was occurring was the final rather messy collision
of a perfectionist with the imperfections of life.

Caron had a number of choices, for the scenic overlooks are numerous in southern Utah and northern Arizona. She had ruled out the Grand
Canyon as being too melodramatic, too obvious. She wanted to be more
subtle than that. Island in the Sky north of Moab was also out of the

question. Although the overlooks were among the finest on the plateau—Green River, Grandview, Dead Horse, the drop below Mesa Arch—they were also too popular and easily accessible. She wanted to be alone for this. Anything in Zion would work, but would also require a three or four hour climb. She might change her mind along the way. That left Muley Point or the Goosenecks Overlook, neither of which had ever done much for her, or the obscure Needles Overlook north of Monticello. It was the last that she finally chose. The view was to the horizons and few people ever took the time to make the fifty-mile round-trip drive. It would be ideal at sunset, the amber light streaming across the low desert from the Henry Mountains. One accidental step away from the tripod, and she would join Van Gogh and the others in the starry night.

At Moab she got an extra five gallons of gas just to be safe—even she could see the humor in this—and then drove south on U.S. 191. The radio was off and the car was silent and she drove without a thought on her mind. She was purposefully not thinking. She had somehow found the courage and the determination to come this far, and she did not want any unforeseen problems to disturb her fragile plan. So she pressed on with her unlikely journey, simultaneously present in the vehicle, and not. It was March and a front was blowing in from the west. The car shuddered a little in the gusts and she had to turn the wheel constantly to the right to keep from drifting over the yellow center line. The late afternoon traffic was light. There were a few ore trucks from the uranium mines in Dry Creek Basin heading north to the rail line, and the occasional delivery van returning to Grand Junction from Monticello and Blanding. Once there was a school bus, a quarter-full of children. That was about it. Spring break was still two weeks off and the tourists were still back in the cities. The whole plateau was taking a long deep breath before the summer season.

The sky was solid blue to the east, but from the high scattered clouds to the west she knew that by morning there would be a fresh blanket of snow at the higher elevations. By then she wouldn't care anymore about icy roads. She drove past the turnoff to Paradox Valley, a place she had always wanted to explore, and the familiar hole in the red rock known as Wilson Arch, and the long dry watercourse called Hatch Wash, and the slickrock formation known as Looking Glass Rock. These were all familiar features to her, and she remembered the times she had passed by them with this person or that person.

She started to make a list. The Jewish people at Masada had done it *en masse*. Socrates had made the same choice, drinking the hemlock as Plato put his face in his hands, and Hamlet had contemplated the possibility with considerable eloquence. Meriwether Lewis went out that way. So did all those young men who cried out "It is a good day to die" in another language as they galloped off with loaded rifles toward that grassy hill above the Little Bighorn. So did the kamikaze at Midway, and later Yukio Mishima and Yasunari Kawabata. Hemingway certainly knew where to find the key to the gun cabinet. Brian Jones, Jimi Hendrix, Jim Morrison, Al Wilson, Janis Joplin—the list from the Sixties was prodigious. And of course there were the modern poets—Anne Sexton, Sylvia Plath, John Berryman. Dylan Thomas could probably be added, though he chose an indirect route, as did Jack London. And then there were the actors—Marilyn Monroe and Judy Garland and possibly James Dean. It was a noble band, an exclusive fraternity, and she would soon be among them.

Seven miles north of Church Rock she turned right on a pot-holed asphalt road that headed straight into the west. She put the visor down, because of the glare of the setting sun. She would encounter no more traffic beyond this point. South of the road there was a long white and buff-banded wall of red sandstone, divided here and there into smooth basins and bowls. Everything to the north was open desert—prickly pear cactus and yucca and empty stretches of sand. The road passed the Windwhistle BLM Campground—vacant, as always, this time of year—and then turned in a gentle curve back in the direction of Moab. On the right was Hatch Rock, an orange-gray piece of sandstone that rose in a sculpted mass from the desert. All around the rock there were islands and archipelagoes of cedar.

The road kept going, well over twenty miles in all, forking and turning over the mesa top until finally she came to the parking lot at the end of the road. She parked in the first available space and got out to stretch. Her ears were still ringing from the long drive, and her legs were stiff from having been crammed in the same position for six hours. She walked to the edge and stood there for a moment and looked out at the landscape. The wind was gusting in an irregular sort of way and she instinctively stepped back a foot. She was at the farthest point of a vast mesa that was shaped like a peninsula and rose above the stone wasteland below some two thousand feet. To the north thirty miles was Island in the Sky, an isolated mesa near the confluence of the Green and Colorado. The horizon to the west was dominated by the Henry Mountains, pale bluish-violet and some sixty miles distant. To the southwest was The Maze—a tangled wilderness of red rock—with intermittent views of the Colorado River beyond. Due south were the Abajo Mountains, a closer version of the Henrys. All views to the east were obscured by the junipers and pinyons.

She turned to get the tripod and camera and proceed with her plan when she noticed there was another car in the further loop of the parking lot. The car had been obscured by the intervening trees. She stopped dead in her tracks. This had not been part of the plan. Everything instantly changed. What was she to do now? The plan would not work unless it was sunset and she was alone. That was an essential part of it. Who was this person? What were they doing up here at this time of year? She pondered her next move. She must determine who they were and how long they intended to remain. The sun would set in less than one hour. After that, she would have to wait another day. Could she maintain her resolve for that long?

She walked over to the car and looked inside. There was nothing except a highway atlas and an empty plastic quart of water. The plates were from a state in the east. The car was dusty, as if it had been driven for a long time. There was a sticker in the window indicating it was a rental car. The doors were locked. She looked around. No sign of the driver anywhere. Where could this person be? She decided to wander off to the left of the parking lot, where the cliffs looked directly down upon the flats of Indian Creek and, at a greater distance, North Sixshooter Peak and South Sixshooter Peak. Both had been featured prominently in *The Comancheros*. She recalled the time she had met John Wayne twenty years earlier in Los Angeles, when he had come to the film class at the university, and had answered all their questions until they had no more questions to ask. Even with his one lung, stomach cancer, broken back, and bad heart he had managed to do that, and with an occasional smile.

She walked off through the cedars parallel to the cliffs, looking for a sign of the owner of the car. Perhaps she could persuade them into leaving earlier, make up some kind of a story. She walked across a flat of exposed rock and then crossed a slight drainage and it was when she was coming up on the other side that she thought she saw something unusual—a bit of unexpected color—in the trees ahead. She walked slowly now, looking to her right and left for any sign of a person or people. She stopped for a moment and studied the color. It was something blue. It definitely didn't belong naturally in the desert. Perhaps it was something that had blown up here from the parking lot. Closer now, she realized it was a blue jean. It was the leg of a person lying under the tree. Perhaps, she thought, the person is tired and is taking a nap here.

She stepped closer.

She was ten feet away now, only the back and legs and part of one hand visible.

"Hi."

Nothing.

"Hellooooo."

Still nothing.

There was something not quite right. No squirrels were chattering. No birds were singing. There was nothing but the wind in the trees.

She walked closer and it was at this moment that everything came together and she realized that the strange dark thing the man was holding in his right hand was a revolver and that a large part of the side of his head was missing. The man had crawled here under the tree and shot himself.

She was horrified at first, then indignant, then angry, then sad, and then all of those feelings again in a blur of emotion. She had never seen anyone dead before except in a funeral home and the sight of this man with his brains on the ground sent her retching into the sagebrush.

When that was over she took one last glance of the man, noting the details of what was there, and then turned away. She ran back to her car and got inside and locked all of the doors. Her hands were shaking. She was thinking quickly. He was a young man. He was half her age. It was one thing for her, a person over forty to contemplate such a thing, but what would cause a young man, and a handsome young man, to take such a step. Why in the world would he waste those really good years from twenty to forty? Was it love? Did he find out he had some disease? Had he committed some awful crime? Had he always been plagued with melancholy, and was this the natural conclusion? Had he lost someone he loved? What in the world would cause a handsome young man to kill himself, and in such a violent way?

She closed her eyes and said a prayer for the young man, for she was a person who always said her prayers, and as she prayed she recalled a poem by Rimbeau—"Le Dormeur du Val"—and her favorite line— *Nature, berce-le chaudement: il a froid.* "Cradle him warmly, Nature: he is cold." It was a sonnet about a young man who appears to be sleeping in a meadow but is actually dead, a soldier slain by gunfire in battle.

With an audible sound of revelation—a resounding "Yes!"—she opened her eyes and suddenly realized why she had been drawn to this place and what she now had to do. She had to find out everything she could about this young man and write down his story. She would work with the authorities to find out who he was and where he came from and what brought him to this place. She would meet with his friends and relatives and uncover the source of his despair. This would be her story. This is what she would write about. Perhaps by writing it down, by telling the story in film, she could save a suffering soul who might then go on to do some good in the world.

She started up her car and sped down the road to the ranger station in Monticello, some sixty miles distant. It was evening now and she turned on her headlights to avoid hitting a mule deer or a jackrabbit or one of those other creatures of the night.

Yes, she resolved to herself, I will make certain that all of this was not in vain.

The Quiet Season

IN THE GEORGIA O'KEEFFE MUSEUM in Santa Fe there is an Alfred Steiglitz photograph that I have always admired. The black and white image features a pair of hands on the skull of a cow. The photograph was taken indoors under diffuse lighting with Steiglitz's favorite camera, a four inch by five inch Graphlex. The skull had evidently been on the ground for some time, because there is no tissue remaining, and the blood stains have been washed away by the rain. It is a graceful object, resonant and white, and the surface of the bone glows white with the purity of death. The skull lies flat on its right side and dominates the field of view. O'Keeffe's hands enter the picture from the lower left. Her left hand has found a natural contour along the top of the skull, with the long fingers extended over the smooth cavern that held the right eye. Her right hand is resting along the right mandible, with the fingers splayed over the molars. Her hands and fingers are darkened by the sun, for O'Keeffe spent a portion of every day in the out-of-doors. They are the hands of an artist, strong and flexible and accustomed to the creation of beauty.

The photograph, entitled *O'Keeffe's Hands with Skull*, was taken in 1930, probably at Steiglitz's studio in New York or at his family retreat at Lake George. That year O'Keeffe spent the whole of June, July, August, and September traveling in New Mexico, and stayed for a time with the artist Mabel Dodge Luhan in Taos. Both O'Keeffe and Steiglitz were in their most productive periods. Steiglitz had just opened his gallery An American Place and O'Keeffe had recently exhibited her paintings at the newly constructed Museum of Modern Art. She would in that year, among other things, complete one of her signature paintings, *Ranchos Church*, as well as her *Jack-in-the-Pulpit* flower series. She had by that time already seen much of the desert—places such as Blue Mesa, the South Rim, Zion Canyon, and Bryce—and the images had begun to fill her paintings.

The photograph can be looked at in several ways, the sum of which is something more than a photograph. It can, first, be viewed simply for what it appears to be—a skull and two hands. It can, alternatively, be thought of as a fairly straightforward variation on the traditional still life. It can also, perhaps more profitably, be considered as a metaphor, as a bit of allegorical play with ordinary objects. The last has always provided the most useful insight to me, as I have seen the image as an elegiac commentary upon winter. The skull is as much a symbol as the hands. The visual essay is as much about the figurative as the literal. Winter is, after all, a time of death, of austerity, and of quiet modulation. The days grow short and the nights become long. A deep cold settles on the landscape. The cottonwoods shed their leaves. The cactus lose their fruit. The coyote in the trap is soon a thing of bones. People turn inward, as much as they flowed outward in May or June, and they rest in the quiet moments that are found between the seasons of change.

The sky on the desert in the winter has a pale transparence. All of the warmth has been removed from it, and it curves overhead like a blue juniper berry or a piece of glass that has been in the river for a long time. The sunsets are muted burgundy and rose-gray, and the ravens roost in the river trees long before the last of the light disappears. The clouds are different as well. No more the heavy brooding cumulus of summer, or the hard-edged white storms that bring rain and hail. Now the clouds are high and thin and scattered. Or they form a lens over a mountain range, the vapor smoothed by a chinook. Or they appear as a gray wall on the horizon and shortly deliver a benediction upon the world.

On the snow you can see who is in the neighborhood. Sometimes it is surprising. A restless bear that didn't eat enough and is out roaming around for berries or acorns or whatever else it can find. A flock of turkeys that has discovered the rose hips by the stream. A rabbit that lives under the house. A ring-tail cat in a canyon where none have been seen in years. Other times you recognize the tracks of a familiar deer, or the splayed feathers of a sage grouse rising from a drift, or a place in the snow where a desert shrew came up to have a look. The snow is its own world. It lies flat and cold over the imagination, so that we live inside walls within and without. It is a poem as well as a painting, and tells stories as well as any raconteur in the valley—the place where the five coyotes chased the deer, and the deer nearly escaped, were it not for the fall over the ledge which broke its leg; or the route the woman took as she snowshoed in the fresh powder and the rock where she stopped and had an orange; or the smooth slide where the otters returned to the river when they scented something on the breeze.

The lower desert in the winter is like an abandoned furnace. One can walk anywhere in the Maze or the Burr Desert at that time of the year without any concern about the heat. Snow can be gathered and melted, and so water is in a sense everywhere. It is strange, sometimes, to be out on the desert and to be cold among rocks that would be too hot to touch in August, but that is the way it is. Or to walk in the Coral Pink Sand Dunes that at certain times of the year lift heat waves to the sky and to see nothing but a washed glass sort of clarity. It seems at times that every-one in the world has disappeared. That some sudden plague or unantici-pated turn of events has taken every other person from the planet. You stand alone on the normally-crowded portals of Delicate Arch, for ex-ample, and are amazed to look in every direction and see not one other soul. Or you put in at a popular place like Spanish Bottom and note that there is not a single fresh track on the sand anywhere.

The trout begin their spawning run up Nankoweap Creek and Bright Angel Creek in the Grand Canyon as early as December. At times the clear water is dark with trout, and the bald eagles gather wherever the fishing is good and use their beaks or their talons with precision. Their black wings are tucked around their bodies and their chests and hoods are brilliant white, and they look very distinguished in their fine plumage. It is almost as if they dressed for a formal banquet, although at times the tuxedos are stained with blood. After awhile they sit in the upper branches of the cottonwoods, looking heavy and over-fed, their sharp eyes closing a bit if the sun is out. It is not unusual at that time of year to see a dozen bald eagles at a single bend in a stream, some fishing and others resting and still others cleaning their feathers. Golden eagles are usually in the neighborhood, as well, and the ravens are always abun-dant. The ravens wait like pirates for a morsel to drop, and when it does they gather around in a flock and claim it as their own.

The smells of winter are the essence of the season: the cold clean scent of snow on the wind and the fragrance of cedar branches burning in a campfire. The wet fish tang of the river drifting up a canyon and the humus odor of leaves turning to earth in dark places during a January thaw. The lingering musk of a mule deer in an old day bed and the heavy sweat of a horse on the trail just up ahead. The reek of a carcass that a chinook has found and the sharp sulphur after a rifle is fired. The bitter-sweet aroma of dry sage leaves crushed in the fingers and the fragrance of onions and venison coming from the stovepipe in a sheepherder's wagon. The scent of the February sun on the sandstone as the warming rock gives up last night's light snow.

At night in the winter the stars flicker in the high winds that swirl between the earth and space. Each one is a sun, and you think of the deserts between the worlds, and of the deserts on other worlds. Every few years there are violent storms on our local star and the radiation that drifts through space afterwards causes the auroras to appear, sometimes as far south as northern Arizona. You walk outside after midnight and there they are, flickering like colored rainbows against the ivory black of space. You wonder, then, about the ancient ones and what they might have thought of these events, and you realize how lucky you are to live at a time when things can be explained. You wonder, too, what posterity will think of us, and how we had this or that wrong idea about something that we saw and thought we understood.

There are winters in space and winters on earth, winters of the landscape and winters of the spirit, cruel winters that hold merciless reign over an age of history and cool winters that come as a relief after a long hot autumn of the imagination. Shakespeare wrote a play called "The Winter's Tale" about how forgiveness can only arrive after a season of repentance. Winter is, he suggested, a time for healing and for deliberation and for retreat. In another one of his plays he has a future king speak of "the winter of our discontent." Winter can also be a time for secret plots that reach their climax in the spring. It seems that wars always settle down in the winter, as generals prepare for sunny days and dry roads. Winter is a time for reading, as well, for introspection and for looking backward as well as forward. It is a season fit for philosophy, as spring is for the lyric, summer for the novel, and autumn for the ode.

The older I become, the more I realize that life has many winters, and that there is not just that well-known one toward the end, but that they actually come and go and that you can be in the midst of a dreary winter at seventeen as well as at seventy. They appear and disappear, and you become accustomed to their rhythm. I am forty-seven as I write these lines. As I age, I look increasingly to my elders for guidance on the journey. Both Steiglitz and O'Keeffe lived a long time and stayed active to the end. She in particular remained close to nature, and was always involved with art and literature and the creative life. Her library at the Ghost Ranch had everything in it from James Joyce to D. H. Lawrence, from the Japanese Noh plays to the classic works of Chinese literature. She loved to listen to Beethoven on the record player at night after dinner, and after she went blind she continued to work, creating objects with clay that she would then fire and glaze in the kiln. Through it all, the desert was at the center of her existence. She saw in the end, and this is evident in her letters, that life is best viewed when the sun is to the west and the valleys are in shadow and only the peaks are visible. On the day she died, March 6, 1986, she had just completed her ninety-eighth winter.

The desert has much to teach us of winter. We watch how the cottonwoods stand in the wind, and how the canyons endure, and how the cactus shrink into themselves, and we take note. Some animals gather seeds and hoard them, as the ground squirrel does, though a strong rain or a curious fox can ruin the plan. Others live from moment to moment with no future plans, like the mountain lion. Others rely on the support of family, like the coyote or the aspens gathered in a communal grove. Still others go to sleep, like the lily that shrinks into its bulb or the bear that seeks its den. Death will find them all, and often in the winter months when the breath frosts the air.

When the final moment comes it is no doubt a bit like Land's End— a dizzying gulf where the wind blows strongly and the ravens cry out.

One can be sure of this much. It will have a panoramic view.

The World Behind the Sun

IT WAS AN OUT OF THE WAY PLACE in an out of the way part of the country. Twenty-six miles north of U.S. 89, fifty-one miles south of Escalante, and a quarter of an hour by foot from the shores of the reservoir that had once been a river. And on every side but one, the desert. A father, a grandfather, a granddaughter, and a hired hand lived there, maintaining a ten table restaurant, a gift shop, a campground, and a two-pump gas station called "The Flat Rock Outpost." The summer had gone fairly well until the flash flood washed away the bridge at Emery Canyon. Then all of the county road equipment was sent to fight the Bridger Knoll fire on the North Rim. The most recent estimate was that repairs on the bridge might not commence until the autumn snows fell. It might even be a late winter project. No one drove down from the north now, because the gravel road was no longer a hundred-mile short-cut to Arizona. Day after day the four residents of the outpost had little to do but tend to the wilted vegetable garden, read library books from Escalante, or listen to the radio, the power cable to the satellite dish having been cut in two by a now-deceased ground squirrel.

The wind was blowing from the east that day, and that meant they would not be smelling the thick acrid smoke of century-old ponderosas—thousands, tens of thousands of them and each its own kind of world—going up in flames. A day or two without smoke was fine with them. But it did mean that a new Gulf storm would be coming soon, another pitiful late August storm with little rain and much lightning that would start more fires, perhaps some in the pinyon mountains just to the west, and that would pretty much take care of the deer hunting season, as well.

The granddaughter, whose name was Joan, had found a shaded place under the largest cottonwood tree in the lower canyon. She came to the place often in the late afternoon when the heat became unbearable. The air was fifteen degrees cooler under the trees than on the rocks and the wind made a sound in the leaves like waves shifting pebbles on a beach. The sound reminded her of the beach—not of Lake Powell, which she hated as an artificial body of water that had drowned a lovely canyon— but of the ocean in the novel she was reading. The novel took her far away from the spare desert landscape where she lived, to a place where the rain clouds hung about the mossy cliffs and the white-feathered gulls called out over the waves and a strong and simple people made their living from the sea.

She was a solidly built young woman of twenty-two summers. She had light hay-colored hair that fell to her shoulders and a finely sculpted nose and clear blue eyes that often looked toward the sky. Her lips, her jawline, her eyebrows, her forehead, her cheekbones—all of the features on her face had come from her mother, Isabelle Seurel, whom her father had met in Paris while he was avoiding service in the Vietnam War. It was a classic Gallic face of the sort that inspired people like Francois Villon and Pierre de Ronsard and Edouard Manet and Claude Debussy. When people saw her at Flat Rock they would avoid looking at her as they avoided staring at the desert sun. They would observe her as they did the sun, without directly looking or perhaps with a quick side glance. Her presence at the desolate location seemed absurdly out of place—she was either just passing through, or she knew something they did not, or she was a serious harbinger of some sort.

As she read the book she could hear steps steadily coming towards her—the smallest sounds carried far in such a quiet place—but she did not look up. Nor did her two Australian sheepdogs, Tess and Rascal, who were asleep in the shade beside her. It was Kevin, the hired hand, who had worked at the outpost since April, when his car broke down. He had been on the way from Salt Lake City to see his uncle in Albuquerque, looking for work, and was taking the shortcut to U.S. 89 when he hit a rock the size of a tank mine that disabled his transmission, permanently. Her father Lewis had offered Kevin a job and like the idiot he was Kevin decided to stay. He was twenty-one years old and stood just short of six feet and weighed two hundred and seventeen pounds. His face had no distinguishing feature—a person who spoke to him for a few minutes in the morning would not be able to describe him in the afternoon. He had played football in high school and for one year at junior college, before the career-ending injury to his right knee. Now he was just another high school graduate searching for an equitable situation in an unjust world.

"I knew I would find you here," Kevin said, hopefully.

She said nothing, reading the book.

"Lewis and Cyrus might go out fishing tonight with the full moon. What say we head up to the spring?"

There was a spring in the rocks above the canyon from which they obtained their drinking water through a series of raised pipes. Back in the 1950s, her grandfather had built a swimming pool in a natural basin below the springs. This was before the dam was built and Flat Rock was still a busy desert crossroads for the uranium miners. One June night in a moment of indifference Joan had gone swimming there with Kevin. It had been a mistake. They had not made love, but they had come as close as two people can and now he considered themselves a couple. He would often say, half seriously—"You know that in some parts of the world we would now be considered legally married." To make matters worse, her father liked him, even if her grandfather understood the awkwardness of her predicament.

He asked the question again.

"Is that all you think about?"

He smiled his broken front tooth smile.

"What are you reading?"

"You wouldn't like it."

"Maybe I would."

"It's a love story by a Japanese writer named Yukio Mishima called *The Sound of Waves*."

"You are such a romantic."

"Not with you I'm not."

"Just give me one more chance Joan. Please, I—"

"—Oh Kevin stop begging. It doesn't do anything for you."

He took off his baseball hat and scratched the back of his head.

"I can think of something that's a lot more fun than reading."

"Don't you ever stop?"

"I read. I'll bet you didn't know that. I read sometimes. You know what I read?"

She didn't look up.

"That a person alone is like half a pair of scissors. It's useless. It takes two to make a functional unit."

"A functional unit? Oh Jesus, Kevin, stop it already."

"Can't you see? I'm in love with you."

"You're in love with yourself. Go back to the city. There are plenty of girls who will love you there."

"But I love you."

"If you keep this up Dad will fire you."

"Keeevvviiin."

"There, see, he heard me. He's calling you. Go see what he wants."

Kevin ran off to help her father fix the diesel generator.

She returned to the story. It was an adaptation of the old Greek Daphnis and Chloe tale. Hatsue was the lovely maiden, trained to dive for pearls. Shinji was the young man with the pure heart who worked as a fisherman. The story was so beautiful at points—the cormorants over the sea, the fog in the trees, the secret liaisons at the lighthouse—that it brought her to tears. When her mother had died she had not shed a tear, but reading this book could make her cry. In fact, sometimes when she was alone she would cry into her hands and pray for a miracle. Her father knew nothing of this, nor did her grandfather. Only the rocks knew.

Several minutes later she heard steps and thought it must be Kevin coming back but when she turned it was a tall young man with sandy sunbleached hair and a partially grown out auburn-colored beard. He was wearing Bermuda shorts and sandals and he had the lean muscular body of a marathon runner. His body was even more deeply tanned than hers. He took off his sunglasses so that she could see his eyes. The dogs were up and smelling his feet, wagging their tails as they always did when a friendly stranger appeared with interesting new smells on him.

"I was wondering if I could get a meal?"

"Where in the hell did you come from? You about scared me half to death!"

She stood up to face him, dressed in the t-shirt and shorts she always wore in the summer.

"I'm sorry. I left my kayak at the dock. The map said there was a restaurant here. I'm still a long way from Page."

"I'll say you are. That's forty miles over the water from here."

"Well do you?"

"Do I what?"

"Do you serve meals?"

Just then she heard the annoying roar of the diesel generator as it started back up and she waved in that direction and said "I guess we do now."

They walked up the trail through the cool trees and the hot sun to the restaurant, not talking. When they got inside he found a table and she went behind the counter to prepare the three black bean burritos he ordered. There were mounted deer heads and rainbow trout and the hide of a mountain lion on the walls. A weathered Winchester 94 thirty-thirty with a rusted barrel hung from a gun rack over the fireplace. A fan in the corner moved the air around.

"Where is everybody, anyway?"

She told him about the flash flood and the forest fires.

"So you're the only person who works here?"

She explained that the men were fixing the diesel generator and that then they had to take the boats out to fix a warning buoy in the reservoir for the park service. The burritos were ready from the microwave and so she brought everything over on a tray and sat down at the table beside him as he ate. The dogs wandered in through the door and lay down near the fan.

"Are you part of a group?" she asked.

"No. I'm running the Colorado River by myself. I started last month in Rocky Mountain National Park."

"It'll be interesting to see how you run the Glen Canyon Dam."

"Well," he smiled. "I will have to make a few portages."

"Why are you doing it?"

"Some kind of a vision quest, I guess."

"What's your name anyway?"

"I'm Thor. Thor Hamsun."

She introduced herself and they shook hands.

"What do you do for a living?"

"I was in the Air Force. But now I'm out."

"Have you ever been to France?"

"Sure."

"Tell me about it. Tell me all about France. I want to go there someday."

"Why?"

She told him the story of how her mother had grown up in a farming village in the Loire Valley and had fallen in love with her father while visiting Paris. The two of them married and then moved out to his father's place in the desert. Her mother had the European country girl's dream of Navajo blankets and wild horses and scenery from the John Wayne movies, but that wasn't exactly what she found. By then it was too late. She was pregnant. Many years passed. One day she was cleaning the storage room and she was stung by a scorpion. It was not a giant hairy desert scorpion, which are relatively harmless, but a tiny deadly Centruroides scorpion. Her father had tried to save her life, but she died before he could get her to the clinic in Page. When the sting is on the neck, there's not much that can be done. Her mother Isabelle Seurel was buried in the canyon above the spring, covered with the sand of the desert she had dreamed about from afar but had hated once she saw it.

And now, Joan explained, the daughter of that woman was trapped in purgatory, staying on for the sake of her grieving father but realizing that life should be taking her elsewhere. Most of all she wanted to travel to her mother's home town of Bourguen and meet her relatives. The Loire was the last truly wild river in western Europe and it still had sea-run salmon and she wanted to walk across the country her mother had known when she was a girl—a landscape of sunny pastures and shadowed beech woods, limestone hills and wandering hedgerows, gray owls and golden orioles. The only thing her mother had left her was a wooden box full of journals and diaries and Joan had read them and wanted to write the story of her mother's life as a novel. It would be a sad and sometimes dark story, but it would be struck through with hope and happiness and humor. It would be like life.

She spoke like this without stopping for twenty-five minutes and when she was done, the words suddenly ending like a sea-swell turning back from the beach after having expended itself, there was a long silence and she was surprised at herself, for she rarely uttered more than a few sentences at a time, and preferred silent observation to the spoken word.

Thor sat back, for it was his turn to talk, and related quiet stories of his travels in France—the museums and galleries of central Paris, the hiking trails in the maritime Alps along the Italian border, his visit to the grave of Theo and Vincent at Auvers-sur-oise—and he would have continued with his experiences in Norway but then he realized the lateness of the hour and stood up, ready to leave.

"How long has it been since you had a hot shower?" Joan asked.

He thought for a moment and said probably about two weeks.

"Well you need one. You stink. You really need to take a shower. The bathhouse is that green building across the road."

She pointed at the bathhouse and said "Go!"

He walked over to the bathhouse where he would find clean towels and soap and shampoo on the bench and she ran to her cabin and opened her lap-top computer and began a search on the name Thor Hamsun, United States Air Force. After several minutes of waiting—she nervously looking out the window to see if he was done yet—a front page article from *The New York Times* came up on the screen. It was dated a year earlier almost to the day. It read as follows:

Air Force Captain Shakes Up Officials At Awards Ceremony

At a ceremony in Bahrain during which he was to be awarded a Bronze Star and a Purple Heart from the Secretary of the Defense, Air Force Captain Thor Hamsun instead delivered unexpected criticism of a recent U.S. action in the war. Six weeks ago Hamsun, the pilot of a F-117 Stealth fighter/bomber, dropped a one thousand pound laser-guided bomb on what was believed to be a command bunker in Baghdad. It turned out to contain the wives and children of Iraqi senior officers. According to the Iraqi Foreign Ministry, eighty-three non-combatants were killed. While returning to his base on the same mission, Hamsun's plane was hit by a ground-to-air missile and he had to eject over the Iraqi desert. The pilot spent two days on the ground evading enemy patrols before being rescued by U.S. forces. It is believed the wreckage of this plane was later sold to the Chinese. Hamsun claimed intelligence operatives had provided the theater commander with target information known to be questionable, and that officials had then lied to cover up their actions. The White House had no official comment, but sources speaking on condition of anonymity said the military was looking at providing Hamsun, a distinguished Air Force Academy graduate and son of an Air Force general, with an early but honorable discharge.

Joan sat back, her head spinning. It had to be him. She understood now why he had been so reticent about his past, and why he was on this journey through the desert. And she remembered, too, the strange bullet-like scar on his right shoulder that she had not asked him about.

Suddenly he was at the door.

"I thought I saw you in here," he said.

She looked up, startled, her heart racing, and turned off her computer.

"That's quite a library."

The cabin had three bookcases and each had four shelves and every shelf was full.

"Reading time is one thing we have a lot of."

He looked at his watch and said he had to go.

"Why don't you spend the night? We could put you up in a cabin with a real bed."

"Thanks but I've got ten more miles to go today. I'm on a tight schedule."

He was already out the door and on the porch.

"Can I ask you a question?"

"Fire away."

"What's that scar on your shoulder from?"

She reached out and touched his shoulder with her fingertips. There was a purple welt there about the size of a dime and there was another identical welt on the opposite side, as if something had passed through his body in a straight line.

"Long story."

"Is there a short version?"

"I was riding my bicycle and took a fall."

This was spoken almost in the tone of a question.

"Has it bothered you with all the paddling?"

"No."

He turned to leave.

"Wait. Let me walk with you down to the dock."

They stepped off the porch of her cabin and just then Kevin, her father, and Grandpa Cyrus came up the trail. Kevin saw the two of them leaving her cabin and his face turned red.

As they passed by, Joan told her father who Thor was and said she was walking him to the docks.

"Best be careful, young man," said Grandpa Cyrus. "The ranger said there's three guys escaped from a prison in Texas and now they've got a powerboat out on the lake. Word is they're headed into the Escalante Country to hole up for awhile. One of them grew up there. I think I might have known his dad from the old days."

"Well, thank you sir, for the heads up. I'm sure I can take care of myself, though."

"You and me both, partner. You tangle with Cyrus Rawlins and you tangle with the man."

Grandpa Cyrus then related a story they had all heard before, except for Thor. It was a tale that had begun as an account Cyrus overheard, and then became an action in which he participated, and then was embellished further so that he became the chief player. It involved a group of notorious cattle thieves led by Willis Clayton up in Davis Gulch, a loosely organized sheriff's posse, and a dramatic shoot-out at a desert watering hole in the Escalante Wilderness.

"Back then this country was wild with a capital 'W' I'll tell you. Yes it was. That's a fact."

Everyone had politely listened to the entire account, which changed slightly every time it was related. Cyrus started to tell another story about a prospector named Buster Bailey and his dealings with the Red Mesa Gang and Thor said he really he had to go. He smiled and gave Cyrus an informal salute and started down the path.

Joan followed.

"I'll come along," said Kevin.

Joan turned and gave Kevin such a furious eye-bulging glare that he stopped in his tracks. Both her father and her grandfather saw the exchange. Her father did nothing but Cyrus reached over and grabbed Kevin by the belt and pulled him back toward the restaurant.

Thor saw none of this.

When he and Joan got to the dock, he began to prepare the kayak for departure.

"Will I ever see you again?" she asked.

"Could be."

"But how? I don't know your address."

He found a pen and wrote his e-mail address on a scrap of paper. "I won't be checking it for about a month, but that's always one way to stay in touch."

She pulled a restaurant menu from the pocket of her shorts. It had her address on it. She gave it to him and their hands touched.

They were standing there facing each other and there was a moment of awkwardness and he cleared his throat and said "Well, I guess this is where we say good-bye" and she said, "Well, at least let me give you a little hug."

When they hugged she didn't let go until he kissed her neck.

He turned to leave.

"Wait," Joan said, "I know we just met, but I want you to have something."

She took off her gold necklace, from which hung an opal that she had found in the clay hills behind the outpost. It was small and egg-shaped and the color of white if white also contained every other color in the form of miniature rainbows. It was without flaw or blemish. The purity of it was such that it seemed a desert sunrise had formed itself into a single translucent tear. In the sunlight the opal was softly luminous. It had an unusual weight in his hand.

"I can't take this."

"I'll be insulted if you don't. Besides I can find opals like that all over around here. I want you to have it because it will protect you in your travels."

"Alright then, thanks." He thought for a moment. "But I don't have anything to give you."

She smiled.

"You can give me your promise that I will see you again."

"Alright. I promise."

He got into his kayak and pushed off from the dock and then began paddling across the cobalt blue waters of the lake. She watched until he went around the point of rocks at the far end of the cove, and she was hoping he would turn and wave, but he didn't. He just kept paddling. After awhile even the ripples were gone, and it was as though he had never been there.

She then walked back up the canyon to the outpost.

Two hours later, Kevin was still pestering her about Thor as she tried to make dinner for everyone. Kevin had just said "I still can't believe you gave your necklace to a complete stranger" for the third time in an incredulous tone of voice when Grandpa Cyrus ran in and said that three men were coming up the trail and the dogs were barking and it didn't look good.

Before they could do anything the three men walked into the restaurant. Two of the men had revolvers and the other, the short one, had a bolt-action hunting rifle. The men were dressed in clothes that did not quite fit them properly, for they had been stolen from an RV in Oklahoma. The men were sunburned as people are who have been indoors for a long time and who are suddenly exposed to the desert light. They looked nervous, tense. Everyone was silent.

Finally Cyrus spoke. He asked them if they were hunters and they started to laugh.

"That's funny," said the short one with the broad face and the close-set eyes who appeared to be the boss. "That's really funny. You've got a good sense of humor, Pops."

"Why's that?"

"Everybody knows that hunting season don't start for another two months, isn't that a fact?"

"So why the guns?"

"I guess you heard there are three prison escapees in these parts. Well, we don't want any trouble. I guess you don't want any trouble either, do you?"

Cyrus shook his head.

The man laughed again, and then his companions did as well. They seemed to take their cues from the short muscular man with the rifle. He was their leader, such as he was, and had until recently been serving a sentence of one hundred and ninety-nine years without the possibility of parole for a series of crimes the exact nature of which was, even among his peers, as much of an enigma as he was. His two companions were felons of the ordinary variety—one had robbed a pizza parlor with his uncle's shotgun after he saw a cable program describing a similar crime; the other had stolen a station wagon with a grandmother asleep in the backseat, which had led to the kidnapping conviction and the mandatory ten year sentence.

"Alright. Here's how it's gonna happen. We're gonna spend the night here and we're gonna be kings of this place and then we're gonna leave in the morning. If you cooperate, nobody will get hurt. Do you understand?"

"I guess we don't have a choice in the matter," said Joan's father.

"That's right. You don't. Cody—grab that rifle on the wall. Now you there—what's your name?"

"Joan."

"Fix us some cheeseburgers or something and stay where we can see you. And bring us some beer too while you're at it. Do you have a telephone?"

"Just this cell phone."

"Give it to me."

"Lucas, will you go shut those dogs up?"

"Sure Duane."

The man walked out and shot the two dogs and Joan screamed "No!" and ran for the door but the short man named Duane grabbed her and told her to get back to the kitchen. Kevin stood up and said to leave her alone and the man struck him in the face with the butt end of the rifle and Kevin fell to the floor with a fractured cheekbone, moaning.

It all happened in thirty seconds.

"I thought we had an understanding, people. I thought we had an understanding."

He was still holding Joan around the waist and the old man gulped then.

Several miles away, Thor suddenly remembered that he had left his camera hidden in the bushes back by the dock. He always left the camera bag in a secure dry place off the kayak. That way he wouldn't lose his film if the kayak drifted away. This was the second time this oversight had occurred on the trip, and he would have to develop a better system. He thought for a moment about continuing on, and buying a new camera in Page, but then he decided he had no choice. He had to return. He laboriously turned the kayak around and began paddling back toward the cove. The wind was behind him now and it was easier. There were pleasure craft out on the lake—houseboats and ski-boats and sailboats—but there was no one near him, on the western side of the lake. He had the western waters alone.

As he paddled his thoughts drifted over the landscape in front of him and he found himself as he often did when he was alone again flying out of Baghdad

on a vector that would take him over the lights of Basra and then across the Gulf and back to the base in Bahrain. He was reviewing a checklist in his mind and staying focused on the flight when suddenly the computer came on saying missile, missile, missile, and put the plane back into his hands. He went into an ungodly spiral they called the mind-eraser because of the seven g's and the computer was saying six thousand yards, five thousand yards and he turned hard right and started to climb, then banked hard left and went into a dive, releasing clusters of phosphorus decoys along the way, but the missile was tracking true on the exhaust. At five hundred yards the explosion came from behind and the plane shuddered and lost all forward motion. It was going down now in a flat spin, the tail blown away and the voice was now saying, a calm female voice in his helmet, eject, eject, eject and he couldn't reach the handles behind the helmet brace. He was trying but the forces were building and then suddenly the canopy blew off and he was rocketed out parallel to the earth at eleven thousand feet. The air was cold and he fell for a long time, watching the plane break apart in burning pieces. The parachute deployed and he used the guide lines to angle himself as far as he could from the plane. Five miles, ten miles. It was a windy night and when he landed it was a soft landing in a pasture and a dog was barking and someone was calling to the dog in Farsi. For the next two days he did not sleep, always stayed awake, spending most of the time in the date palm grove and he remembered search and rescue finally coming in a Blackhawk, and how he was almost there when some farmer shot him from behind and a marine came out and dragged him in.

An hour later he paddled into Flat Rock cove and noticed that a power-boat was tied to the dock. He remembered what the grandfather had said and something about the scene seemed or felt strange to him and so he anchored his kayak in some rocks about fifty yards from the dock. He then took an alternative route to the outpost, climbing a side ridge that would carry him above the canyon.

When he had the outpost in sight, he crouched down, for he was sky-lined, and peered through a clump of rabbitbrush.

He saw the two dead dogs lying in pools of blood and then he saw that three men had Joan pushed against a tree. There was a rifle in her chest. They were telling her that if she cooperated they wouldn't kill the others, but she had to cooperate. They told her to take off her clothes, that they wanted to look at her. She was crying, the men standing around her. One man raised his voice and slapped her twice and she slowly removed her t-shirt and then her shorts. Underneath she had on a one piece bathing suit. She was trying to talk, but they told her not to talk, to keep her eyes closed and do what they told her. The short man told one of the other men to get some music. He wanted to see her dance. They were all drinking beer from cans.

Thor sat back, his heart racing. His every impulse was to rush down the hill and put a stop to it, but that would just get everyone killed. He needed a plan, and he needed a plan fast. He had no weapons. He had nothing that came close to a weapon. He thought back to his training, to all those weeks in the field at Pensacola, and to what he had learned in that other desert. He understood that he needed a diversion. He needed to get one of the men alone and get that man's weapon, and then he would be in a position to deal with the others. His mind was working with a speed and focus now that it normally did not possess. He forced himself to look away from the tree to the rest of the compound. He saw then what he had to do.

The music was playing loudly from a truck radio and the men had her dancing. The men were drunk and becoming drunker and they did not hear or see Thor run down the hill to the kitchen. Once inside, he found a length of wire—a knife wouldn't fit into his plan—and put an aerosol can in the microwave and set the timer on four minutes. Just as he was about to leave he saw the others tied on the floor of the restaurant. The grandfather was the only one who was conscious and he was looking at Thor. He had his mouth taped shut. Thor put his finger to his lips and nodded and Cyrus nodded back.

When the can exploded the short man named Duane made a profane observation and told the other two to go check. Neither wanted to go and an argument ensued. One of them was finally ordered to go. The other wanted to keep watching. When the man walked into the restaurant he saw nothing unusual. He walked through the kitchen and again saw nothing. He stepped out the back door and was looking to his right and left when Thor jumped from the roof onto his back. There was a scuffle and the man kicked over a garbage can as the wire tightened around his neck but the music was so loud the others couldn't hear.

The rifle was a Remington 700 BDL and there was one round chambered and four more in the magazine. Thor had hunted elk once in the Medicine Bow Mountains of Wyoming with a similar rifle when he was at the Academy. He was familiar with its operation. He worked the action several times to make certain the rifle was functioning properly. The barrel was clear and the iron sights were in place and everything was as it should be.

He dragged the man into the bushes and climbed back into the rocks. He saw then that he couldn't risk shooting from there, because the men were positioned between him and Joan. They were standing in front of her. If he shot either man the bullets might glance off a bone and hit her. The one hundred and eighty grain lead-tipped Winchester bullets were designed for fragmenting inside the body of an elk or a moose.

There was no time left. They had tied her hands to a branch over her head, and were about to cut off her swimsuit.

Thor shouted in a generic voice "Hey guys! Come quick! He's getting away!"

The music was so loud and they were so drunk they didn't recognize the unfamiliar voice. They only heard an indistinct male voice that sounded like their companion calling for them.

"What?" the short man called out, his brow furrowed.

"Over here!" responded Thor, in a muffled voice.

The two men started down the canyon, revolvers in hand, calling their companion's name.

"Lucas! Hey Lucas! Where you at?"

Thor dropped into some sagebrush where he could not be seen and yet where he would have a full view of the upper canyon. He lay down and prepared himself for what he had to do. He could hear a dove calling in the cottonwoods and the blue shadows on the canyon walls were lengthening, but the upper canyon was still as hot as the air over a flame. He smelled the sharp astringent scent of the sagebrush all around him and he could see bits and pieces of the men now through the green leaves as they came down the canyon. They were about fifteen feet apart, each on a different side of the trail. They both had revolvers. He was waiting until the short man reached the sunlit place and he would have a clear shot. He would shoot him first and then he would shoot the other one. He had the chest of the first one in his sights now and he could feel his heart thumping against the sand and the ants crawling up the side of his face. He could hear Joan calling "Dad are you ok?" and when the short man stepped into the light and turned to the other man and opened his mouth and said "That bitch just listen to her" Thor began shooting.

Part III

Navajo Mountain

IN THE DESERT ALL TRAILS eventually lead to the mountains. They beckon to us from afar and rise with prominence from a flat country. They offer a ladder to the sky and a vision of the world below. When they speak it is always in the language of metaphor. They are older than the rivers, and they are covered with the scars of their antiquity. They are eminences before they are anything else, and in the deepest sense of that word. Like each person, each mountain is different, and has its own unique personality and presence. Some are grave and foreboding, and loom over the landscape with steep slopes and severe angles. One thinks of the San Francisco Peaks above Flagstaff. Others are less heavy and solemn in their lines, and present a milder aspect. Sleeping Ute Mountain is like that. Some are beautiful—as with Mount Tukunikivats—and others are nondescript—the Kaibab Mountains. In the Red Rock Desert most of the peaks are part of ranges—the Henrys, the La Sals, the Blues. They live in groups that resemble families. They enjoy the intimate company of their immediate surroundings and, looking up at them, you can identify family members by their various characteristics. These are communities that quietly endure for millions of years.

Navajo Mountain is located at the center of the desert. It is the hub. The other desert peaks are connected by invisible spokes to Navajo Mountain. Everything in the region turns around it. The Navajo have long known this, and regard the mountain as one of their sacred summits. The mountain can be seen as far north as Muley Point overlooking the San Juan River. It rises on the horizon like the end of your thumb if your thumb was colored a pale violet blue. It can also be viewed from State Route 98 east of Kaibito. There the mountain resembles a gray-blue turtle. If you stare at it long enough, in the vibrating shimmer of heat, it becomes an enormous desert tortoise. You can see the wrinkled neck, the antiquarian-like eyes, the bulky weathered shell, the clawed reptilian feet straining to break free of the earth. You blink and the mirage loses its effect. At Page the mountain rises in the redrock country east of town like a recumbent breast. Navajo Mountain can also be seen from the canyon behind Rainbow Bridge. There it looks like a loaf of blue Navajo cornbread.

Approaching Navajo Mountain from a highway to the south, I see the mass rising without peer from the surrounding countryside. It comprises the aesthetic heart of the country—one senses that immediately. It singularly commands the attention of anyone and everyone on the lower desert. The spirit is as naturally drawn to the mountain as the body is to a waterhole. Fifteen miles from the highway, traveling now on a little-known reservation road, the pavement is left behind and the surface steadily deteriorates. Switchbacks follow, scattered rocks and gravel, and then the road straightens out, at least for awhile—a brief respite before the really bad part certain to be waiting ahead. Every backroad has its really bad part, especially every backroad to anyplace worth seeing. Gradually the road winds its way across an extensive mesa and valley country, the surrounding mesas covered with pinyon and juniper. Everywhere there are acres and acres of rabbitbrush. The plain is covered with ragged yellow blossoms. If these flowers were gold, the Navajo would be the wealthiest people on earth.

But they are not.

Twice I see the local residents walking on the side of the road, and twice I offer them rides, but they decline, saying they are just going up to their neighbors. The men wear cowboy hats and jeans and plaid shirts and cowboy boots and the women wear long satin dresses and shining velveteen blouses. They walk slowly with great dignity and I think of T. C. Cannon's painting *Mom and Dad Have the Going Home to Shiprock Blues.*

Navajo Mountain looms larger now, and its appearance does not soften at close proximity. The gentle aspect was an illusion, as is often the case. The flanks are covered with talus rock slides and hanging coniferous forests. All around the base are stony buttresses that arch toward the top of the mountain.

Several more miles of sun-baked desert and wind-blown dust and I reach the end of the road. A road-grader is pulled over to one side, having apparently died on this stretch. I get out and walk, onward and upward into the heights, following the jeep trail the Navajo have built to their radio transmitting towers. Eventually I detect a short cut to the top and set out on foot up a talus slide. The rocks range in size from a little one the size of a television set to larger specimens the size of an automobile. The route is precipitous, set at an angle of fifty or sixty degrees, and is guaranteed to help you shed a few pounds, even if you don't need to. Shortly the pinyon and juniper are left behind, and I enter the zone of the ponderosas. These are lovely trees, and scent the air with their sap. Squirrels chatter, birds sing, mountain flowers blossom. Interesting rocks, primarily of volcanic origin, present themselves. I press on, not inclined to stop or be distracted, drawn to the summit. One climbs, or at least I climb, not to conquer—only a novice to the faith would phrase it that way—but to be conquered, to be humbled, to be in the presence of an entity that invigorates and inspires even as it exhausts.

I travel carefully, for I am far from any formal trail and navigating only by line of sight and no one knows that I am here. This is where the hiker exercises caution; if you fall, you may not be found until your child is a grandparent, if then.

The major challenge are the thick patches of wild rose. This is a diabolical plant, each branch covered with hundreds of thorns. They catch on your jeans, your shirt, your hands. One false move, and I'll be in a scene from a science fiction movie, drawn into the mother plant, awash in blood, tingling with pain.

I press on, using what was once a short aspen tree as both a walking stick and a wild rose deflector.

Gradually the annoying rose zone is left behind. We enter—my walking stick and I—the world of spruce and fir. We are nearing the heights of 10,388-foot Navajo Mountain. After an hour and a half of steady scrambling and sweating, I take a short break and prepare myself for the final assault. The loyal stick is discarded. I briefly take in the view—but only for a moment, as it will be much more complete from the top.

Onward and upward, through the rocks, sometimes backtracking and trying an alternative route, pausing at times to catch my breath, always alert for rattlesnakes, never making the mistake of sitting down, ignoring the blisters.

Higher now, the summit within reach.

False summits, several of them, the top playing hard to get, and then finally a staggering out on what must be the highest ground. I scan the horizon and confirm that, yes, there is no higher point in sight. This rolling open country among the trees, indeed, is the rather broad and extensive summit of Navajo Mountain.

The first order of business is to sit down, more like collapse, and take a restorative drink of water.

A little later I wander west along the ridge and discover that the view, as I had always hoped, is wonderful. The whole lower desert country is visible, spread before me as on a map. Places that I have known for years are now identified and located in their larger context—canyons, mesas, cliffs, buttes, forests, wandering dry washes, various rivers, standing rocks. Most prominent is Lake Powell, the cobalt blue water inching up into every side canyon for one hundred miles. North and east is the deep cut of the San Juan River and, nearby, the Escalante Country where Everett Ruess—the John Muir of the Red Rock Desert—disappeared in 1934. To the west is the long blue rise of the Kaiparowits Plateau. Southwest are the Vermillion Cliffs and the Paria Plateau, the country where Clint Eastwood filmed himself as the Outlaw Josey Wales. Somewhere in the red rock directly below my feet is Rainbow Bridge and the surrounding canyons where the Navajo hid from Colonel Kit Carson, who is either a war criminal or a national hero depending on with whom you talk. Due south is endless sun-baked desert, with scattered mesas and mountains rising like islands—the Kaibito Plateau and Black Mesa, Ward Terrace and the Moenkopi Plateau of the Hopi Reservation. There are villages and placenames on that land from another language, another culture, another cosmology: Kykotsmoui, Shugopavi, Mishongnovi, Secakulu. There are a people who still practice the old ways, of planting melons and corn, and hunting the deer, and listening to the tales of Coyote and Raven.

On the mountaintop I see again what I have glimpsed before—that the fullness and the clarity of the vision on a summit leads either to faith or heresy. Here is the home of lightning and thunder, causality and free will. Nothing here is bound to render any form of mercy. You remember that Prometheus was bound to a rock in the Caucasus, his reward for having brought fire to the human race, and that his nemesis Zeus dwelled on Olympus, and that people do not live on mountaintops because they would likely be killed by nature if they tried.

An hour passes, two hours pass, and it seems, in that radiance, a Blakean moment.

The sun has crossed the meridian and is sinking to the west.

I turn to leave, but then pause.

One always searches for something to carry away from a summit. Once I came upon the carcass of a golden eagle—only the feathers and bones remained. Another time I found the skull of a bighorn sheep, the rings on the horns indicating the ram was fourteen years old. A few years later I discovered a ten thousand year old vision quest site in Rocky Mountain National Park—the government archaeologists subsequently took that place apart with tweezers and flat trowels. I have spent much time in the western peaks, wandering around, looking for whatever treasures and treats persistent curiosity and random chance might reveal. Sometimes you find nothing. In fact, most times you find nothing. But about once every decade, hiking steadily every summer, you happen upon the unexpected.

The older I become, the less inclined I am to search for things, in the sense of material objects, and the more interested I have become in establishing facts, distinguishing subtle but significant differences, identifying truths, finding connections, apprehending patterns. Half a century after the heretic pharaoh Amenhotep invented the idea of monotheism, Moses, the adopted but estranged son of Rameses, climbed a mountain in the Sinai desert and returned with ten principles to live by. Whether from a divine encounter or not is impossible to determine, perhaps even irrelevant. What we do know is that, after a period of reflection, he descended from the arid heights with a set of truths that have endured for thirty-three centuries. Over the years I have often thought we should add an eleventh. On Navajo Mountain, in the brilliant rays of an August sun, I considered one way to phrase it: "Thou shalt not harm the earth, or any other world on which you live."

Superstition is cowardice in the face of the divine, of course, and I do not embrace anything that does not pass the sixth grade reality test, but the fact remains that goodness is a mystery, and evil is everywhere. If we describe the world in terms of these things, a world that has a long and brutish history, then we eventually reach the ultimate paradox—the light that is clothed in darkness. Unless we have been misled by the philosophers, there seems to be such a thing as grace, and the life well lived. We each move as best we can toward that. With those thoughts and little more I descend from the mountain that stands alone—as I do—in the center of a desert, forever the outsider, not connected to any other range, a solitary peak that rises toward an ever-changing sky.

Navajo Mountain has a spirit. I felt it that day. If the mountain revealed one certainty, it is that time is not endless and that nothing is made in earnest. If the choice is between either being bewildered or saddened, then I will turn from the void each time. Resolutions, revolutions, revelations. Life is full of them. Sometimes, though, it is enough to climb a mountain, and to praise it.

The Dead

SHE LOVED THIS TIME OF THE YEAR and it would have been good to be home except for what they had gathered to discuss. The peach orchards were all in blossom. They had reached their peak the day before. Every tree was covered with a light cloud of pink flowers. There were hundreds and thousands of flowers, and whenever the breeze blew through the house it brought with it the lingering grace of a sweet fragrance. In a day or two the petals would begin to fall, but for now the trees were in their glory. Honeybees were everywhere, and the warblers and vireos were singing from their nests high in the branches. In the morning the birds in the valley were so loud that they woke people up an hour before the sun rose.

But it was hard to be disturbed at such a beautiful music, and so everyone rose in good spirits, knowing that they lived in a special place.

When the petals fell they would drop quickly, like the leaves in the fall, and the ground would be covered with a layer of soft pink that would soon melt into the green. The petals would be on the earth, but like certain other fallen things—the feathers of birds, the snow—they would seem not really a part of the earth. Wildflowers grew there, in the radiant shade of the trees, flowers such as the lavender verbena and the white anemone. The tiger swallowtails loved these flowers. Out along the irrigation ditches the yellow desert marigolds flourished and they gave off a fine powdery scent and down by the grassy banks of the Colorado River there were whole banks of color where the orange globemallow and the violet-blue irises grew. Her favorite were the stream orchids, tiny unexpected lanterns that brightened a delicate world close to the ground. When Gretchen was a little girl she thought there were a fairy people who lived there in the grass among them, and touching the flowers she felt in possession of a wonderful secret all day.

The argument was now in its second hour. During the first hour, the oldest sister, Carol, had raised her voice twice, and so had Gretchen, the youngest daughter. A book had been thrown against the wall and a middle finger had been raised and the "f" word had been used several times. The middle sister named Lois had tried to mediate between the two ancient adversaries and had met with uneven results. They were assembled at the dining table to discuss the fate of the three hundred and sixty acre farm they now owned. Two months earlier their parents had been killed in an automobile accident in the resort town of Winter Garden, Florida. No one was prepared for the event—their departure was not supposed to occur for twenty or thirty years. Now it had arrived, though, and it was a fact, like a new-born baby or a marriage, a court summons or a draft notice, that could not be ignored.

The lawyer from Salt Lake City had come and gone, explaining the curious world of state and federal estate taxes to them, and they had read the letter from the Nature Conservancy stating that although the property had scenic value, it supported no "at-risk" species and was not an essential wetland area and therefore was unfortunately not a tract in which they would have any preservation interest. The discussion then moved to an offer on the table from a businessman named Gilbert Whitehead in Plano, Texas, who was offering them ten thousand dollars per acre. He was a professional developer who intended to subdivide the land into one-acre lots and build an exclusive subdivision for the local gentry and for those with money from elsewhere who were looking for a comfortable place in the desert. He would sell the lots for prices ranging from fifteen thousand to twenty thousand dollars, and he would make a profit there, as well as in the mark-up on the houses his firm would construct. The trees would all be cut down—all fourteen thousand of them—and wood-frame homes would be raised on the lots and a strange people would come to live on the farm.

These new residents would know nothing of the land, and there would be no memory on it of the old peach trees with crutches under their sagging branches, or of the grape arbors with tender green sprouts among the gnarled branches, or of the cottonwood trees in which the magpies and the gray squirrels lived. The deer and the elk would not winter in the pastures anymore. The songbirds would be killed off by the house cats and the free-ranging dogs would run the rabbits and the fawns and the elk calves to death. Diesel trucks would come every few weeks and empty the septic tanks, and the truck radios would blare the angry and forlorn music of the underclass across the valley. Eventually the home owners would learn that the valley was, in fact, a desert, and that it was too hot for people in the summer. They would also discover that there were no jobs in the area at all, and that the valley was as boring as an art museum. They would sell their houses and move elsewhere. The houses would remain, though, and many would come to be owned by people who left them empty for most of the year. What had been a lovely farm that travelers would stop and photograph along the side of the scenic state road west of Fisher Towers would become just another Southwestern ghost community.

It was, for Gretchen, a possibility too horrible to contemplate.

The older daughter Carol was staring at Gretchen as they sat on opposite sides of the dining table and she wished for a moment that it had been Gretchen who had been killed in the car accident and not her parents. She felt guilty about that thought, but that was the way it was. Carol lived in a dark place thick with regret and she had always secretly hated Gretchen because Gretchen was the only naturally born child. Both of the first two children had been adopted. Gretchen had come along as a happy accident, after her parents had given up on conceiving their own child. Carol and Lois felt that her parents had always preferred Gretchen. For one thing, Gretchen was a physical version of her mother—tall and thin and dark-haired—while the other two—who had the same mother but different fathers—were both short and brown haired and heavy boned. For another, Gretchen had more of her parents' calm and generous spirit. These were facts that were difficult to ignore, even among the most loving and well-intentioned of people. Carol and Lois had both married right after high school to local working men. Gretchen had gone off to college in California. She had never married and was an artist in Sedona. She had a studio and was successful at what she did.

"You know," said Carol. "It's easy for you to pass on this offer. You lead this carefree existence as an artist and you have independent means."

"I'm not rich."

"But you don't have bills like we do. We have children. We have college to think about. Do you know how expensive that is?"

"That was the choice you made when you two decided to marry Al and Roger and have children."

"Anyway you look at it, life is easy for you compared to us."

"No it's not. I work like anyone else."

"The way I see it," said the middle daughter. "We really don't have a choice. I mean, where are we going to get the money to pay the estate taxes? Three hundred thousand dollars is a lot of money."

"Like I said before, we could take out a mortgage," Gretchen said.

"Alright, but what if we have a bad year with the peaches?" Carol said, "And we can't make the payment on the note. Then what?"

There was a silence.

"The bank would work with us," said Gretchen. "After all, we've banked with them for fifty-three years."

"Maybe we could try a different compromise," suggested Lois, who had already argued unsuccessfully for a partial sale of the land. "Maybe we could go ahead and take out the loan and then if things got bad we could sell. Put off a decision for now."

"But would we get an offer like this again?" asked Carol.

"Even if we did," said Gretchen, "Why would we want to even consider it? The rest of the valley is all either public land or conservation easement. A subdivision here would ruin the whole place."

"Who cares?" exclaimed Carol, "If you want a farm so bad, go buy a farm somewhere else. It's only land."

There was a knock on the door and it was Carol's husband Al. Gretchen's face became red and she reminded the other two sisters that she had insisted that there would be no husbands. That wasn't fair. Then they would be ganging up on her like they did when they were little. She had taken that crap when she was little but she wasn't afraid of them anymore and she wouldn't stand for it. She would leave if he came in and then they would never get the third signature they needed on any kind of agreement.

The husband got in his car and drove away.

"You know," said Carol, "He just wanted to know how things were going. You didn't have to be so mean."

Gretchen knew he was a parasite just waiting for his wife's inheritance. He would then likely divorce her and take half of everything. He was the worst kind of human being. She had no respect for him. She was so mad she knew it was best to say nothing.

There was another knock on the door and Gretchen got up, ready to tell the husband Al off but it was Ramon Pacheco, one of the field workers that came up every year from Hermosillo in the state of Sonora. They were opening the head gates and flooding the hay meadows. The family had twenty acres in alfalfa down by the river and they got two tons of hay per acre, which they used to feed the riding horses and her father's longhorns in the winter. The man wanted to know where the boards for the side gates were and she told him where to find them. She spoke to him in an easy, fluent Spanish and as he walked away she wished that she was off working in the fields instead of trapped in the house.

It was quiet in the dining room. Carol had gone into the kitchen to make more coffee and Lois was reading through the proposal again, looking for something perhaps she hadn't seen before. Carol brought in the coffee and she and Lois began talking again. Gretchen was not really listening. She was looking at her parents' wedding photograph on the table beside the picture window. There was Grandma Claire and Grandpa Virgil and her parents Lee and Roslyn at the church in Grand Junction where her father had met her mother in a bible study class. It was a long time ago and they were smiling and everyone looked young. They were all dead now and she realized that she had to speak for them. If they were here they would be saying exactly what she was saying, and her sisters would have to listen to them. The land was what made them different from other people. It had to somehow stay in the family.

She lifted her eyes from the picture to the fields beyond the window where the workers were already placing the boards at the side gates. The boards created a series of miniature dams, which spread the water evenly out across the fields. The hay fields would be green in a week. Beyond the fields was the river, slow and brown and muscular, and beyond that were the red sandstone cliffs, streaked here and there with desert varnish. Above it all was the blue sky. There were clouds in the sky, and they were drifting in lazy shapes.

"So Gretchen, I'm asking you. What difference does it make?" asked Carol.

Gretchen said nothing.

"Gretchen, are you listening to me?"

"Yes, you said 'What difference does it make?'"

A Very Long Time Ago

HE WAS EIGHTEEN YEARS OLD and did not own an automobile and so he took a Continental Trailways bus from Denver to Grand Junction and then hitched a ride on a delivery truck for the last one hundred and thirty miles. At Dry Creek Basin, a windswept crossroads in a wide and waterless sagebrush valley, he met his new boss, Clyde Graves. Clyde lived with his wife Gladys and their twelve-year-old son Daryl in a log-cabin home, the first floor of which was a combination grocery, restaurant, liquor store, natural history museum, taxidermy studio, lending library, pawn shop, indoor cactus garden, and Navajo art gallery. Clyde was employed by a man named Grant Wood, who pretty much owned the western half of San Miguel County and flew around in a single-engine Piper Supercub, landing wherever he pleased—new-mown fields, mesa tops, the middle of the road.

The young man's job in the Basin was to guard North Mountain, Grant Wood's private hunting preserve, from local poachers. Not the mountain, of course, for it was too large to be stolen, but the resident deer and elk. For this task he was provided with a fifteen-hand Appaloosa named X-Ray and a 1949 Willy's jeep, to be used on alternating days. He soon learned the assignment was impossible. North Mountain and its associated terrain sprawled over forty-five square miles. Additionally, most of the poaching occurred at night, when he was asleep. He also soon learned that he was not entirely unsympathetic with the locals, who were for the most part just trying to feed their families. He had read a short story in high school entitled "How much land does one man need?" and he now understood Tolstoi's point.

During the day he ranged all over the country. It was a vast landscape, with aspen and spruce in the highlands and pinyon groves down lower and then the coyote desert and the red rock canyons. There were wild horses in Disappointment Valley, and bald eagles wintering in the breaks along Dry Creek and every so often someone would spot a mountain lion track in the snow. On his backcountry patrols, which often took him to the top of the mountain, he enjoyed the quiet grace of the land and the panoramic views. Toward the east was Lone Cone, an extinct volcano, and to the west, across the Dolores River, were the La Sal Mountains. On a clear day the Henry Mountains were also visible, stretching in a pale blue wave from north to south.

On his off days he would drive around the desert and become acquainted with the people. He had grown up in the city and had never met people like them before. There were Augustine and Vermeil, the Basque sheepherders who lived in an old line cabin in the purple sage at the base of Pony Draw. They conversed in a language older than Spanish and kept a collection of bear skulls on their propane tank. On the back side of Hamilton Mesa there was the Navajo woman Lucy Blue who made sandpaintings that she sold for ten and twenty dollars, depending on the size, in Clyde's art gallery. She had no contact with anyone in her family down in Klagetoh because she had married a man from the Sky City on the Acoma Reservation. And there was Lester Burnett who lived in a cave with a wooden door beside his uranium claim on Bull Canyon. He sold his yellow cake once a year to the government buyer in Nucla and then went to Las Vegas for a week. That was his entire life, other than his son the veteran and daughter-in-law who lived in a tepee with an upside-down American flag somewhere near Paradox Valley.

And there was Duffy.

No one knew his last name. His age was somewhere between fifty and sixty, most likely, although for that matter he could have been a very poorly aged forty. He had perhaps ten or eleven functional teeth—most of the others had been pulled out with vice-grips by himself or his best friend Ray Niederhaus. He was as short as the gas pump in front of Clyde's store, as strong as a tow cable, as indestructible as a cinch ring. When he smiled, and he smiled often, you saw his philosophy of life: grin and bear it. He lived in a coal-heated cabin at the far end of Big Gypsum Valley, feeding the cattle, deer, elk, antelope, and wild horses from the back of his pickup truck. He would care for anything that came to his door: a red-tailed hawk that had lost its ability to fly after landing on a power line, a pine squirrel that had reluctantly surrendered most of its tail to a gray fox, a blind prairie dog that had somehow survived a rattlesnake bite. It was a lonely impoverished life and every Saturday night he would drive into Dry Creek Basin and buy a six pack of beer for the local teenagers. One Saturday night in January a couple of the kids borrowed Clyde Graves' snowmobile and shot out across the desert under the stars. A few minutes later they ran into an ore truck from one of the vanadium mines and both were decapitated.

Not long after that Duffy showed up at the young man's residence, which was a converted tack room in a barn to the extreme rear of Clyde's property. Duffy needed someone he could trust and he knew he couldn't trust anyone in the country except his best friend Ray Niederhaus who was moving Grant's longhorns to the other side of the Dolores and perhaps this new kid with the honest face who had come from another place far away.

He explained what had happened and asked the young man if he could spend the night. He couldn't return to his cabin because the deputy sheriff was looking for him and he had left his horse Big Mac at the bottom of an arroyo to the west. The horse could not be seen from the road and would be out of the cold wind that was blowing across the land. He would die if they sent him to prison, he said. He would not have his animals or his open spaces and he would die. He would die an awful death. He talked half the night and finally fell asleep in the middle of a sentence while sitting on the floor with his little dog Junior.

The next morning around six-thirty Ray Niederhaus showed up on horseback having followed Duffy's tracks on the snow. It was awhile before Ray could talk because he had been riding into the wind. He moved slowly and sat on an orange crate next to the coal-burning stove. When he took his cowboy hat off there was a sharp line where the skin was brick red below and pale white above. He never straightened his back, even when he was indoors, because he had been hurt once while working as a stunt double in *The Searchers*. Ray finally was warm enough to talk and he related a new development. There was a boy in the Basin named Eric Houtchens and Eric was secretly engaged to one of the victims, Jolene Terry. After Eric learned the news he went to the storage shed behind his father's house and chose one of the worst ways to leave this world—a few gulps of fertilizer. His father, Preston, had tried in vain to save his son's life by sucking the caustic liquid from the boy's mouth, and had nearly destroyed his own lips and mouth in the process.

The three men, two with silver in their hair and the other still with the face of a boy, then had a long talk about what should be done. After awhile the course of action became clear. All the world would ever know was that the man with no last name who had always asked to be paid in cash and showed kindness to any living thing that came to his doorstep had disappeared like a piece of paper you see blowing by on a windy day. You reach out to grasp it and then it is gone and it is all you can do to keep your hat on your head.

The Woman Who Came
with the Spring

i.

THEY HAD DRIVEN FOR A WEEK. Driven steadily west and north from
Artesia, Alabama. Followed the blacktops wet with spring rain across the
gloomy pitch pine country of Mississippi and over the great mile-long
bridge and through the hilly brown oak woods of Arkansas and then finally out beneath the broad blue sky of Oklahoma. They had stayed at
private campgrounds or in state park campgrounds where the father and
the slow-minded son slept in the half-dome tent that carried with it forever the memory of freshwater bass, and the mother and the three daughters, the two identical red-haired twins and the older blond daughter,
slept on mattresses in the Dodge van. After one hundred and forty-three
planting seasons in Chickasaw County, the Dixon family, or what remained of it, had surprised no one and everyone and picked up and left.
Six generations of Dixons laid to rest in the cemetery, and that antique
statue to Captain Willard Dixon, C.S.A., charging on his bronze horse
through the city square, and they finally left. What choice was there? First
Senator Quintan Shelilah collapsed and died while reading a statement
about the international peace-keeping force in the Balkans into the Congressional Record at the age of ninety-seven. After a decent interval the
Department of Defense quietly closed Davis Air Force Base, causing a
third of the residents of Chickasaw County to become unemployed. A
month later Hurricane Beryl boiled up from the Gulf and destroyed the
new school and the old school and even the historic pioneer school. Then
there were the late autumn floods that washed away the paper mill and
the covered bridge everyone depended on to get to Mobile without taking the hundred-mile coastal route through the Florida panhandle. Worst
of all was the tornado. It was the tornado on that Sunday morning when
everyone was in church singing God's praises that did it, lifting the

Dixon's two-story wood frame home across Pumpkinseed Creek and dumping it in the middle of a neighbor's cow pasture, upside down and crumpled like a toy a child has grown bored with.

That is what they felt like—a toy in the hands of something no longer disposed to kindness or mercy. For the first time the Dixons questioned their faith. It was a question of faith, really, a faith that the upheavals of two centuries had not shaken. At one point that strangely calm and sunny afternoon, picking among the drenched remains of what had been the center of their world, Donna, the wife and mother, actually hurled the family Bible with a curse across the field, where it was thoroughly examined by fire ants for an hour in the grass, until she felt guilty and cleaned it off and placed it in her broken suitcase with what remained of her best handmade clothes.

There was no insurance on the house and the bank had filed papers to take possession of the heavily mortgaged property and so the Dixons salvaged what they could from the ruined pile of lumber and carpet and rusted pipes and twisted electrical conduit and filled a horse trailer and drop-bolted it to the trailer hitch of their nine-year-old Dodge van with 160,000 miles on it and, one foggy cold morning in mid-March, started west, where no Dixon had ever gone before. For years they had heard about Arizona, where Rufus Crippen (who was not a physician but had been called Doc ever since he kept records for the high school football team) claimed that the fishing was like the fishing must have been in Alabama when Hernando de Soto passed through, where Hardin Barksdale at the feed store said there were deer and elk and lions and bears in the high mountains, and wild turkeys in the oakbrush, and where the knowledgeable commentator on CNN flatly stated there were jobs in the robust state economy for all who wanted to work.

For one entire day now they had been driving across New Mexico. There were no trees, except what they saw far off, scattered wide and thin along the watercourses that carried not running water but upon closer inspection only clean washed sand. It was a dry vacant wind-blown land, with the flat shriveled pads of prickly pear cactus and the spiked bayonets of the yucca and the bittersweet-smelling sagebrush, a country unlike any they had ever seen, or imagined, and none of them liked it much. That was the sole point, amidst frequent bickering, upon which the six

occupants of the van could unanimously concur. They missed the familiar green trees, the comfortable intimate feeling of being surrounded by
friendly woods, of being presented with a view at best to the next hill, or
down the valley a ways, and no further. They missed the daily rains that
cleansed the air and washed the leaves and filled the pig troughs and bird
baths and the places where the peeper frogs lived. They missed the stately
live oaks draped with Spanish moss and supporting various hammocks and
swings and climbing ropes. This new country was nothing like back home,
and its spaciousness and dryness and emptiness made them feel small and
vulnerable and each of them missed home and wanted to return, but there
was no future for them on the other side of the big river, and so they drove
on towards the place where the sun was setting. Sometime after three they
passed a road sign welcoming them to Arizona the Grand Canyon State
and the twin seven-year-old girls and their brother clapped and yelled, hoping to cheer their parents who had only moments before agreed it was best
not to speak for one hour so as not to further upset the children.

Polite conversation resumed in a subdued manner after this and one of
the twins said she had to use the bathroom and so they pulled over at a
truck stop in Sanders, twenty miles farther down the road. The older
daughter, who would have been in her second semester of college had life
been more reasonable, stepped out to stretch her legs, noticed a quarter
sparkling on the asphalt and went into the convenience store to buy a
newspaper. When the clerk was not looking she slipped a *People* magazine
into the pages of the classified ad section and as she walked back to the
van a truck driver with silver-toed cowboy boots standing by his rig smiled
at her and she smiled back. She was tall and broad shouldered, with fine
legs and hips that swelled in a Matisse curve and a chest she carried with
her swimmer's shoulders held back. Her hair was straight and blond and
fell to her collarbones and looking at the parents the trucker wondered if
it was genetically possible that such a woman could come from such
parents. In fact, Megan had known since she was a little girl that her father
was not Lester Dixon, but was a Navy pilot who had been assigned as an
instructor to the Davis Air Force Base for six weeks in the summer of 1978.
The young lieutenant had met her mother in the officers' club where she
worked as a hostess, and later at several other quiet places around Artesia,
and after Lester arrived at the front gate one night demanding justice the

pilot was transferred back to Pensacola. For years Lester had confronted his wife over this matter every time he got drunk, but then he had found religion and changed his ways and began to realize that this source of discontent might at some later time prove valuable to the Dixon family. Gradually a truce was reached—not the sort of solemn covenant drawn up by diplomats and signed at a public ceremony in a medieval castle, but the sort of informal agreement that time produces of its own logic and according to its own leisurely schedule. The Dixons may have been poor, but they were possessed of a beautiful daughter, and even the father understood that in this world such a gift can bring good fortune.

They were driving on Interstate 40 now a few hundred yards north of the humble trickle that was the Little Colorado River. The father had the map spread over the steering wheel and the wife told him to be careful of the truck traffic, which was heavier than in New Mexico where they had driven once for twenty-two minutes, listening to a radio minister in Tucumcari relate the story of Absalom in a soft mesmerizing storytelling voice, and not seen another vehicle.

At a desolate windblown exit eighteen miles west of Winslow, Lester turned south and his wife asked him what he was doing. He said that he wanted to see the world's largest meteor crater. His wife Donna reminded him of his promise that she and the girls would be able to stay at least one night in a decent motel before arriving in Flagstaff, so that they could properly bathe. He said that one night more of camping wouldn't kill them. A terrible fight ensued and the older daughter put her hands over her ears and stared out the window at the pronghorn antelope feeding on what grass could be found.

"Look!" she shouted.

Her parents followed her gaze and the dusty van and trailer slowed and there was a discussion about whether they were deer or antelope and finally it was decided they could not be deer because deer were not colored that way. So these cream and tan creatures with the odd black horns must be antelope. The Dixons had not seen antelope before and so they watched the herd for awhile. The animals were colored like African gazelles and had tiny fragile bodies and impossibly thin legs built for escaping the cheetahs that had once shared the grasslands with them during the Ice Age. The father resumed driving and said that they were only

an hour from Flagstaff but that he didn't want to arrive in Flagstaff at
nightfall. He liked to arrive in a city in the morning. At night the trav-
eler was at a disadvantage because the motels all were charging double
what they had ten hours earlier. Tomorrow night Donna would have her
bath. Lester Dixon began to look for a place to camp. He drove past the
turnoff to the crater—the country now as broad and flat and featureless
as a billiard table—and after a few miles spotted a lonely gravel road heading southeast. He turned onto this nameless side road, the van and trailer
pulling a rooster-tail of dust that dissipated quickly in the chinook that
was blowing with considerable strength from the snowy mountains.

After two miles a sign said they were entering public land, Kit Carson
National Grasslands, and should close the gates behind them. The road
was transit straight and there were windmills every half mile, drawing
water from what remained of the aquifer to rusted stock tanks. On one
tank they saw an immature bald eagle with a dirty white hood, and as
they watched the eagle flew off heavily toward what appeared to be a distant prairie dog village. Another six miles farther the gravel road dead-
ended on a bench above a broad dry streambed. There were gray-barked
cottonwoods along the banks of the stream, which was not straight but
moved over the earth like a prairie rattlesnake advancing slowly across
warm sand. A hundred yards east of the turnaround was the burned out
hulk of an adobe home where a family had lived before the Dust Bowl.

Lester drove down the grassy track to the abandoned homestead and
parked around back, so that they would not be visible from the main
road, such as it was. Here the Dixons would be hidden and out of the
way and able to sleep without disturbance for the night. He turned the
hound loose and stepped from the van and stretched and told everyone
they should really get out and see this fine new country, which was different from the Pecos Valley where they had stayed the night before.
He was happy to finally be on public land, where they could camp for
free. There was not much public land in Alabama, and he knew from
the maps that half the state of Arizona was public land. He liked that
idea, having recently lost his own parcel and not having any prospects to
ever have a piece of earth like that again. Here at least he could have the
feel of owning a lot of land. The women began to prepare camp and he
told his son to go down to the streambed and bring back some firewood

because there was no more propane in the propane cooking stove. He walked over to the adobe house and studied the walls that were made of earthen bricks and were two feet thick. He had never seen a home constructed in such a way and marveled at its durability.

"Just think," he shouted to his wife. "During the homesteading era everything around here was for free. A man staked his claim and started plowing. God those must have been the days."

In his mind he was thinking that it would not be much work to put a roof on this old homestead, and then raise a floor. Windows could be refitted to the casements and the fireplace could be cleaned out and the resident bats sent flying. Rooms could be framed and walled in and insulation laid under the roof. The well outside could be redrilled and made to pump water enough for the house and the garden. There would be no telephone, no electricity, but there could be kerosene lamps and telephones were a nuisance anyway. The fortress-like walls would keep the house warm in the winter and cool in the summer. That was the whole point of such walls in such a climate, he could see, and if he wanted more additions he could just build a mud pit and make more bricks from the earth in the front yard. Set the bricks in the sun for a few days and let them dry and then raise more walls. With a little work, Lester was thinking, a family could comfortably live in such a place.

"This land is worthless, Lester." Donna had read her husband's every thought as all wives can and laughed mockingly at him as she carried the cardboard boxes from the van to clear an area for sleeping. "This land'll be empty til Jesus comes again. A mouse would starve on this land. The worst land in Alabama is a hundred times richer than this. And you said Arizona was—"

"Don't start."

"If we had only listened to my sister. "

He turned from the wall to face her. He was a man of medium height who from the upright way he stood appeared taller, a sturdy man whose body was all honest muscle, with hands grown thick from milking cows, and forearms that were like hard tree branches from swinging an axe over a woodpile day after day. His black hair was cut military short and he had no gray at forty-two and his face was permanently sunburned from having worked outside all his life. It was a happy face, even if it was a

dull face. He stared at his wife but did not see a red-haired woman who was still slender and attractive at thirty-nine, who was his companion on the journey, and the mother of his children, but saw rather an annoying burden, a chronic nuisance, god's punishment on him for something he had done in a previous life.

"Your sister. Your sister. Always your sister. Wait til you see mountains higher than the clouds, Donna. Wait til you see waterfalls the height of a church steeple. Wait til you see canyons so deep it takes a rock five minutes to reach the bottom. Wait til you see herds of wild horses running free on the range and a bull elk with antlers out to here and mountain lakes full of fish. Then you'll be singing a different song."

"Clouds is right. You've got your head lost in the clouds."

"Better than having it stuck up my ass."

"What did you say?"

He thought for a moment.

"Better get supper ready fast."

"I thought so."

After a simple dinner that did away with the last of the ground beef and the canned potatoes and carrots Lester saw what appeared to be an official sign nailed to a couple of four by four posts just down the hill. He and the son, whose name was Adam, walked over with the dog to have a look.

It was to his surprise an historical marker, a weathered wooden plaque erected by the Arizona Historical Society, according to the sign, through a private endowment in 1936. Lester and his son stood in front of the sixty-year-old wooden sign that was overgrown with morning-glory vines and the father read it aloud as his son pulled the dead vines and dried tendrils away.

Dry Creek Massacre Site

On November 29, 1864, there stood on this location an encampment of over 100 Navajo Indians, the site established by order of the U.S. Army Commander at Fort Defiance. Early that morning the Navajo awoke and saw the camp was surrounded by the mounted soldiers of the New Mexico Volunteers, led by Colonel Kit Carson. The Navajo hoisted an American flag and a white surrender flag to convey that the camp was peaceful. Ignoring this signal, Carson ordered his troops to attack the unarmed Indians. When the attack was over forty-three Indians, mostly women and children, lay

dead. The attack was denounced in congressional hearings, but none of the
participants were ever held accountable for what they did.

Adam asked what that meant and Lester tried to put it into simple terms
for him. When Lester and Adam returned with melancholy faces to the
campfire they explained about the sign and so the mother and daughters
hurried over to read it for themselves in the last light. There followed a general agreement about how the Dixons had no reason to feel sorry for themselves when others had suffered so much more. The family actually felt
somewhat better to know life could be far worse and the father led a prayer.
After the sun went down the wind died and the air grew calm. One by one
the stars came out and they sat around the fire and watched the flames
grow large and then settle back and then flare up again and the rhythms
of the fire and the smell of the woodsmoke and the coolness of the night
on the desert began to put them to sleep. After awhile the fire was gone to
a bed of dull red coals and they looked again in amazement at the Milky
Way and the stars which they agreed were nothing like the stars in Alabama
and crawled into their sleeping bags and fell asleep.

In the morning after breakfast the van wouldn't start and there was a
spirited discussion about whose idea it was to camp eight miles from a
paved road. Not long after this they saw a cloud of dust spiraling like a
tornado behind a truck coming north on the dead-end road and five
minutes later a white pickup truck from "Charles Hughes Land and
Cattle Company" pulled into their camp. A sundarkened man of about
fifty winters with a white Stetson and a walrus moustache jumped from
the truck. His gut sagged grotesquely over his belt in some sort of a
statement to the world.

"You people can't squat here. This is private land."

Lester saw his own face, his entire family, reflected in the man's sunglasses.

"Mister, I'm really sorry but the sign down the road said this was public land," said Lester in a voice gentle enough to disarm a bomb.

"I know about that sign. That sign is my damnation. I've had this discussion a hundred different times with a hundred different hunters. Sunflower County is a checkerboard patchwork of BLM and private. This
side of Dry Creek is private. I should know. I own it just like my Daddy
did and his Daddy before him."

"You Mr. Hughes?"

"Yes I am."

"Well, Mr. Hughes we were just here for one night. We'll be happy to leave if you'd give us a jump."

"A jump?"

The man was going to make a fuss about giving the trespassers a jump when the older daughter stepped from the van, stuffing her partially buttoned blouse into the front of her blue jeans, and his demeanor instantly changed.

"I'd be delighted to give you a jump."

The man pulled his truck around and popped the hood and Lester attached the red and black battery cables to the positive and negative terminals. After they started the van the man insisted on waiting and letting the battery on the van fully charge.

"You never can tell about these things," he observed authoritatively. "You don't want to lose power somewhere out on the highway where anything could happen."

Everyone stared at the engine.

There was a silence, the wind picking up now as the sun rose higher in the sky.

"Where you folks headed?"

"Flagstaff," said Lester.

"You're on vacation?" the man asked reflexively, realizing the absurdity of the question even as he spoke.

"No. We heard there are good jobs up there. Housekeeping, maintenance. That sort of thing."

The man couldn't suppress a chuckle.

"What's so funny?" asked Lester.

"All those type of jobs in Flagstaff are taken by the students at Northern Arizona University."

"Well," said Lester as he disconnected the copper battery clips from the terminals on the battery and held them apart so they wouldn't touch, "we'll have to see about that."

Lester walked over to the man's truck and disconnected the clips from his battery.

"If you're looking for good steady work, you oughta stick around here."

"What kind of work could you find in a place like this?" asked Donna.

"There's always the feed lot."

"What do they pay?" asked the older daughter.

"Five something an hour."

"We couldn't live on that," said the father grimly.

"Housing is cheap around here. You wouldn't believe housing in Flagstaff. Rent can go twelve hundred a month even for a small house. Here you could rent a house for three hundred."

"What do you do in a feed lot, shovel shit?" asked the father.

"No. The whole operation is mechanized. My brother-in-law runs it. You should see. It's all scientific."

"Thanks, but we'll be moving on."

"Suit yourself," said the man, with an expression of surprise that anyone would rather live in Flagstaff than in Sunflower County.

"What do I owe you for the jump?"

"Nuthin' at all." The man paused, looking at the family with pity but realizing they were strong country folk and didn't want his pity. "Good luck to you."

"Good luck to you too mister," said Lester.

And so they loaded up the van and climbed aboard and returned to the highway and drove north and then west, past the world's largest meteor crater they had never seen, angling steadily toward Flagstaff, the father trying not to appear concerned about that peculiar thumping noise in the engine, the mother concluding she was too tired to worry anymore and that it would be God's mercy if they were all killed at a railroad crossing, the boy watching the beautiful clouds over the mountains that no one else was watching, the older daughter reading about Bruce Willis and Demi Moore in *People* magazine, the twins playing house with their dolls in the back among the boxes.

ii.

LUTHER BOYD HAD LIVED AND WORKED in Flagstaff for most of his life. The son of a prominent architect, he had grown up with every comfort and privilege. He had attended Stanford University, majoring in American Studies, and later graduated from Pepperdine Law School.

For several years he had practiced family law in Flagstaff, but now, at the age of forty-five, he was working, as he had for the past seven years, as a cab driver. The account of his unlikely descent through circumstance and class would make an interesting novel. The short version of the story is that he was afflicted with an illness that no one could name or cure. Each therapist had a different diagnosis, and each clinic had a promising new treatment, and he had tried them all and none of them worked. The symptoms described any one of a half dozen maladies. His moods were as varied as the weather. He could range in a single evening from brilliant *bon vivant* to vulgar nuisance. Not to mention the unpredictable pacing, whistling, nervous tics, and bizarre outbursts. Only after converting to Buddhism, and chanting for an hour each morning and evening, had Luther been able to bring himself into a state of equilibrium, but the remedy had come too late to save his once-promising legal career. By then, his options were limited, or at least seemed that way to him. After his mother died of cancer, his father had remarried a younger woman. In the years that followed, his stepmother had gradually driven the father and son apart, having calculated the inheritance. As a result Luther was estranged from his family and lived alone in a rented basement apartment that not one person with his last name had ever visited.

Luther was working the afternoon shift on St. Patrick's Day, which is always a good day in the cab business, and he had just made a medicare run to the dialysis clinic when he saw a van with out of state license plates broken down on Old Route 66 east of town. He was en route to the Museum of Northern Arizona to pick up the assistant curator who needed a ride to the airport and he would have roared past the travelers but then he saw the statuesque blond staring disconsolately in his direction. He immediately pulled over. Luther's unique gift, which had been of some use during the years he practiced law, was his ability to directly see to the heart of the matter. After a brief conversation with Lester Dixon, he understood precisely what needed to be done, and in what order. The alternator needed to be replaced, and they needed a place to live.

He offered to help, to spend a couple of hours with the Dixons just for the sake of the good kharma.

"And you mean you'll do all this for free?"

Luther said yes and Lester gave his wife an "I told you so" look. Five minutes earlier she had been on the verge of leaving him. Now she was willing to remain in the marriage for at least another hour.

It was the good fortune of the Dixon family to have met the one person in Flagstaff who was best suited, by disposition and experience, to help them. Every community has a person like Luther, a roving ambassador of good will who variously functions as a sort of unelected mayor, unofficial city manager and self-appointed inspector of restaurants, delicatessens, bars, bowling alleys, and highways. Within an hour Luther had arranged for a free tow from one of his drinking buddies to a garage where there was a mechanic who owed him money. The man would perform the replacement in exchange for the discharge of the loan. Luther then took the family to a mobile home park where he knew the manager from an old personal injury case and the Dixons soon obtained a decent safe place to live for five hundred a month, no security deposit required. In keeping with his faith, Luther hoped that these selfless deeds would cause some positive energy to flow back into his life, even if, as a realist, he suspected that such a turn of events did not seem to be part of the general plan of the universe.

A week went by.

One afternoon Luther drove to the trailer park to see how the Dixons were adjusting to their new life in Flagstaff. With him that day was Jack LaSalle, who was killing time before the Aerosmith concert. Jack was the son of "Big Mike" LaSalle, who owned several businesses in Flagstaff— the Ford-Lincoln-Mercury dealership, both downtown McDonalds, a Blockbuster Video franchise, and the Ace Hardware Store next to the mall. Jack was twenty-seven years old and had so far successfully avoided any of the conventional responsibilities of life, such as marriage and children or career and community service. After eight years of part-time attendance, he had graduated from Northern Arizona University with a 2.75 average in "general collegiate studies." He worked about four or five days a month as an "information consultant" for his father (who still declared him as a dependent on tax forms). He and Luther had met two years earlier, when Jack's Saab had broken down on the South Rim of the Grand Canyon and Luther was the lucky driver assigned to the call. He and Luther had a spirited conversation on the way back to town, and shortly discovered that they were both Grateful Dead fans, that they both had seen all of the films of Stanley Kubrick, especially *Dr. Strangelove*, several times, and that they both loved the game of tennis. It was an odd friendship on the surface—a cab driver and a trust-funder—but they actually had much in common, especially in ways that people could not see. Over time the association blossomed, and now they spoke to each other over the phone every day, and frequently went out for dinner together. Jack enjoyed all of his strange acquaintances in the lively underworld of Flagstaff, which was part of his ongoing rebellion against his parents, whom he delighted in annoying.

When they pulled up to the trailer, Jack asked Luther to leave the radio on because he wanted to listen to the rest of the live interview with Steve Tyler, the lead singer of Aerosmith. Luther insisted Jack come in and meet the family. When Jack said no way, Luther threatened to begin singing "Bohemian Rhapsody" by Freddie Mercury out the car window to the whole neighborhood if Jack did not join him. Jack finally relented and exclaimed "This better be good, Boyd-Master!" Jack had invented a number of playful nicknames for Luther, including "The Boyd-azoid" and "Da Boydster" and "Boyd-man" and "Boy Boyd."

When the door to the mobile home opened it was Adam. He explained that everyone was gone but his sister, who was baby-sitting him. He showed them in and they sat on the couch that had just come from the Salvation Army store and smelled of moth balls. The television was on and it was a Walt Disney cartoon on a cable channel. Adam resumed playing with his Lego toys on the floor. He was building an elaborate spaceship.

A moment later Megan got off the phone with her best girlfriend Ashley Lowndes in Artesia and walked in. She was wearing blue jean cut-offs and a white t-shirt that said "Gulf Islands National Seashore, Pensacola, Florida."

Jack was sitting back with his basketball shoes up on the coffee table, not able to see too well with his dark Armani sunglasses and already thinking about the concert that night at the university field house, when he saw an extraordinarily poised and lovely young woman step from the hallway. For the first time in his long and brilliantly successful career as a board-certified ladies' man with multiple advanced credentials in flirtation he was rendered silent. When he stood up to shake her hand he nearly fell over the coffee table. Each time he tried to say something it came out as a stutter. He was reduced to the role of mute buffoon, a part he was unaccustomed to playing. As a result, Luther did all of the talking, determining that the twins were already enrolled in elementary school, that Lester had gotten a temporary job as an assistant manager at the Seven-Eleven, and that Donna was working as a teacher's assistant at the school. Megan said that she had put in a few job applications, but Luther could tell from the sound of her voice and the way her face changed that this event had not yet occurred. Like all lawyers, who are themselves skilled masters of dissimulation, Luther could easily apprehend when a person was creating a fiction.

Jack and Luther were halfway back to town when Jack told the Boyd-azoid to turn the cab around. He was going to invite Megan to the concert. He had regained his composure. He had glimpsed Everest. If he had faltered at first, and who would not at such a sight, he knew now what he had to do. Like all mountaineers, who measure themselves by the loftiness of the summits they attempt, he would now begin the perilous ascent.

"But what about Erika Fox?"

"What *about* Erika Fox?"

Luther smiled, for his plan had worked. He had become in a sense, the older brother that Jack, being an only child, never had.

Jack and Megan went to the concert that night, Megan complaining throughout that the singer Gwen Stefani in the opening act No Doubt wore too much makeup and that the loud rock anthems were nothing like the music she was accustomed to. Afterwards they went to a small out of the way Italian restaurant and had cheese ravioli because Megan was a vegetarian and drank coffee and talked in a side booth until the place closed. They discovered that she was a Democrat and he was a Republican, that she was a Baptist and he was an Episcopalian, that she liked figure-skating and he liked football. They had nothing in common and disagreed about almost everything and it was partly those differences, paradoxically, that drew them together. He liked the fact that she was unlike the women in Flagstaff—that she had been to France as an exchange student for a year when she was fifteen and could quote from

books he had never heard of and played classical piano, and was continually full of unusual surprises. Her most appealing virtue was her conviction that the future would be a good place to live and that all of this
current misery was only a temporary distraction.

Before Megan got out of the car Jack gave her a hug and kissed her cheek.

When Megan walked in at twelve-twenty-three her mother wanted
to know if she had gone out with that over-the-hill cab driver Luther
Boyd, and Megan said that no, it was one of the cab driver's younger
friends. They had gone to the concert and now it was late and she
wanted to go to bed. Megan knew nothing of Jack's family background,
only that he made her laugh and was fun to be with and that partially
made up for the fact that he was not the best looking or the smartest
boy she had ever been out with.

The mother went back into her room and whispered in Lester's ear. The
only thing that Lester wanted to know is when Megan would get a job.

"It's just not proper," he said, raising his voice so that Megan could
hear in the next room. "She's nineteen years old. It's time for her to work.
Who does she think she is?"

Megan thought about those words the next morning. She weighed the
injustice of not being able to attend college yet against the necessity of
her current situation, and she decided to give Luther a call. Naturally he
had the perfect "job that would not even seem like a job" for her. By
evening she was a full-time route driver for a medical laboratory. She
gathered samples at clinics around Flagstaff and brought them to the
hospital for testing. The job came with a free late model automobile
which she could keep on the evenings and weekends, as well as a gas card
and a cell phone. Her salary was a little more than twice the minimum
wage. It would at least work for awhile, until she could figure out a way
to pay for college.

Lester was delighted that the family now at last had one reliable vehicle
for shopping and sight-seeing. The first priority was to show everyone, especially his wife, the Grand Canyon. Lester was convinced that seeing the
Canyon would change the family mood and finally restore his wife's faith
in him. He was growing weary of the averted gazes and dropped plates.

Two weeks passed. Jack called every night at eight o'clock and Megan
spoke to him for periods ranging from one hour to three hours. They

talked about everything and nothing, and even when it seemed to others as though they were not discussing anything they were actually talking about something. Her friends in Artesia would try to call and the line would be busy until it was one A.M. in their time zone.

When Jack learned of Lester's interest in the Grand Canyon he picked up a ten passenger van from his father's lot, where he was now working full time as the new car sales manager, and personally drove the family to the South Rim. It was a Saturday in April and the park was not crowded yet. They had just passed the visitor's entrance at Desert View when a herd of two dozen elk crossed the road. The elk moved slowly with dignity and the cows were noticeably heavy with their spring calves. The bulls had just begun to grow antlers in velvet. Their shoulder manes were as dark as the shadows under the trees and their bodies were the color of winter grass. Adam was so excited he shot almost an entire role of film with his new camera before Megan could stop him. At Lipan Point they pulled into the parking lot and walked cautiously forward in one group holding hands. A great light was coming from the earth and when they walked to the edge and saw what was making it they were speechless and struck with awe, as all pilgrims to the place are. Twenty miles due north was the North Rim and seventy miles to the northeast were the Vermillion Cliffs near Page. It was a clear day, and everything nearby and faraway was sharply defined. A mile below the cliff was the Colorado River, glistening like burnished silver in the sunlight. Layer after layer of rock rose from the depths. The red and pink and orange canyon was as much a revelation of time as it was of space. Lester looked not so much at the canyon as he did at his wife's face, which appeared radiant in the reflected light of the canyon. She looked young again, and happy, and he remembered again for the first time in months why he had married her.

They had a picnic in the junipers and pinyons just below the rim because it was too windy on top. They ate boxed sandwiches and potato salad and soft drinks that Jack had brought from a delicatessen and mostly talked about their former life in Alabama, as people who have moved to a new place always do for awhile. Later they went to the Desert View gift shop and Jack bought Donna a pair of turquoise earrings because it was her birthday. Each of the children received a gift as well. Driving back they stopped to watch a band of mule deer in the pinyons and junipers and Lester commented that he could not wait to begin deer hunting again. He would hunt them with a longbow he had made himself from a piece of hickory back home in Alabama. He was a deadly shot and he observed that it sure was going to be different hunting here with the one deer limit. Alabama permitted the hunter to harvest four deer annually. The mule deer, though, appeared to be larger than the white-tail, and so would have more meat on them. Lester loved venison, especially venison sausage which he made himself.

Through all of this, Jack was trying to befriend Donna because he sensed that she was the ultimate authority in the family, and could be an ally or an adversary depending on his approach. She had at first written him off as a worthless rogue of a species she was once familiar with, but was now beginning to see some promise.

iii.

TWO MONTHS LATER, toward the end of May, Megan and Jack met for lunch in the city park, as was their custom. It was a sunny hot afternoon, a preview of the summer to come, and they sat in the shade under their favorite cottonwood tree near the central fountain. People were walking their dogs and playing frisbee. Somewhere a college student strummed a slightly out of tune twelve-string guitar. Quiet conversations drifted back and forth on the breeze. Midway through the meal Megan mentioned as matter-of-factly as she could that her period was now about a month late. There was a silence and then she also confided in a lower voice that she had tested positive on a home pregnancy test from the Wal-Mart pharmacy that very morning, although those tests could sometimes be wrong. When Jack mumbled a sentence with the word abortion in it she began crying uncontrollably and he realized that option was out of the question this time. People were staring from a block away and so he put his arm around her and held her close, although he was actually more concerned about appearances than anything else.

To avoid any more loud cries, he assured Megan that he would do the right thing and she looked at him with flushed cheeks and brimming eyes and asked in a hoarse voice "What's that?" He gulped and after a full minute during which his mind turned into a pocket thesaurus searching for a synonym that does not exist in the English language or any other language he said he would marry her. His tone of voice carried with it no sense of conviction—it was as flat and empty an utterance as someone might mumble in their sleep—but the unambiguity of the statement would prove impossible to retract.

She gave him a wonderful kiss in the car on the side street where no one could see except a retired librarian peeking through her upstairs curtains and the duration and quality of that kiss partially changed his mind, at least for the afternoon.

That night he met Luther Boyd at a place called the Bear's Lair Saloon. The name derived from the stuffed grizzly bear head on the wall behind the bar. The bear, the last of its species on the Mogollon Rim, had been taken by a legendary hunter named Ben Lilly at the beginning of the last century, when Arizona was still a frontier. It was a female named Old Sally that had reputedly killed sheep and cattle for years on the government pastureland before finally being taken in a set-gun trap. One New Year's Eve a drunk torpedo mate home on leave from the *U.S.S. Los Angeles* had crawled up on the counter when the bartender wasn't looking and put a cowboy hat and sunglasses on the bear. There they remained and their absurd presence pretty much summed up the Bear's Lair Saloon. It was the sort of place, and there is one in every town, where men go to be with other men and attempt to understand the opposite gender, where men in the midst of divorces obtain advice from elders, where boyfriends who have been dumped by girlfriends drink their blues away, where old bachelors who have given up on the sporting life watch the sports channel. A quarter of a century earlier, Willie Nelson and Waylon Jennings had played the Bear's Lair a few times during their wilderness period, and there was a framed picture of them on the wall behind the pool tables. This was back when Willie's hair was still red and Waylon Jennings still had his original liver. And there were photographs of other performers from the Seventies—Kris Kristofferson, Rita Coolidge, Michael Murphy, Don Henley, Warren Zevon, Tom Petty, and a very young John Denver. All had played at the Bear's Lair Saloon when it was a well-known venue on the college town circuit.

The music now was canned rock and roll—the juke box was playing the Love Shack song by the B-52's.

Luther and Jack sat at a corner table drinking Australian beer as Jack morosely described his predicament. Luther listened attentively to the narrative. Like any good counselor, he remained silent through the account, absorbing every fact and slowly developing a sense of the situation. Jack would likely follow his advice, and so Luther realized that he had to be extremely careful about what he recommended. This was, after all, someone's life.

"Luther, you're the closest thing I have to a lawyer. What do you think I should do?"

"Do you have a picture of her in your wallet?"

"Uh-huh."

"Take it out."

Jack took the photograph out and put it on the table. It was a picture that Adam had taken of Jack and Megan together on the South Rim that day in April. The two were embracing at Lipan Point with the Palisades of the Grand Canyon in the background.

Luther turned the photograph around so that Jack could see it.

"Jack, take a look at that. Take a good hard look at that. Look at the smile on your face. And look at who you're with."

Jack glanced at the photograph.

"I'll tell you, man," Luther continued, "you can search the rest of your life and not find someone better. If you lose her you will regret it until your dying day, and I suspect most especially on your dying day. My advice is to marry her. And I would suggest that even if she wasn't pregnant."

Jack didn't say anything but vaguely nodded his head in affirmation as he stared at the picture and drank his beer.

The next day he brought Megan to the family home and told his parents the bad news. Much to his shock, they were both delighted, though for different reasons. His father saw the pregnancy and marriage as a way to control his son. He could use Megan, the ultimate weapon, to finally persuade his son to make something of himself. After all, Jack would now have to provide for a wife and a child. His mother thought immediately of the beautiful grandchild that she could now love and spoil as she had her own son. And she also discerned that Megan was a woman, like herself, whose uncommon beauty would bring good fortune to her husband. Later there was a dinner meeting with the Dixons at the Flagstaff House, the finest restaurant in town. The conversation ranged from Lester's dream of being a professional bass fisherman with his own line of products to Adam's accomplishments in the Special Olympics to Dale Earnhardt and the incredible sport of stock car racing. Following that evening the LaSalles had a few mild reservations, but both were philosophical enough to know that accidents and injustices do occur to families and that they do have a cumulative effect. No situation was perfect, and they both agreed that night when they were alone in the darkness of their bedroom that even with its problems this was a better situation for their son than his previous state of perpetual hedonism before Megan.

The Dixons were equally happy, having learned by then exactly who the future father-in-law was. Within weeks, Lester was working as manager of the service aisle. Big Mike had finally found someone the mechanics were happy to work for. Donna got a job in the finance department of the dealership. Mike had searched for years for someone who could be trusted with accounts payable. Who could be better than a relative?

The wedding was set for June 20th, the day of the summer solstice, marking the end of the spring and the beginning of a new season. Announcements were made and invitations were sent out and the entire community of Flagstaff took interest in this major development involving one of its most influential families. Everyone at the Ponderosa Country Club and the local watering holes who had bet that Mad Jack LaSalle would never marry now had to pay up. Some of these were rather sizeable bets. All of the young women who had thought they had at least an outside chance with the last living bachelor of his generation now realized that they had to look elsewhere. And all of those girls agreed that they truly hated Megan Dixon and would always hate her for any one of a number of reasons, even though they had never met her and knew nothing about her. A minister was contacted, flower shops and caterers made their plans, and a church and banquet hall for the reception were reserved. Day by day, hour by hour, the two young people, each still as independent as a free-floating atom, moved closer to becoming the bonded molecule, a man and a woman, that is at the center of human society.

It was now June and the wedding was about to occur.

About thirty minutes before the appointed hour, Luther, as best man, was performing his essential duties at the liquor bar when he glanced out the window and noticed that Jack LaSalle was running toward the parking lot. It was a sort of modified one hundred yard dash in a tuxedo. Luther had the ring in his pocket and so he knew there was only one reason that a groom would be bolting.

He excused himself from the discussion of tort reform with the other lawyers and, as soon as he was out the door, jogged off at a brisk pace in the direction of the parking lot. He caught up with Jack just in time. The car door was closed, the engine was running, and the transmission was in reverse.

"Jack, what are you doing?"

"I can't do this Luther. I just can't do this."

Jack's face was a portrait of the word panic.

"Ok. Just relax. Calm down. Put the car in neutral and talk to me for one minute. Just one minute."

Jack cooperated.

"Alright then, have you decided where you are going?"

"I'm just gonna leave town for a few weeks until things quiet down. I'll drive to Tucson or something. Maybe drift over the border to Puerto Penasco. Stay at Blind Willie's. Just hang, you know."

"Well, I guess that would be an option."

"You're not mad?"

"Jack, it's a free world. I'm not here to hassle you. I'm your friend. But before you go I want you to see something. Just give me five minutes and you can take off."

Jack turned off the ignition and they walked across the lawn to the minister's home, where the women were preparing Megan for the wedding. Luther and Jack crept forward to the edge of a lilac bush that was taller than they were and looked through a break in the leaves.

Ashley Lowndes, the maid of honor, was adjusting the back straps on Megan's flowing white gown. Megan's mother and sisters, and her future mother-in-law, were preparing various aspects of her dress. The room was in a state of quiet disorder, although it was filled with grace and harmony. A cat was playing with a ball of ribbon. The twins were looking at themselves in the mirror, making faces. The voices were soft, low, now giggling and now mildly serious. It evoked a scene from a Mary Cassatt painting that captures an intimate moment among women—the young and the soon to be married and the old, and all bathed in a mild summer light.

"Look at that, Jack. Tell me you can actually walk away from that and I won't stand in your way. I'll still be here and I'll be your friend when you come back, but she won't. She won't ever talk to you again, except through her lawyers. But more important than that, think about this. That is your child inside of Megan's body. One day soon she will be born and you will want to be there for that moment. That little girl will look up at you with eyes filled with unconditional love and trust and you will always want to be there to protect her. And you'll want to be there for her first Christmas and for her first birthday and for her first tennis lesson. You'll always want to be there for her. And somewhere along the way you'll learn that the most wonderful word in the English language is Daddy."

Half an hour later the vows were exchanged and by noon the next day the happy couple was getting sunburned on a white coralline beach in Barbados.

THIS WAS ALL SEVERAL YEARS AGO, before Jack was elected to Congress and Big Mike LaSalle saw to it that Luther Boyd was appointed his chief-of-staff.

Sandpainting

ONE NOVEMBER AFTERNOON many decades ago I bought a sand-painting from a Navajo woman named Nillie Bryan. She sold it to me at a place called Dry Creek Basin in western San Miguel County. She needed the money for groceries. Her husband was a cowboy in the valley, and they had a new baby. On the back of the sandpainting she wrote in pencil "The Seed Blessing Way Chant—The rainbow Natseelit sur-rounds and protects the seeds that make the plants necessary for life. All sand are [sic] natural colors." Nillie once told me that a sandpainting was a kind of altar—a place, originally on the floor of the desert itself, where a healing ceremony took place. Balance with nature was restored to the person who sat within a sandpainting, which was traditionally destroyed after the ceremony. This particular sandpainting was made on a piece of plywood twenty inches square. The background was pink sand of the sort found in Monument Valley. A rainbow of green and brown enclosed an inner circle of corn stalks—each with a human head—and an array of animals—a raven, a lizard, a coyote, and a songbird. At the center of the painting was a circle that was half dark and half light.

When I returned to Denver that spring I gave the sandpainting to my mother as a belated birthday present. She had it framed in wood. The frame was weathered gray-brown wood, as from an old barn, and it formed a natural border for the painting. For several years the sand-painting hung in their living room in Littleton. It bore silent witness to the struggles of the family at that time. When doors were slammed, it shook on its hanger. It also heard the laughter at various parties, for my parents were fond of entertaining. It was there when my brothers moved back from Santa Fe after their rock and roll band "The Rockonauts" dis-banded. And it was there one Christmas when I received a wonderful present—Richard Ellmann's biography of Joyce.

Eventually my father's work took him to Boston and my parents moved to a place called Swampscott on the North Shore. The windows were always open in the summer and you could smell the seaweed and dead fish on the beach, which was only a short walk away. When I visited the cats would come in and lick my face in the morning and as I walked down the hall I would see the sandpainting and it would remind me of the desert. At that time in my life the Southwest was a faraway place, both figuratively and literally, and I kept a map of it with me at all times, tracing my fingers over favorite places. Seeing the sandpainting reminded me of where I should be and kept me connected, if only by a gossamer, to a place that truly felt like home.

The sandpainting then traveled with them to Washington. They had a home in the Virginia countryside that I never saw. I am told that it was surrounded by a forest. This was for awhile a good time in their lives. The sandpainting—which hung in their study, I believe—came to know the thick humidity of the Potomac Valley in the summer months, and the long gray winter dusks. Eventually they returned West, moving to a house near the Presidio in San Francisco, and the sandpainting came to know the Pacific Coast as it had the Atlantic. My brothers and I would come out for the holidays each year, and inevitably there would be long meals in the dining room, where the painting hung. My brothers would always ask for the famous story of the 1979 disaster hunt, and I would repeat the familiar episodes of the wall tent burning down and the horses breaking out of the corral during the blizzard and many other catastrophes too numerous to list here. We would smile and laugh, and then my mother would relate her stories, always cautioning my father not to interrupt as he tried to correct facts.

After ten years in other cities they returned to Denver. They lived in several different homes, for my mother loved nothing more than to decorate a new home. The sandpainting moved from place to place. All the while her health declined. She kept the sandpainting either in her art room, where she had done many of her best paintings—watercolors and acrylics in the abstract expressionist mode—or in her bedroom. Eventually she suffered a heart attack, caused, the doctors said, by a lifetime of smoking. After the heart attack she would rise every morning at four o'clock, because she had read somewhere that heart attacks most often occur at that time of the day.

In those final anxious years she spent a lot of time reading. I see now that, approaching the end of her life, she instinctively sought books as

part of a search for meaning. She read histories only, and never any form
of fiction. She was particularly fond of Will Durant's eleven volume history of western civilization, and of one volume in particular—*Caesar
and Christ*. At that point entertainment and diversion were not as important for her as faith and understanding. What was this thing that had
just happened to her, this thing called life? What was to be made of this
other event about to occur, which would lead to the opposite of life?
Those books, as mirrors of life, provided her with a sort of clarity and
comfort that no physician, no priest could. When hope dwindles and
nature stymies reason, when suffering intrudes and science is con-
founded, there is always the solace of the ages.

All the while the sandpainting hung over her bed.

One morning she went to the hospital and when she returned four
days later it was in the form of ashes. After about six months my father
gave me the sandpainting. He was giving away possessions with too
many memories.

And so I hung the sandpainting to the right of my photography table
and over a bookcase with all of my favorite Southwestern books. The
sandpainting always cheers me up when I look at it, which is the first
thing I do every morning when I go into my study to work. Much has
changed in my life over the past twenty-five years, but the sandpainting
has always remained a constant. It belongs to that odd species of mem-
orabilia that are so fragile as to be indestructible. It is a fixed object in a
world of flux. To another person, it would have little or no value, but it
carries for me a whole series of memories. We hold onto things like this
because they measure what we have lost as much as what we have gained.
Perhaps it is too much to say that the sandpainting has healing power,
but I have always found in its images a certain reassurance. I have often
thought, too, of the woman who made it, who lived in a coal-heated
cabin without electricity or plumbing, and who had a sick baby and not
enough food, and who stayed up late one night, arranging sand on wood
by the light of a candle.

Points and Lines

HISTORY RECORDS THAT HE WAS BORN in the second century B.C. in the Urk Desert at the foot of the Gol Mountains in central Asia. His name was Ashka, and he was the son of a goat herder named Zhar Ket and a woman named Prang. The family was part of a nomadic people who wandered from the Yar River on the west to the thermal springs of Carsk in the east. In his seventeenth summer Ashka was told by his grandfather Sunar of a mystery that was five days' walk north of Carsk. There was, Sunar confided, an immense basin as large as a small mountain turned upside down and at the bottom of the void was a powerful rock. The rock was the length of ten camels and shaped in the form of a sleeping tortoise. If a black stone of the sort that could be found in the cliffs of Umk was held to any point on this rock a spirit in the rock would try to take the stone. This presence could be felt and it was not in the imagination. Whoever could tame that spirit would have power in this world.

The next day Ashka left, for the tribe was resting at the medicine waters as they always did in the eighth month and he was an energetic youth filled with a boundless curiosity. With him he took a gourd of honey, the skin of a Varan lizard filled with dried berries and sunflower seeds, and a hunting bow and several arrows. The moon came full and waned and came full again and Ashka did not return. The snows were descending the mountainsides, each night a little further, and so the tribe turned south for the winter pastures. The grandfather left his mark at the message wall beside the thermal springs, indicating they would return in eight or nine moons.

The next year when the tribe came back to the place that was always scented with sulphur Ashka was there waiting for them.

But he was no longer the person that he had been. He had the beginnings of a full black beard and his dark brown eyes were charged with a strange energy and when he spoke it was with the confident bearing and carefully chosen words of a white-haired elder. When informed of the death of Sunar, Ashka replied that he knew where his grandfather was, and that he had visited him there and that it was a good place. His mother was frightened, and thought perhaps the desert spirits had taken possession of him. She wanted him to undergo a purification but he said that he no longer believed in the desert spirits. He had sat on the rock he called Imlac many times during the day and night and the rock had spoken to him. He had watched the sun and the clouds and the stars and he had listened to the silence and everything had become clear to him. There was only one spirit that infused all things, and it was older than the sun and the moon. He called this spirit Dar, the mighty one, and made statements such as "the radiance of a hundred suns is less than the splendor of the mighty one." A skeptical young man in the tribe named Og Kasran scornfully demanded direct proof that this mighty one existed and so Ashka produced two rocks and placed them apart, and the two rocks moved together and became one.

Og played with the rocks for hours, pulling them apart and watching them magically come together, and became Ashka's first disciple.

Ashka had also found a myriad of clear glass beads near the rock— they were as numerous as grains of sand—and he presented a glass bead to each member of the tribe. He then showed them how to make a fire by focusing the sun's rays through a glass bead on a dry leaf. Now even a child of four could easily build a signal fire at any time. The whole tribe felt in possession of a wonderful knowledge that separated them from other people.

Later that same year Ashka was summoned to the court of Khar Khagd, who presided in the walled palace of his ancestors over two parallel river valleys. In exchange for one-fifth of all the herds and crops, Khagd provided a trained army to defend the people against the barbarians who came on periodic raids from the north. King Khagd was doubtful of Ashka's new observations and beliefs. He was, after all, a veteran soldier, a practical man who believed only in the strength of his arm and the sharpness of his sword. The real power in his regime, however, resided with his chief wife Balzhag. It was Balzhag who had prevailed upon her husband several years earlier to abolish the practice of human sacrifice, and who had thus won the gratitude of the masses. She listened to Ashka carefully and soon saw that this popular young man could be of some use to the kingdom. For one thing, his optimism lifted people from despair. For another, his moral code was conducive to civil order. Finally, there was his novel concept of the afterlife, which gave the suffering some hope of relief beyond this world. Eventually Ashka was invited to live in the court. Not long after that King Khagd died suddenly while eating a bowl of fruit. Within a few months Ashka was wed to Balzhag.

Ten years passed. Over that time Ashka transformed the kingdom from a secular to a religious state. His simple philosophy of love and forgiveness made it easier for people to live in larger communities, and soon even the most devoted of the herding folk were learning how to plant seed and cultivate fruit. The people began to converge in what would become two cities, and at the heart of those two cities were two identical temples—one outside the walled palace of Ashka and the other at Imlac. These temples were immense circular buildings with massive colonnades fashioned from limestone. On the sides of the colonnades were incised sculptures of wild animals and other scenes from nature, all glorifying the power and kindness of the mighty one. At the center of each temple was an open space of light and air where the faithful could gather and pray to Dar.

Ashka and his devoted follower Kasran jointly ruled the kingdom, with Ashka presiding over the society, which had been established to promote virtue, and Kasran administering the government, which had been convened to restrain vice. The kingdom flourished as do all experiments founded in kindness and common sense, and word began to spread of the prosperity and happiness of its people. One autumn Ashka was visited by a delegation of scholars who had journeyed by camel for many months from the Indus River far to the south. These visitors were in possession of a written language. After listening to Ashka, they directed their scribes to preserve his chief sayings on clay tablets, which Kasran's workers then kiln-fired and placed in the temple at Imlac. These five hundred proverbs addressed questions of good and evil, freedom and justice, life and death. They became known as "The Book of Imlac by Asha." After the untimely death of Asha (the "k" having been lost somewhere along the way) from a scorpion bite, Kasran ruled over the kingdom for another thirty years, during what archaeologists refer to as the First Dynasty. As a result the faith became known, even in its earliest stages, as the Kasranian faith of Asha.

It was now twenty-three centuries later. The Kasranian religion was practiced by five hundred million people around the globe. These people, by and large, formed a peaceful society, and like all people were bonded together more by what they loved than what they did not love. The chief ceremony of the faith was the journey to Imlac. Visitors prayed in the Imlac temple for three days, consuming only water and never looking at the light of the sky, before being led to the center of the impact crater (as it had been determined), where they were permitted to touch the meteor remnant. After completing this ritual, and swearing allegiance to Dar and to the principles of Dar, they were accepted into the faith and promised a place in the afterlife with Asha.

Like all faiths, Kasran had known its schisms and internal battles over the centuries, with this or that side contending for this or that interpretation of the sacred text. Some of these disputes had grown into feuds. Several had festered into wars. All had been concerned, whatever their religious appearance, with the control of power and wealth. In the late twentieth century, a new threat emerged in the person of Javahd Xanthes, the nineteenth son of a wealthy oil and gas magnate in the Kasranian state of Trgit. Xanthes was a dogmatic fundamentalist, and adhered to a strict interpretation of the Book of Imlac. He would not abide any divergent views, nor would he tolerate non-Kasranians on Kasranian soil. Although he was at first regarded as a minor nuisance, he eventually became so volatile that even his father would have nothing to do with him. Only his mother maintained contact with him. All others in the family had disowned him.

ii.

A STILLNESS FILLED THE SAN RAFAEL DESERT of southern Utah. The stars seemed at once to be near and far away, simultaneously capable of being touched and as remote as the abstract thought of a star. They were sprinkled in little groups of light across the ivory black sky and through them ran the long twisted radiance of the Milky Way. Far to the west a young moon was sinking into the mountains. It was as perfectly formed as a shaving from a jeweler's bar of silver. After awhile it turned gold and then it dropped away from view beyond the rim of the earth. Although the sunrise was still an hour off, the first meadowlarks had begun to sing. Their song was not loud, but in the silence of the pre-dawn it seemed so. Back and forth the birds called out from various locations on the desert, each marking his place in the world. Gradually a few faint streaks of gray appeared in the east, and then a rose-gray presence made itself known across the horizon. Almost all of the stars were gone now, and breezes were stirring about the landscape, carrying with them alternately the sharp tang of sage and the sweet pollen scent of rabbitbrush. A coyote howled once from a dry streambed, and then another answered from a distant butte. After awhile a prairie dog whistled the all clear. Soon the entire colony began to emerge from their burrows in the earth.

A man was sitting on a flat rock in the middle of the desert, with his head resting on the palm of his hand. He had been there for an hour and was gazing steadily toward the east, where a cloud shaped like a lens was turning bright red. His face was warmed in the crimson light for a few minutes, and then his eyes tightened as the sun peeked over the edge of the world. It was a youthful face, even if it was a thoughtful face. He had a prominent nose, crow-black eyebrows, and short-cut black hair. His cheekbones were distinct and his dark brown eyes were deep-set under a prominent arch. He often came to this rock at this hour, before work. It was the only time in his life that he felt truly free. At such moments it seemed there was no duty or responsibility, no evil or injustice, no sickness or no death. There was just the earth and the sky, and the sort of a calm and security one might find in a place where there was no earth or sky, only infinite space and eternal time and a thought so pure it could only be revealed as a light.

The man's name was Gabriel Calderon. He had grown up not far from the spot, at a town called Two Waters on the Uintah Reservation. His mother Irene Grayhills, a member of the Uintah nation, had been a school bus driver. His father Hector was from a village in the Sierra Madre Occidental and had worked as a sheepherder on local ranches. When Gabriel was seven both his parents were killed in a propane gas explosion. Beginning that year Gabriel evidenced a precocious ability in mathematics. By the age of twelve he was solving complex problems of differential and integral calculus in his head, without pencil or paper. His mentor in this enterprise was a man named Paul Alberic, who was a Franciscan teacher at the mission school in Two Waters. Although Brother Alberic tried for many years to convince Gabriel to attend his alma mater, Notre Dame, and become a mathematics professor, Gabriel decided instead to study computer science.

After awhile Gabriel saw a jeep on the dirt road, trailing a beige cloud of dust, and he stood up and walked over to the end of the road. He had a briefcase in his hand and was wearing the uniform of an Air Force captain. There were two people in the jeep, a man and a woman, and the three of them went to the door of a low flat concrete structure. Not much was said, because, to them, this procedure was so routine as to be boring. A minute later the heavy steel door creaked open and two other officers emerged, one squinting in the light and the other wearing sunglasses. There was a brief signing of papers attached to clipboards, some sort of a joke about the quality of the air in the bunker, and then Gabriel and his deputy commander, First Lieutenant Lisa Oxnard, lowered themselves down a thirty foot ladder into the earth. Once safely in their office beneath the desert, they commenced their daily activities, which consisted of various equipment tests, computer simulations, and practice launches. All of these involved the three missiles located in the silo field a quarter mile east of their position.

Their life in the bunker was at the same time mundane and exciting. At any given moment, they could be called upon to launch an attack against a distant adversary, but, given the conditions of the modern world, that eventuality seemed about as likely as the sun rising in the west. Once in the bunker, their environment was not unlike that of a submarine or a long range aircraft. The facility consisted of a ten foot by thirty foot steel cylinder. It contained an instrumented work area, as well as a sleeping room and a bath. The light was entirely fluorescent, and the lights never went off. The only advantage of this situation was that it produced an ideal habitat for African violets. The wife of the base commander had provided potted plants for each of the six bunkers, and there was a long-standing monthly competition to see which bunker could produce the best blossoms. The winner was provided a meal at the home of the base commander. Some of the teams took the game seriously, and sent away for liquid fertilizers and high-intensity grow lights. Others regarded it as an idiotic diversion, and completely ignored the plants.

Gabriel's work space consisted of a metal desk and three computers, each connected to one of the Titan II missiles. Each computer was equipped with several monitoring screens. The screens could provide information on the current status of the flight systems, the location of various targets, and the condition of the ordnance, which consisted of two independent warheads in the payload compartment of each missile. There was a telephone to his right that connected him to his chain of command—Colonel Bodine, the commander at Cheyenne Mountain, and the president. He and Lieutenant Oxnard spent two twenty-four-hour shifts together in the bunker each week, with two days of rest in between. While inside, they were completely cut off from the outside world. As a result, they had become good friends. Gabriel had never had a sister, and Lisa had never had a brother, and so their relationship had evolved as such—close siblings in the extended family of the base.

Gabriel often spoke about his fiancée, Eileen Burgess, who was completing a master's degree in science education at Rice University. He kept a framed picture of her on his desk. They had met during the "math olympics" when he was in his senior year at the Air Force Academy. They had been engaged for two years. Lisa had recently confided to Gabriel that she was pregnant by her boyfriend Jon, who worked as a consulting engineer for a firm in Salt Lake City. She kept a photo of him and her border collie Archimedes on her desk. The two enjoyed giving each other advice on all the secrets of the other gender, and discussing the various shapes the future might take. They each also kept a calendar on which they carefully marked off the days until their tour of duty on the range was completed, and a well-earned promotion would take them each to a better posting far away.

The subsequent twenty-four hours passed as tediously as all the others spent in the bunker. They ran through the usual checklist of assignments, as well as a test of the quick launch sequence, which was conducted once a month. This procedure was designed to rapidly launch the weapons in the event hostile missiles had been confirmed inbound over national air space, and the silo field was in danger of being breached.

It circumvented normal guidelines and provided the silo team with unusual latitude in their operations. They could, for example, input new target coordinates at the last moment or disable recall codes if it had been determined a computer attack had also occurred. On this day Gabriel established a new record for the base—three minutes and fourteen seconds.

During the shift both Gabriel and Lisa took a seven hour nap in the sleeping room, and both prepared several meals in the microwave. They also had time to read—Gabriel a new history of the Army Air Corps in World War II and Lisa a copy of Mark Twain's story of Joan of Arc. Eventually they received the welcome signal that the relief shift had arrived. They then put the six master computers on a two minute safety hold and climbed up the ladder. When they emerged into the blinding desert light the security officer, a staff sergeant with a permanent sunburn named Karen Joyce, said that she had just received word that Colonel Bodine had ordered an all-base meeting for 0700 at the alpha hangar on the main runway. The staff sergeant had no idea what it was all about.

The drive across the desert took them down the "valley of the dead," as they called it, and up a series of switchbacks that climbed an exposed ridge of limestone. The mesa top was higher in elevation, and there were scattered woodlands of pinyon and juniper. It was noticeably cooler than the lower desert. As the three approached mainside—an assemblage of thirty or so drab government buildings beside an airfield—Gabriel noticed that the base flags were at half-staff.

Inside the hangar several hundred military and civilian workers were seated on folding chairs. A low hum rose from the group, as from a beehive, as people whispered back and forth. Gabriel sat in the first row with the other officers and did not listen to the enlisted personnel behind him. He would learn the purpose of the meeting soon enough. He guessed that it was an announcement about the base being closed, although the flag at half-staff suggested that perhaps a government official had died.

Several long minutes passed.

Finally Colonel Bodine walked in and a master sergeant brought everyone to attention.

The colonel stood at the podium with his hands behind his back and put his unit at ease. Everyone sat down. The huge space was entirely silent. He was a tall, lean man with short-cropped silver hair and a craggy, suntanned face. He cleared his throat and announced that, effectively immediately, the 163rd Strategic Missile Group was being put on alert status, and that this was not a drill. One hour earlier a tactical warhead the size of a suitcase had exploded in Houston, Texas. The detonation had occurred, as near as could be determined in the preliminary assessment, somewhere on the campus of Rice University. Much of the surrounding area, including the oil refineries east of town, had either been leveled in the initial blast or was now being destroyed in the radioactive fires. A man named Javahd Xanthes, leader of the radical Kasranian sect, had assumed responsibility for the attack. He had made three demands: one billion dollars in reparations from the western powers for various grievances; the removal of all non-Kasranians from the central Asian republics of Kasran and Trgit; and the cessation of all western support for Hesiba, a small democratic country south of Kasran whose people were members of the Xia faith. If these demands were not met within three days, he would turn his attention to another city in either the United States or Western Europe and would continue to do so at random intervals until his demands were met.

The colonel then dismissed the force to the direction of their immediate superiors, and hurriedly left the hangar for a teleconference with the secretary of defense.

People poured out of the hanger like ants from a crushed anthill and Gabriel found himself in a group just outside the east entrance, standing in the blaze of morning sunlight. Everyone was dazed and confused. Some were stunned into silence. Others couldn't stop talking. Few could recall what they had been doing a few minutes earlier or should be doing now. Gabriel noticed that his unit commander, Major Scott Weathers, was trying to call his parents in Galveston on his cell phone and Gabriel asked him what he should do. Major Weathers said that he should rest and prepare normally for his next shift in forty-eight hours. The whole function of the base depended on the ability of the silo teams to successfully perform their essential duties.

Gabriel stood there for a moment with his hands in his pockets staring blankly at the ground, wondering what to do, before deciding to walk over to the chapel and pray.

The chapel was a white-washed wooden country church that actually predated the base. It had once served the desert mining camp of Bonanza before it became a ghost town. The antiquated place of worship looked quaintly out of place among the government buildings. Gabriel went in and removed his cover. It took a moment for his eyes to adjust to the half-light. The air was heavily scented with incense. He walked to the first wooden pew and knelt down, his forehead resting against his folded hands. As he prayed his mind wandered off, and suddenly he felt an emotion well up inside him and that emotion unsettled him and so he stopped praying.

After awhile he smelled something other than incense. Lieutenant Colonel Junger, the base chaplain, had a small apartment in the basement of the chapel and evidently he was cooking in his kitchen.

Gabriel walked down the stairs and stepped inside the doorway. Father Junger was busy with a steel pot on the gas range. His back was to the door and he couldn't see Gabriel. The room was about twice as long as it was wide, and was furnished as simply as a monk's cell in a monastery. Against the left wall was a small desk, several chairs, and a bed just wide enough for one person. On top of the pillow on the bed was a copy of the Bible. Against the right wall was a wooden bookcase with hardbound works of Greek and Latin and a scattering of novels and histories in the original French or German. Above the bookcase was a framed black and white photograph of Father Junger's parents, Ingrid and Klaus, who had been killed during the fire-bombing of Dresden in 1945. The photograph had been taken in a studio, under controlled lighting, and the couple looked young and happy. There were two candles beneath the photograph, as well as several rocks covered with fossils from the desert. Together they formed a sort of shrine. Farther down the bookcase was a potted prickly pear cactus, an old-fashioned record player, and an upright case with records of classical music.

On the floor was an elaborately colored and patterned rug that Father Junger had found in the coastal fishing town of Izmir in Turkey.

Gabriel knew the apartment well, for he visited nearly every Saturday night to play chess or discuss books or simply have a decent meal. Here he felt about as close to home as he ever would, and as close to someone resembling a parent as he would ever get.

Gabriel cleared his throat. Father Junger turned and saw the high wistful look and walked over.

The two men stood a few feet apart. Father Junger was neither short nor tall, although he was stocky. He had a youthful chubby face and hair that had now gone completely white. His face was friendly and honest. He was the sort of person that other people instinctively trust.

"I was thinking about you," said Father Junger.

"I'll be alright."

Gabriel was trying to be brave, and was at least appearing to be so.

"You can be truthful with me."

There was a silence.

"You prayed?"

"Yes."

"Before you came in I was thinking about that line from Proverbs— 'As silver is tried by fire and gold in the furnace so the Lord trieth hearts.' Right now we have all been thrown into the furnace."

Father Junger held the ladle over his left hand so that the soup would not drop on the rug.

"But you know," he continued, "fire can create as well as destroy. Who knows where this will lead? Of the dead, including our own, they have found a grace beyond imagining. What is that line from Corinthians? 'Eye hath not seen, nor ear heard, neither hath it entered into the hearts of man, what things God has prepared for them that love him.'"

Gabriel nodded. The words were soothing, even if a rather large part of him doubted at the moment their veracity.

Father Junger turned and motioned to the stovetop, where a pot was filled with simmering vegetable soup. He had been reluctant to mention anything of Eileen. It was simply too much to talk about just then, even for him.

"—No, no, go right ahead."

Gabriel sat at the table. As Father Junger stirred the final spices into the soup, Gabriel's stomach began to growl.

"Can you believe it?" Father Junger spoke more loudly now, for he had turned on a fan in the window. "I am not permitted to leave the chapel grounds. Colonel Bodine has restricted all unnecessary movement. Now let me ask you, why confine the base chaplain at a time like this? I feel like I am in middle school again, and must get a pass from the home room teacher to walk to the library. You know, it really is a shame. I could be of some use. A lot of people had relatives in ..."

He was talking over his shoulder and his face suddenly registered an expression of regret at his choice of words. Gabriel made a gesture with his hand, as if sweeping away a fly, to say "that's alright."

A thoughtful silence followed.

After awhile the soup was ready, and Father Junger poured them each a large bowl, then cut some homemade bread into slices and placed the plate between them. The brightly painted bowls had been made in the farming village of Kisolo in the volcano country of Uganda, where Father Junger had worked as a missionary in his youth.

"I hope you don't mind. I can't have the radio on. It is all too much. They were playing the latest message from Xanthes when I turned it off. It's like listening to John Wilkes Booth rant about Abraham Lincoln. The man should be making pot holders in an asylum."

"And yet there he is."

Father Junger nodded. He was becoming more animated as he ate.

"I knew a man once," he said, dipping a piece of bread into the soup, "who was on a pilgrimage with his good friend to the Holy Lands—" Gabriel paid close attention, for whenever Father Junger began with "I knew a man once ..." you could be sure he was talking about himself "—and when the two of them reached the gates of Jerusalem his friend looked up and pointed at something and then suddenly collapsed on the ground. His face was turning red and he was holding his chest and it was clear to everyone that he was having a heart attack. The poor fellow got out just one last word before he died. The word was 'Why?'"

Father Junger paused to chew and swallow a piece of bread. He took a full drink of his iced tea and then continued.

"And that is the only question isn't it? Everything else is a variation of that question: Why are we here? Why do we suffer? Why must we die? Why? Why? Why? That is the first question that Heraclitus asked and the last question that Camus asked. And yet, you can stack all of their books from here to the ceiling of the Sistine Chapel and get no closer to the truth."

He reached for another piece of bread, and spread a thick layer of margarine upon it with a butter knife.

"What did the one man say to the other?" Gabriel asked.

"The one man?"

"You know, in the story."

"Oh, he said something like 'It is God's will,' but he didn't know if the other man even heard him. The eyes of the other man were awfully still by then, you know."

Gabriel's beeper went off and he walked over to the phone on the kitchen wall and called a number and spoke to someone. When he came back he said it had just been Major Weathers checking on his location.

"You see," Father Junger continued, "you and I are in the same predicament. All of this is happening to the world and yet we are both stuck here, like two useless potatoes in a grocery store vegetable aisle unable to do anything."

Father Junger got up and poured them each a second bowl of soup. Neither had realized how hungry they were. Gabriel actually felt more empty with each spoonful.

"You know, Gabriel, the life of the mind is two forces. We have the necessity to believe in order to live and we have the necessity to reason in order to advance. There are times when the will to reason is paramount, and there are other times, like now, when faith must be supreme. Without faith, there is no way to endure."

"Do you think what happened had a purpose?"

Father Junger paused.

"In terms of my faith, yes, but still, I am a reflective person."

"Can I ask you a difficult question?"

"They are the best kind."

"What if there is no God? What if this just happened?"

"Well, we will not know until we die. Until then, we have a choice. We do, after all, have free will. We can decide whether to believe or not to believe. For me, I see evidence everywhere. All of this organized beauty can not be accidental. You are a scientist—what would the chances be of that randomly occurring? No, something definitely made all this, and it is open and free, like the spirit of its founder. We are free to choose between good and evil. And that is why we have evil. Some people choose good and other people, like Xanthes, choose evil. The story is as old as Cain and Abel."

Gabriel nodded in agreement. He finished his soup and pushed back from the table. Father Junger brought over an apple pie and cut them each a slice.

"The question now," Gabriel said, "is what to do."

"Exactly. You know, I have heard they might capitulate."

Gabriel made an incredulous face.

"They see themselves in a checkmate. You see, the leaders of Trgit are afraid to turn Xanthes over. I mean, he could do the same to them. Besides, he supports them with his opium trade. So there he sits, in his desert fortress, threatening civilization with apocalypse."

"So what are you saying?"

"Let me suggest a metaphor. Think of this ideology, this fanaticism, as a tree. Now the civilized world is going to try to chop it up with axes. But when you cut the branches, the roots remain. With a little water and fertilizer, the branches will grow again. We must get at the roots."

"Does that—"

"—You see, they are trying to destroy our way of life, which is based on freedom. It seems to me that we should now—"

"—But what about the Sermon on the Mount?"

Father Junger raised his eyebrows, as if to say, "I am glad you asked that!"

"I seem to recall that the same god who parted the seas for Moses also drowned the army of the Pharaoh. Look, Gabriel, these people hate us and they are not afraid of us. We can not change their hate but we can make them fear us. In the end, the choice is simple. Either they destroy us or we destroy them. Even the pope has condoned the use of force."

The mention of the pope caused Gabriel to pause in his thinking. The two finished the last bit of their dessert in silence, each privately considering everything that had been discussed, which had provided a different sort of meal. After awhile there was a knock at the open door. It was a group of enlisted men who wanted to be led in prayer. Father Junger told them he would be right up. Gabriel helped clear away the dishes.

"This has been a good talk," Father Junger said, putting his hand on Gabriel's shoulder. "Let us talk again soon. Some good may come from this, yet."

iii.

GABRIEL WALKED UP THE STAIRS into the sun-drenched desert, blinking at the intensity of light, and returned to his quarters across the street. The usually busy street was empty and the base was filled with an uncommon quiet. His quarters were even more spartan than Father Junger's—two rooms and a bath, with no kitchen because the mess hall was a block away. Even the view was terrible—a parking lot and the runway. He tried calling Houston once, but there was only a recording that said all lines to the area code were busy because of the high volume. After that, and this was in keeping with Uintah tradition, he methodically removed all reminders of Eileen from his dwelling—framed photographs, a box of letters, a pair of ceramic rabbits from a vacation to San Francisco, all of those artifacts that each of us collects along the way.

He then sat down for a moment to reflect.

Although his mind functioned in logical ways—flowing down pathways and through branches of circuitry that could, if given sufficient time and means, be mapped out to the farthest twigs of ganglia—there was something new and unfamiliar inside him. It was an alien fissionable material surrounded by spheres and shells of reason, but it was still capable of its own kind of explosion. It was an anger that had washed him clean of everything that was benign and emptied him of all that could pass for hope. This new force was there now, in his core, and it was changing him in ways small and large. Even with the physical reminders gone, buried away in a cardboard box at the bottom of the hallway closet, he could still recall the smooth and polished arch of her brows, the small straight nose, and the way her eyes grooved merrily when she smiled. And whenever he thought of her, one part of him grew while another part of him diminished.

Hours passed, and he did not move from the chair. Try as he might, he could not wrap himself around what had happened. It was too vast, too sudden, too intractable.

Eventually the room began to darken and he looked at the clock, surprised to see the entire day had passed and he had not moved.

He went to bed, then, and fell into a sleep that was marked by dreams that took him far away, dreams that pained the very sense they were

meant to please, dreams that pulled him to the edge of life and then over
a porous boundary into what lay beyond. He awakened in the hour before dawn, hearing birds, and opened his eyes to see a star burning outside his window.

By degrees it disappeared.

He rose then, when the world was light again, and pondered things
ranging from the innocuous to the ruthless. He knew that history is a
broad and deep river. He knew that people do not matter much to the
current, which can one moment uncover a sandbar and the next wash it
away, gently fertilize a field and then violently drown a city, and all according to a momentum that obeyed only the laws of physics. He also
knew that systems tend to exist in equilibrium and then fall into chaos
and then reorganize themselves in a new state of harmony, and that this
rhythm is pervasive across time and space. He, finally, understood that
at moments of rapid change a single person can have an effect that is am-
plified by the energy around them.

What had occurred had, in this sense, liberated him. He had no parents,
no siblings, no relatives at all. He was alone, and free to act in a way that
others could not, however much they might wish they could. The government might be restricted in certain ways, but he was not. The world
might be confused, but he could apprehend with clarity. The nation could
feel fear, but he could remain calm. He had, in a sense, died when the
bomb went off, and was now leading a posthumous existence. He was a
phantom, a specter, an apparition. As a result, he was now free to wander
between and among the worlds and to act as he truly wished, though always in accordance with the nature of the spirit that had created him.

Suddenly it became clear to him. He saw among the many possible
worlds that could begin tomorrow, or the day thereafter, an alternative
history, a future that would flow from an event that he would initiate
and that would be both a culmination and a new beginning.

A few minutes later he knocked at Father Junger's door.

iv.

OVER THE NEXT DAY the two men had several more talks. Gradually
an understanding was reached, and a philosophical solution that was also

a practical plan was formulated, even if its particulars were only vaguely alluded to. Nothing was ever stated explicitly. Everything was communicated in implied statements and telling gestures and shared looks. The two men spoke discreetly around the obvious, as people often do when developing a plan that can not for whatever reason be revealed in words. The closest to a specific reference about their thinking occurred when Father Junger asked "But would one person, even with your computer skills, be able to——."

At which point Gabriel raised his hand to prevent him from speaking further, and simply nodded in affirmation.

In their last conversation Father Junger inquired of Gabriel if he had reached a decision on the matter they had been considering. Gabriel replied that he had. Father Junger asked him if there was any assistance that he could render. Gabriel said no. He would take care of everything himself. It would not be that hard to do. Father Junger then said, "Let us go to the chapel and pray."

Kneeling in the first pew in front of the altar, they recited the Twenty-Third Psalm and the Lord's Prayer. Father Junger then spoke a prayer: "Almighty and merciful god, whose designs are inscrutable, whose glory is without boundary, whose compassion for our errors is inexhaustible, in your will is our peace and our salvation. Mercifully hear us as we pray tonight for your guidance as we make our way on this journey. Help us to see clearly and to act justly in accordance with your will. Amen."

v.

TEN HOURS LATER Gabriel was standing once more outside the bunker in the San Rafael desert as he did every Thursday morning. A wind was blowing steadily from the west and a thickness of clouds was holding the sun off the earth. There was the smell of rain in the air. The whole desert was dull and gloomy in appearance, and the shapes of the mountains had changed. They were no longer brilliant violet, and studded with luminous blue shadows, but had become flat mounds of earth rising from an ordinary ground.

After awhile another jeep could be seen driving across the valley. By degrees it neared and finally it stopped.

Lieutenant Oxnard stepped out slowly. Like many people, she had a stiff back from another sleepless night. To be polite, she asked Gabriel how he was doing. He smiled at her in a way that suggested he was barely aware of the fact that she existed, and that his mind was thousands of miles away.

She said nothing more, but regarded him strangely.

As they waited for the door to open Gabriel turned and looked over his shoulder. The others were talking but he could not hear them. His eyes were resting on a missile silo in the distance.

Grand Gulch

THERE IS A LITTLE-TRAVELED HIGHWAY in the Cedar Mesa country that runs south from the highlands to the Arizona borderlands. Along either side of the road there are low rolling hills with pinyon and juniper, interspersed with the occasional dry watercourse or old grass pasture turned to sage. The asphalt pavement goes on, straight and narrow, for miles and the only radio station comes from Window Rock on the Navajo reservation. Frequently all you will hear is a group of men chanting to the beat of a single drum. From the south the sky is brighter than in any other direction, and that brightness is the reflected light of Monument Valley, which is largely exposed stone. On the day I am thinking of I had planned to continue on to photograph the Mitten Buttes, but on passing the trailhead to Grand Gulch, a half-million acre archaeological preserve, everything changed. I am one of those souls who can not resist an opportunity to hike into the backcountry, particularly on a sunny spring morning, and so I parked the car at the Kane Gulch Ranger Station and filled the pack and set off.

Northern Arizona would have to wait until tomorrow.

The trail began on the west side of the road and dropped by degrees into the upper portals of a canyon. In places the sage and junipers were shoulder-high and the trail, the main trail, was easily lost among the cattle trails. Once in the canyon the converging trails became a single narrow path and the stone walls lifted toward the sky and the air became still and cool, with the intimate quiet of a contained space—a place of worship, a library retreat, a museum exhibit space. A mile farther there was a cattle guard and I opened and closed the gate and stepped into that other world—the one from which all livestock and machinery are excluded. The sign read *Grand Gulch Primitive Area, administered by the B.L.M., San Juan District, Monticello, Utah—No motorized vehicles, or equipment permitted—Violations punishable under Public Law 16 U.S.C. 551 and 16 U.S.C. 1131–1136.*

Instantly there was the feeling of exhilaration that always attends one's entry into the wilderness. Deeper and deeper the canyon carved into the plateau, curving like a serpent with sinuous bends and darkly streaked overhangs and quiet alcoves set in the stone. At first the stream was dry, but shortly there were dripping springs and standing pools and spurting waterfalls. In places the trail was no wider than my shoulders, where it passed through a tangled patch of willows. In other places it could accommodate two horses side by side. Steadily the canyon walls rose. From twenty to thirty feet they were within one mile one hundred to one hundred and fifty feet in height. Looking up you saw white Cedar Mesa sandstone, unclimbable overhangs, the formidable palisades of the netherworld.

Spring progressively became more evident—the swollen pussy willows, the partially leafed cottonwoods and oaks, the budding yuccas and prickly pear cactus, the singing sage sparrows, the chanting canyon frogs, the green sprouts of what would in a few days become the blossoms of pink mariposa lily, red paintbrush, blue penstemon, white peppergrass, purple shooting star, and yellow prince's plume.

A pleasant surprise in the first two miles were the aspen trees, scattered here and there in the deep shaded alcoves, elegant white-barked visitors from the high country.

Another unexpected discovery were the fine waterfalls cascading over polished green slickrock into deep clear pools. The natural gardens around these basins were more perfect than anything an arboretum gardener could create. Not one of these were marked on the topographic map, and so I named each for a lovely woman. Terri Falls, Monica Falls, and so on.

Everywhere there were huge perched boulders. Picture a two and a half ton truck poised on its right front headlight. Or a locomotive balanced on its cowcatcher. Judging from the desert varnish on the rock (desert varnish being a thin veneer that slowly forms on rock surfaces exposed to the atmosphere), the boulder had been *in situ* for a very long time. Somewhere I read that geologists consider balanced rocks to be a natural indicator of seismic stability. If that is the case, the high desert must be one of the most geologically stable regions on the planet.

After four miles the side canyon opened into a larger canyon and it was there, above a grassy triangular bench, that I came upon the remnants of an Anasazi village. The houses, granaries, and kiva were not on the flats, where the fields would have been maintained, but were perched high in the rocks, in the manner of cliff swallow nests. The most remote structures could only have been reached by rope, for two stories of vertical rock separated them from the ground. In those protected nooks the resident Anasazi would have stored their seed caches of maize, melons, beans, and sunflower in stone pots, safe from rodents and birds. Other dwellings—the bulk of them—were clustered at ground level in an overhang that formed a shallow cave. The cave faced south in such a way that the residents would have been warm and sun-washed in the winter and cool and shaded in the summer. Aesthetically, the Anasazi homes fit into the landscape in a way modern frame homes do not, for they were built directly from the earth—sandstone and mud.

I spent the day exploring the village and that part of the central canyon, which is in its full length sixty miles long. There was much of their world to see—room after shadow-haunted room, pottery sherds with geometric designs painted on them, scattered piles of 900-year-old corn cobs, pipe fragments and reed baskets, well-worn grinding stones, chipping rocks and unfinished arrowheads, a child's straw sandal at the bottom of a kiva. The place was superintended by an irregular squad of collared lizards, their eyes sparkling like imbedded jewels. They stared at you and followed you and in their own understated way let you know you were not welcome to stay long.

Not far from the ruins, nearly lost among the cottonwoods, was a rock panel with petroglyphs scratched into the darkly varnished wall surface. Despite the inherent limitations of the artistic technique, the images had spirit and strength: A pair of deer, tense and alert, their heads raised at some disturbance. A strange spiral. A coyote. A bighorn. A star. A serpent. Handprints, perhaps the artist's attempt at a signature. From what I could discern, the Anasazi had been on the verge of moving toward the next stage: hieroglyphics. From there, it would have only been a matter of time before they began to develop an alphabet, a written language, the most useful tool in the hands of any civilization.

The spare, visionary style of the petroglyphs evoked images to be found in other dry and dusty parts of the world—the desert mountain ranges of North Africa, the ancient canyonlands of Central Asia, the high plateaus of South America. The impulse to create is cross-cultural and global and is not bound by any particular time or place, for it is part of each human being's spiritual endowment.

Evening came early to the bottom of the canyon—a little brown bat with translucent wings flittering among a cloud of mosquitoes, a gathering violet to the sky, one faint star to the east. I headed back up the dark side canyon, reluctant to leave, but deeply appreciative for what I had seen. The Anasazi village, and accompanying rock panels, had provided me with a glimpse of how a group of human beings can live in communion with the earth. The ancient ones have much to teach us. From them we can learn how to look at the landscape, and how to walk through it, and, perhaps most importantly, how to sit in one place and let the spirit of the place—its gentle life, its surprising secrets, its elusive presence—quietly come to us.

Here Today

IT WAS NOON. The Grand Canyon lay sleeping. The gulf was quiet and still except for a light breeze that gently moved through the branches of the pinyons and junipers. Under the trees there was a net of sunlight and shadow spread across the ground. Lizards darted here and there, some of them trailing pieces of shed skin.

The old man and woman were sitting on a rock east of Lipan Point. There was a crowd at the point, as always, people coming and going and much distracting activity, and so they had followed a wandering trail down the ridge to a place where they could be alone with the landscape.

The sky was blue. There was not one cloud. It was as if the word cloud had yet to be invented.

A breeze lifted the old man's buoyant hair and it floated above his head. He had given up on trying to do anything with it. It had a mind of its own, particularly in a dry climate. The woman had tied a scarf around her head. They were both dressed in clothes not normally seen in the park. The man looked like an old world gentlemen with his fine mustache and gold-rimmed glasses and wool jacket. He was wearing a blue dress shirt. The woman was dressed simply in a gray skirt and a blue blouse. Their faces, which once had been quite different, had over the years become similar. They now seemed like slightly different versions of the same person. Sitting there side by side they resembled two trees that have been rooted together closely in one place for so long it is difficult to tell where one begins and the other ends.

"What's the best time we ever had?" asked the wife.

"I think I know. But you go first."

"I think I know, too."

"Well, I'm not going to say anything until you do."

"Alright, then, I've got it. The time on the North Tyne."

"The walk through Wark Forest?"

"Yes."

"It was a special day. It was before Anna——."

"——Yes."

Her face became flat with a memory, but gradually her expression changed as she searched her past. "I remember the fireweed."

"Yes, especially around that old Roman fort."

"And then you——"

She smiled.

He laughed "——we won't talk about 'that.'"

There was a silence then. They were each absorbed in their own thoughts. The old man was reliving a train trip half a century earlier westbound on the overnight from St. Louis to Denver. She boarded at Kansas City and the train was full and she had to sit next to him. It turned out she was dating one of his fraternity brothers, and when the train pulled into Union Station, there was the idiot boyfriend waving from the platform.

Eleven months later he and the girl next to him on the train were married.

A pinecone fell from the tree, bounced from branch to branch, and landed at his feet. He picked the pinecone up and felt its weight and the sharpness of its edges against his fingers. The desert ground was dry and sunbleached and fragrant with wild herbs and it reminded him of a place in Sicily where he had become very well acquainted with a piece of the earth once and he decided it was time to talk.

"What were you thinking about just now?" he asked.

"What we did later that day. Do you remember?"

"We … stopped at that inn on the lane where we got lost. There was that innkeeper with the strange name. Dumphrey something or other."

"It was Humphrey. Humphrey Basil. Oh, those Brits, and he had those two dogs Gog and Magog——"

Suddenly there was a voice behind them. It was a teenage girl with her black hair in two braids. She explained her car had broken down and she and her boyfriend needed a ride. It would only be a few miles. The boyfriend was up on the hill, looking down at them. The sun was behind his head and he was hard to see.

The old man politely declined to help and suggested they wait for the ranger patrol.

After the girl returned to the top of the hill the wife was silent.

"You disagree?" he asked.

"It wouldn't hurt to give them a ride."

"The world is full of all sorts."

They had had this conversation many times before. He was a skeptic. He called himself a Hobbesian. She liked to quote Mark Twain: "I'm optimistic despite the evidence." They had had the conversation about the nature of the world so many times before they decided not to have it again.

That night they were eating dinner at the South Rim Lodge and they overheard a conversation at another table about something that had occurred that afternoon along the road and the wife said nothing, silently regarding the husband, who seemed neither pleased with himself nor ready to discuss the matter any further. He was just staring at her with the same faraway look he gave the canyon.

After dessert she began taking her pills. There were six of them in various sizes and colors and she took them one at a time, gulping water each time.

When she was finished they walked out on the stone patio. Everyone had gone back inside. They had missed the sunset. The sun was gone, and there was a red rim on the western horizon. The rest of the sky was night-blue and rapidly thickening with stars. The brightest stars seemed very near, as if they were fireflies. The depths of the canyon were muffled in a gloomy purple shadow. Masses of solid black bulked up in places. The near rocks seemed like pieces of aged ivory.

They said nothing. They just held hands and viewed the darkness.

Gradually a deep cold began flowing over the heights of the canyon. They shivered at the breeze and turned to go back inside.

The door was locked and so they tapped and after awhile a waiter came over and let them in.

What Does It Mean?

IN HIS BOOK *The Grand Canyon of the Colorado* (1920), Professor John Van Dyke—an art history professor at Rutgers University—asked the question "What does it mean?" He attempted no answer and did not provide any further guidance. He simply posed the question, as a teacher should. But in the absence of an explanation, I have—for I am the eternal student—often pondered his words. It is a good question. Perhaps too good, for it strikes at the heart of the matter, and I do mean matter.

There are two possibilities. Either the canyon—which we can take as an emblem for all of nature—means nothing or it means something. Edward Abbey, in his essay "Down the River," embraced the former point of view: "What does it mean? It means nothing. It is as it is and has no need for meaning. The desert lies beneath and soars beyond any possible human qualification. Therefore, sublime."

Sublime as a response has always seemed to me inadequate. Sublime, a term introduced by the Roman philosopher Longinus, means "glorious, resplendent, majestic." Something is sublime if it causes a "lifting up" (*ekstasis*) of the spirit. How does it help our understanding to simply state that the Grand Canyon, i.e. nature both wild and human, is beautiful? And, if it is beautiful—organized according to regular laws and patterns—how can it then mean nothing? Why should there be beauty—systematically arranged matter—if there is no purpose? If matter had no purpose, wouldn't the reverse be true—anarchy instead of order? Doesn't beauty prove by its very form that its existence is not without reason? And doesn't that design imply a designer?

It is much more difficult to say that nature, both wild nature and human nature, means something, because then you have to uncover that meaning.

To me the high desert is pretty clear evidence of how powerfully change permeates the universe, indeed is the theme of the cosmos. Major Powell, writing in *The Exploration of the Colorado River* (1870), expressed it this way:

Now we have canyon gorges and deeply eroded valleys, and still the hills are disappearing, the mountains themselves are wasting away, the plateaus are dissolving, and the geologist, in the light of the past history of the earth, makes prophecy of a time when this desolate land of Titanic rocks shall become a valley of many valleys, and yet again the sea will invade the land, and the coral animals build their reefs. ... Thus ever the land and sea are changing; old lands are buried, and new lands are born.

The message is clear—change pervades all that we know and can experience with a force that can not be opposed and with a thoroughness that could be called wisdom.

Nor is there anything original about this line of thinking.

Listen to my old friend Marcus Aurelius, dead now some twenty centuries: "Observe constantly that all things take place by change, and accustom yourself to consider that the nature of the Universe loves nothing so much as to change the things which are and to make new things like them." Or his Greek mentor Heraclitus: "Everything flows and nothing abides; everything gives way and nothing stays fixed" and "It is in changing that things find repose."

Read any of the Asian philosophers—Lao-Tzu, Confucius, Mencius—and you will find the same understanding.

What, then, shall we take away with us from the rim of the canyon?

For me, it is simple—the belief that those who embrace change are liberated, and those who resist are annihilated. I can live by this principle with as much trust as if I had heard it in a lecture hall from a venerated scholar. In a sense I have, for the desert is not unlike a great university—a Harvard without doors, an Oxford without dons, a Heidelberg without the hubris. There are department heads that wear the black robes of the raven, and deans with the all-seeing eyes of a desert bighorn, and lecture halls built to hold a generation. Lessons are delivered hourly, by example, on all the virtues Plato extolled. We learn about courage in the face of adversity, and freedom and responsibility, and the price to be paid for avarice or ignorance. The library houses two billion years of history, and the outdoor museums contain the ruins of a half-dozen dead cultures. At night, the classrooms expand to include the farthest visible stars.

Let insincerity and ambition reign elsewhere. The desert will forever be the domain of the sun and the sand, the river and the rock, a landscape from the Book of Genesis or the mind of Thomas Merton. Here destruction and creation, past and present, life and death are one. Here is the kingdom of change, the unchanging. Here a person may stand on Earth and catch a glimpse of eternity, which is—as a wandering carpenter once predicted, and with the confidence of someone who has seen it—an immensely calm and beautiful place.

The Diamond

LONG AGO AND FAR AWAY there was a volcano in a place we now call the desert. It rose from the plains and for a time its fire and smoke dominated that part of the world. Over time, like all things in nature, the volcano grew old and lost its strength. Gradually its rumblings ceased and it forgot what had caused its fury and plants came to live on its slopes. The rains took over then, slowly washing its earth down to the streambeds, where the rocks were further sorted and scattered. Many ages passed. Eventually all that remained was the dense pillar that had been its heart, a battered relict standing upright on a flat valley. It was a grim rampart, a ruined mass, a monumental tombstone for a thing that was already old when the surrounding landscape was young.

One day a people came from the north and settled in the area. They lived for many generations in the cliffs and built their homes from mud and stone. They knew about corn and made bows of oak to hunt the desert bighorn sheep. When the rains did not fall for several years they moved away. For a long time the land was empty. The cottonwood leaves still turned yellow when the deer had lost their velvet and the mariposa lilies still blossomed a few days before the finches returned, but there were no human voices, only the water and the wind and the coyote and the raven. Six hundred winters later another people came from the north. They called the rock Agathla, and settled in the desert, building eight-sided homes they called hogans. Eventually the Spanish came and named the rock El Capitan. They left then, too.

El Capitan became a familiar presence to residents and travelers, for it could be seen for miles, from Wetherill Mesa on the north to Church Rock on the south, from Comb Ridge on the east to Owl Rock on the west. Early pilots flying south from Escalante would welcome its appearance on the horizon, and know from its position that they were an hour from Gallup. During the third term of Franklin Roosevelt a paved road was built about a mile from the rock and large format photographers from places like Carmel and Prescott would stop each summer at the pullouts. Occasionally they were joined by artists from Taos, who would walk farther into the desert and set up their French easels beyond the sounds of the road. People were naturally drawn to the beauty of the solitary rock that edged the turquoise with darkness. It had been, like them, methodically stripped of any aspect that could be called soft or gentle. All that remained was the indestructible core. It was both a thing of beauty and a geological curiosity, a dead piece of rock and a metaphor. In galleries around the country various interpretations were exhibited.

The red soil around El Capitan was fertile, and after a snowy winter the grass grew thick and the local sheepherders, who were of the Navajo nation, brought their sheep to graze. Often they would let their spotted dogs watch the flocks and they would go up into the rocks to explore. They would search in the rubble at the base for pieces of obsidian, which were sharp enough to cut leather, and Apache tears, smooth opaque crystals about the size of your thumb. Their wives and daughters and sisters could then sell these objects at the roadside stands to the north in Monument Valley. On hot days, the sheepherders would take a gallon of water up into the shade behind El Capitan and watch the blue sky or the faraway storms and tell stories. The clouds would rise in all sorts of shapes and they would tell stories they had heard before or that had occurred in their own lives. At such times a man was judged by the stories he could tell, because that is all they had other than the shade of the rock. Sometimes they would look at the distant road and make jokes about the tour buses and freight trailers and cars. Sometimes they would recognize a passing pick up truck by its color or the time of its appearance and they would comment about the driver. In this way they could pass whole days.

ii.

JOSEPH BEGAY WAS BORN NEAR CHINLE in the spring of 1965. The exact month and day is not known because his parents lived far from the road and he was born at home. When he was in his second spring his father Walter who had tended sheep in Black Rock Canyon went to

Vietnam. A year later a bullet found him as he was running toward a Huey helicopter near a place called The Parrot's Peak. The battle was actually in Cambodia but the official letter from the Secretary of the Army reported he had been killed by a land mine in the Mekong Delta. After that his mother Grace moved Joseph and herself to Kayenta to be closer to her family. She worked at the Blue Mesa Trading Post on U.S. 160 and took correspondence courses from the college at Window Rock for her degree in family counseling. One night in March there was an ice storm and when a porcupine appeared on the road she rolled her 1958 Volkswagen on the big curve south of Navajo Mountain. Several days passed before they found the car because it was in the pinyons.

Joseph was eleven then, and old enough to work, and so he left school and began keeping a herd of sheep on the open pasture near El Capitan. For the next five years he worked in that area, living with an elderly man and his wife who lived along Antelope Wash. Lucy and Russell Hale had never had a child and were glad to have Joseph stay with them. To them it was like suddenly finding the month of June in the middle of the winter. On his twelfth birthday they bought him a spotted puppy, and eventually a fourteen-hand Appaloosa that he liked to ride on Sunday afternoons. Like the father and the grandfather he had never known, Joseph was always cheerful, whether he was by himself or with others. Everyone agreed he was a pleasure to have around, particularly if work was involved.

There was a girl named Rose Martin who lived in Shonto. She came to Kayenta on the weekends to work at her Aunt Lorraine's jewelry shop. She and Joseph met one Saturday morning while they were waiting for the grocery store to open. Both were too shy to talk at first but they were still drawn to speak. Everyone from the store was at a funeral for the assistant manager who had drowned in Lake Powell and so they had an hour to talk. He liked the way her shiny black hair fell over her shoulders and sometimes covered her eyes in the wind when they were talking and she liked the way he smiled when he didn't have anything to say. She also liked the breadth of his shoulders, and the muscles that came from walking all day over the desert that made it difficult for him to fit into a pair of jeans. She was a young woman whose face looked best in profile. From all other angles she was ordinary, but from either side she

was lovely. After about a year of seeing each other every Saturday she and
Joseph were married by a minister in Tuba City, because she was a Christian and had him convert.

They lived then on some land the old man and woman had given him.

iii.

IT WAS THE MONTH OF MAY and the grass was still green and Joseph
was climbing on the rock known as El Capitan. On days when there was
no one else around and there was nothing else to do he liked to take off
his shoes and socks and follow the handholds and outcrops and fissures
and angled fractured rock into the heights. Sometimes he would find
personal items that earlier climbers had left in secret places in the rock—
a fine fluted arrowhead made of flint, a bit of broken pottery with a
mud thumbprint, a flat piece of sandstone scratched with the image of
a waving man. He would leave these things for other climbers to find,
because he understood that they belonged to El Capitan in the same
sense that a person owns his freckles or his scars.

Occasionally he would come upon bird nests. The rock doves liked
to nest on the lower reaches of the pinnacle, and their nests of twigs
and mud were always in a safe place on the east side, away from the pre-
vailing winds. The doves mated and bred at all times of the year, even
in the winter. Sometimes there would be eggs in the nest, small and
smooth and white, and other times there would be little birds. Joseph
had learned that the baby birds liked to eat corn and grass seed and the
fruit of the cactus. Sometimes he would bring them treats such as wild
strawberries or shelled sunflower seeds. They would rapidly beat their
wings and shriek as they did when they were being fed by their parents.
Up higher there were the nests of falcons and eagles, but there was no
way to climb that high without ropes. Once he had found the shed wing
feather of a golden eagle. He had carefully put it inside his t-shirt and
brought it down as a gift to the Hales. The feather was as long as the
bone between his wrist and his elbow and it was in immaculate condition and they kept it in a box of cedar.

On this day he had chosen a route he had not taken before. He had
often wondered if there was a way up this part of the wall on the north

side of the pinnacle. After climbing for a quarter of an hour he reached a point about as high as a three-story adobe where there was a ledge and he rested there awhile. Looking out, he could see the country as if he was a bird flying and he noted places that he knew and trails that he had taken. It was all familiar to him, the valleys and mesas and wandering stream courses and standing rocks, and after he had surveyed the local neighborhood he let his eyes rest on the blue mountains far to the east, near Window Rock. He had been there once, for a rodeo on the Fourth of July, and seeing it always reminded him of his mother and her dreams.

As he was about to leave and was searching for a good place to put his right hand he discovered a crystal stuck in a groove where the rock curved outward. He had a folding knife with him and he opened the smaller blade and chiseled the crystal from the rock. It was not difficult to remove the crystal and soon it was sparkling in the palm of his hand. The crystal was about the size of a dove's egg. It had seven or eight flat sides and each was polished to brightness as if by a chamois. The inner depths of the crystal had a pale yellow tint. The outer regions were clear. It resembled a piece of broken glass, or something that had fallen out of the world's largest honeycomb, but Joseph knew that it could not be glass or anything else from where he had found it. He put the crystal in a deer-skin pouch he kept in his jean pocket and climbed back down.

That night after dinner when he and Rose were sitting outside watching the sunset and talking about the day he casually took the pouch from his pocket and showed the crystal to her. He asked her what she thought and she said that she believed her Aunt Lorraine would know. There was an awkward moment when Joseph asked for the crystal back and she reluctantly gave it to him and watched as he put it back into the pouch.

Three days passed.

Rose would not let him touch her during this time and slept with her back to him because he was keeping the crystal in his deer pouch as if he did not trust her. Whenever Joseph asked her what was wrong she pretended as though everything was fine, and said sarcastically that this is the way it always had been and always would be. She had begun to drop things, as well, and to generally make as much accidental noise as she could, while all the time stating that nothing was wrong. Although

Joseph would not admit it to anyone, even the spotted dog that he talked to sometimes, he had begun to wonder how it would be if this new thing did have value, and who this woman was who had recently come into his life, and why she should now be entitled to have a part of something that he had found himself while climbing on that dangerous rock.

On Saturday they drove into Kayenta as always for weekly groceries but they did not talk happily to one another about the small events that held their lives together as they normally did. On their way out of town they stopped at her aunt's shop. Her aunt made jewelry from silver and turquoise and sold it to tourists. She was in a good frame of mind because the summer season was beginning. Busloads of tourists from Phoenix and Las Vegas were arriving nearly every day. She was a short stout woman with silver hair she wore back in a bun. She was always busy, and somehow kept her business afloat year after year even when the economy was bad and the tourists from places like Europe and Asia did not come. She had raised two children alone after her husband died in a coal mine accident and she had long ago stopped viewing life as an equitable or even enjoyable proposition. She lived like a turtle, with a hard shell and slow deliberate movements from one known place to another. At times she seemed as hard as a rock.

She studied the crystal for several minutes under a hand lens and then tried scratching it with a piece of quartz.

She stated that it was worthless, a thing of little or no value.

Joseph asked her what she thought it was.

She replied that perhaps it was some sort of an agate. She said that determining the type of crystal was sometimes not possible. Most of the time it was not even necessary. Perhaps she could sell it for one dollar in her shoe box of loose rocks for children. She yawned and scratched the back of her head impatiently and when Joseph did not answer she looked at her watch.

Joseph asked for the crystal back.

Aunt Lorraine glanced again at the crystal in her hand as it lay flat on the glass counter and suggested that maybe she could give him ten dollars for it, that possibly it was a type of weird topaz or some other transparent mineral she did not know, and perhaps she could make use of it in a pendant or something.

At that point Joseph reached over and took the crystal from her hand and said that he appreciated the offer but that he and his wife would be leaving now.

On the way back home Joseph and Rose had the first serious argument of their marriage. Both of them realized from the aunt's demeanor that she had been deceiving them, but they did not argue about that. They argued about the way Joseph had taken the crystal back. Rose thought that his conduct was not polite, even if her aunt was trying to take advantage of them. Joseph refused to apologize for what he had done and said that the aunt was being evil as evil is defined in the bible that Rose had forced him on many a night to read. He had memorized passages from her bible and repeated them back to her now in a loud voice, and at that point the quarreling only became worse as it always does when voices are raised and sore points are belabored.

Two days later, instead of driving to the pasture in the morning, Joseph drove into town and went to the high school and asked to see the science teacher, Mr. Gray, whom he had met once in a field near Stage-coach Wash. Mr. Gray had been out capturing butterflies with a fine-mesh net. The western tansy mustard plants were in blossom and the pearly marblewings were everywhere. Mr. Gray believed he had come upon a new species of pearly marblewing because of the unique wing pattern. They were distinct from those found on Cedar Mesa, the Paria Plateau, and elsewhere. He had been so excited that he hadn't noticed that his black plastic glasses had slipped down the bridge of his nose or that his Bullfrog Marina baseball hat was pitched on his head ridiculously. He had held his gallon jar up to the sky as if it was a gift from the gods. In fact, he called it that, a gift from the gods.

Joseph had found him harmless and amusing.

The secretary led Joseph to Mr. Gray's empty classroom where he was grading papers from the morning quiz. Joseph introduced himself and said that he had found a crystal on his property and wondered what it might be. Mr. Gray gladly remembered Joseph from their prior meeting and they shook hands. He was a short limber man and although he was fifty he jumped off the lab table with the natural buoyancy of a fifteen year old. He held the crystal up to a beam of sunlight near the window and said it appeared to be an octahedral gemstone. Under the lab table

Mr. Gray kept a standard Mohs hardness testing kit which he used in geology modules. He took the kit out and then tried to scratch the surface with various test points—a copper wire, a piece of quartz, a steel file. Nothing worked. He even tried a bit of corundum, a crystal of aluminum oxide with a hardness of nine. That, too, failed to make the slightest etch. Mr. Gray told Joseph that he thought the crystal might be some sort of a diamond. If it was a diamond, Mr. Gray continued, the crystal would be of interest from a scientific perspective, because there were only about a dozen places in the world where diamonds could be found. Places such as India, Brazil, Russia, and southern Africa. The crystal would also have value because of its size.

Joseph asked how much.

Mr. Gray said that, given the clarity and color, it could be tens or even hundreds of thousands of dollars.

Joseph thought for a moment. He trusted Mr. Gray's judgement and asked him for his best advice. Mr. Gray suggested that Joseph show it to the state district geologist who would be in town on another matter in a few days.

Before Joseph left he asked Mr. Gray not to tell anyone. Mr. Gray readily agreed, but that night in bed before falling asleep he mumbled something about the unusual meeting to his wife. Telling his wife was really not like telling someone else, he reasoned, because they had become so close over the years they resembled one organism in two bodies. The next morning his wife called her sister, who in turn called her best friend who worked in advertising at the regional newspaper in Window Rock. When the paper came out three days later, the story about Joseph's diamond was on the first page. That same evening the Hales came over with the paper in hand and asked Joseph what was going on. He explained the situation, and promised to keep them abreast of any developments. After they left he turned to Rose and accused her Aunt Lorraine of having planted the story. Joseph then mentioned that he had visited the science teacher and this revelation only made matters worse. For the first time in his marriage, Joseph slept outside the hogan in his sleeping bag on the ground beside his spotted dog.

While he was off with his herd the next day a rusted out Pontiac GTO with four drunk men pulled up and they refused to leave until they had been shown the diamond. Rose said she did not have it and stayed in the house with the kitchen table against the door and told them to leave. They remained an hour, shouting obscenities and threats and generally making a nuisance of themselves. Before they left they broke a window with a rock. That night Rose told Joseph that she would have to leave and move back in with her aunt unless they got a gun. She insisted that they needed a gun now, with strange people showing up at their doorstep. Joseph said he would think about it.

The following afternoon he met with the district geologist, who ran further tests from a kit in the trunk of her car and confirmed that, yes, the crystal was a diamond of unusual purity. She suggested that Joseph sell the diamond as quickly as he could, because it was not safe to have a thing of such value at home. She gave him the name of an appraiser from Phoenix who could drive up at anytime. She thought he would give him a fair price and wished him good luck. Before she left she gave him her business card and said to feel free to call if he had any further questions or needed anything. He looked at the card which smelled of patchouli oil and noticed from her last name that she was of the Hopi nation.

When he arrived back home that night the Reverend Mather was already there. The Reverend Mather had come to the reservation six months earlier from a seminary in El Paso. He did not dress in a conventional dark blouse and white collar, but wore ordinary clothes. He was about thirty years old and had never been married. His face seemed handsome at first but seemed less so after he spoke. It was like a painting in a gallery that appears fine only from a considerable distance. He was tall and thin and kept his long blond hair in a ponytail. He wore a silver bracelet on his right wrist and he moved his hands a lot when he talked, as if he was standing at a pulpit and speaking to a congregation. He liked being the center of attention, and could speak for hours if no one stopped him. The story was that he had entered the seminary after he had failed at several other careers. The running joke among those who did not belong to his church was that he could persuade a deer to wear the horns of an antelope.

The Reverend Mather was sitting in one of their two chairs and he asked Joseph to consider donating the proceeds from the sale of the diamond to the church. The money could then be used to help build the alternative school for Christian families and to upgrade the church building. Joseph knew that the minister was sleeping with a married woman in the parish, and that Rose did not know this, and he also knew that the minister was gambling with church money at the new reservation casino in Tuba City. He had heard this from another sheep-herder who only spoke the truth and he had not shared this information with his wife so as not to disturb her faith. He listened patiently to what the Reverend had to say and then said he would think about it and get back to him in a few days.

The next day while he was out with the herd the appraiser from Phoenix showed up unexpectedly at their home and this led to another argument, because Joseph had not told Rose anything about the state geologist or the appraiser. Joseph was becoming accustomed to sleeping outdoors. It rarely rained in the desert, and the stars were nice overhead. The only drawback was that the wind blew sand in his ears and he was developing a cough.

He learned that the appraiser was staying at the Holiday Inn and so the next morning he and Rose went to meet the man, she mumbling something on the drive over about contacting a lawyer in Flagstaff that her brother knew in order to protect her interests. Joseph stared straight ahead and said nothing. He was learning to stare straight ahead and say nothing. The appraiser was a well-dressed city person in his early sixties named Victor Landau. He had the look of a man who has never missed a meal in his life and who has also successfully avoided any form of exercise in several decades. He wore a tailored white dress shirt and designer blue jeans and cowboy boots of the sort that are never dusty because they are worn only where there is carpeting or hardwood floors or concrete pavement. On the ring finger of his left hand was a black onyx set in gold.

He carried some testing equipment in his briefcase and when he had finished confirming what the state geologist told him he said that he could give Joseph four thousand five hundred dollars for the diamond. He could write him the check, right now, from the company checkbook, and they could close on the deal with a nice lunch in the restaurant, on him. He might even go as high as five thousand dollars. Enough to buy a new truck for Joseph's wife. The check was drawn from a long-established account at a well-known bank in Phoenix, and it was good.

Rose who had her hands folded on her purse told Joseph to go ahead and take the money. Joseph said no, that the science teacher had told him the diamond could be worth five or even six figures. He wanted to meet with other appraisers and see what they had to offer before making a decision. Mr. Landau replied that the only other appraisers in the Southwest with his various credentials and certifications were in Los Angeles and that Joseph and Rose should certainly feel free to drive out there and check with the other appraisers. Joseph and Rose then began to quarrel as if they were at home alone in the middle of the night and not in a hotel room with Mr. Victor Landau of Phoenix, Arizona. After ten minutes of listening to them bicker, their host excused himself from his own room and said he would be in the bar if they changed their minds.

He left the room and took his briefcase with him and Rose began crying and saying that the marriage was over, that she had no rights anymore, and that this diamond was a curse upon their lives.

Thereafter all sorts of people began showing up at their home—people who wanted money for surgical operations, people who wanted to touch the diamond and be cured of a fatal disease or annoying affliction, people who were blind and wanted to see, people whose children were not of a complete mind and who wanted them to be made whole by the crystal, people who wanted loans to start up promising businesses or patent brilliant inventions, people who were up to no good, people who were just in the area and wanted to drop by and see it, people from television stations and newspapers and magazines, people whom they had never heard of or seen before from both on and off the reservation. Word soon got out on the reservation that Joseph kept the diamond with him at all times, even sleeping with it out in the desert. Tracks began showing up in the sand around their home—the tracks of people waiting and drinking and dropping a rifle cartridge now and then—and it became clear to Joseph that he really did need a gun.

One day he drove to a pawnshop named Big Ernie's in Tuba City and bought an inexpensive used revolver and fifty rounds of lead-tipped ammunition in a cardboard box.

About a week later Joseph remembered that he had the gun and removed it from the paper bag. He was sitting at the dining table and Rose was standing across the room folding laundry. When he had finished loading all six chambers, he closed the cylinder and the gun went off in his hand. It was a cheap and defective twenty-two caliber revolver. When the cylinder was in place, the merest jolt of the hammer could cause the gun to fire. Rose had just bent over to pick up a dropped shirt when the gun went off. The bullet hit her high in the chest. It did not look bad at first and she stared at the bright red blood on her blouse in surprise, not feeling any pain and wondering what to do. The bullet, though, had passed through an artery and within a minute she was unconscious on the floor. Within another minute her face was as pale as the petals of the evening primrose that grow along the rivers at the bottom of the canyons.

It was as simple as that and it happened just as quickly.

A coyote was passing by the hogan just then, on his way to hunt the deer mice and ground squirrels that lived in the rocks at the base of El Capitan. He took the same trail every night, and stopped here and there to note the scent of whatever had passed through during the day. When he heard the shot, the coyote stopped moving and stood rigidly, having learned that when he was motionless he was less easily seen. The whole desert was silent, alert, listening. The coyote had heard gunshots before, but never in this place and at this hour. A gunshot could mean one of several things, ranging from danger to bounty. He looked down the hill toward where the spotted dog lived. The spotted dog was staring at the house. A human voice could be heard inside. The voice was rising and falling. The dog was pacing and whining.

The coyote watched, attentive.

There was a second shot, followed by a silence. The coyote then continued up the hill toward the black pinnacle that rose among the stars.

Afterword: Work in Progress

IN THE END, we know little of our condition. All around us are vast expanses of time and space. Truths and mysteries yet revealed deepen on every side. We are certain of little except that we are alive a short time. An eternity of perhaps nothing awaits us. Some cling to hopes of future good fortune. Others drift on legends of what might have been. I only know this. There are few things as beautiful as the shapes a desert river carves in the rock of a country, or the way a canyon rose holds its wine-colored blossom toward the sun, or the sound of the wind as you climb to the summit of a solitary peak. To have been among these places is to have known a happiness not often found elsewhere in this world.

A quartz crystal in its angular symmetry reveals the atomic structure of matter. In the same way do our acts of love, however small and seemingly insignificant, present an outward manifestation of ultimate nature. One could sit alone in the desert for thirty years, as with the early Christian fathers or the Indian yogis or the Tibetan monks, and probably advance no further toward that elusive final truth. Love them, dear readers, these lost and lonely lands, and you will find that in the end what you get back is equal to what you give.

SELECTED BOOKS BY JOHN A. MURRAY

A Republic of Rivers (Oxford University Press, 1990)
The Islands and the Sea (Oxford University Press, 1992)
Wild Africa (Oxford University Press, 1993)
A Thousand Leagues of Blue (Sierra Club Books, 1993)
Out Among the Wolves (Alaska Northwest, 1994)
Cactus Country (Roberts Rinehart, 1997)
Desert Awakenings (NorthWord, 1998)
Cinema Southwest (Northland, 2000)
Mythmakers of the West: Shaping America's Imagination (Northland, 2001)